L.SUPERIOR

L.MICHIGAN

L.HURON

L.ONTARIO

L.ERIE

BASIN

PRAIRIES

Mississippi R.

Illinois

Wabash

South

Ohio

Ohio

Tennessee R.

HIGHLAND

Arkansas

Red River

Mississippi River

COASTAL PLAIN

PIEDMONT

BLUE RIDGE

GREAT VALLEY

ALLEGHENY

CUMBERLAND VALLEY

ATLANTIC COASTAL PLAIN

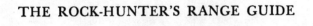

THE ROCK-HUNTER'S RANGE GUIDE

# The Rock-hunter's
# Range Guide

ᐱᐱᐱᐱᐱᐱᐱᐱᐱᐱᐱᐱᐱᐱᐱᐱᐱᐱᐱᐱᐱᐱᐱᐱᐱᐱᐱᐱᐱ

## HOW AND WHERE TO FIND MINERALS
## AND GEM STONES IN THE UNITED STATES

Jay Ellis Ransom

HARPER & ROW, PUBLISHERS

New York and Evanston

*To My Father*

JAY G. RANSOM

1884-1960

*Library of Congress catalog card number: 62-7919*

# *Contents*
/\.\/\.\/\.\/\

# *Preface*
## /\\./\\/\\./\\./\\./\\

As sciences, geology and mineralogy—the study of the earth and its substances—are relatively new, products of only the last few generations of mankind. Nevertheless, the practical aspects of the earth sciences have always been known to man. From earliest history to as late as a century ago, practical geology was something a man picked up by observation incidental to outdoor life. Today, both are still accompaniments to vacationing outdoors. But where the rugged Forty-Niners made a profession of tramping over the canyons and catwalk ridges of America in search of yellow gold, their modern counterparts vacation by jeep, pickup truck, or camp trailer—still searching for mineral substances. Instead of gold, today's prospector, outside the professional class, seeks agate; instead of silver, it is rock crystal, tourmaline, or topaz that brings the glow of excitement to the rock-hunter's eye.

During the past decade, part-time prospecting has developed into a national leisure-time avocation, and probably more people than ever before in history are interested in the mysteries of Mother Earth. While many professional prospectors are in the field, mainly in behalf of America's continual search for new sources of strategic minerals, scores of thousands of "rock-
vii

hounds" are taking to the hills whenever the opportunity permits. These men and women, whose children are often referred to as "pebble pups," come from all walks of life. You will find them on any weekend, poking through beach gravels, in stream beds, along highway and railroad cutbanks—even in the remotest regions—searching for agate, carnelian, chalcedony, jasper, quartz crystals, topaz, or tourmaline. Lovely petrified wood, curious fossils, colorful ore specimens in mining regions, and a great host of other gem stone minerals scattered over all parts of the national compass exert a powerful influence on the vacation plans of countless Americans.

The American west is being literally reopened, as the rock-collecting fraternity follows winding dirt tracks into remote mountain and desert regions. To such enthusiastic amateur prospectors, the finding of a geode filled with fine quartz or amethyst crystals is as thrilling as it was to the Forty-Niner to stumble upon a vug, or pocket, of solid-gold nuggets. Gold has become little more than a curiosity; an amethyst cut into a ring set is as lovely and wearable today as it was in Cleopatra's time.

Since its inception, America has been engaged in seeking out and exploiting its raw materials, such as coal, iron, copper, aluminum, and oil. In this raw, virgin continent Americans have been more conscious of commercially valuable minerals, perhaps, than any people heretofore. Our enormous geologic literature attests to the thoroughness with which professional prospectors and geologists have dug into the mysteries of the American earth and recorded their findings, particularly in mining areas. The training afforded our professional geologists has, necessarily, had to hew to the line of commercial exploration and development.

In the light of today's interest in "pretty" rocks for more esoteric reasons than a money economy, this limited training seems regrettable. In all of the thousands of volumes of geologic literature, encompassing tens of millions of words, we find almost no references to gems or gem stone deposits. It has been largely left to the amateur rock collector to prospect for minerals and gem stones that provide mostly beauty and only now and then a few dollars.

Unlike the search for raw, yellow gold which anybody can

recognize at first glance, or for uranium which responds to electronic instruments, the majority of worthwhile minerals and gem stones requires some knowledge of geology and mineralogy before they can be readily found or identified in the field. Thus, two major problems confront every rock, mineral, and gem stone collector before he even starts to look for them.

First, he must recognize and identify the various mineral species commonly associated with rock collections. To satisfy this requirement, several excellent field guides have been listed in Appendix I: Bibliography, which are invaluable in helping the collector identify rocks and minerals as well as the many varieties of gem stones. These well-illustrated handbooks are available in most bookstores, and every mineral enthusiast should have one as a field reference.

The second, and certainly most vital, problem is where to go to look for interesting minerals and gem stones. Part Two of this book attempts to answer this problem in considerable detail by listing the most important collecting localities alphabetically by state, county, township, district, and landmark. Any attempt to compile a field-trip handbook of rock-hunting sites is, at best, a never-ending project, and no book can ever be completely up to date. New rock fields are constantly being discovered by rock clubs and by individual adventurers who tramp farther and farther from the well-trodden paths. Most such localities achieve local importance and rarely, unless later developed into a substantial mining operation, reach national notice.

There are a number of valuable regional periodicals and private publications listed in the Bibliography, which detail a great many local areas. Many of these publications describe brand-new rock-hunting fields, often with maps that include mileages from some central point. Local Chambers of Commerce and mineral and gem stone societies often provide directions to collecting fields known to their members only.

For the beginning rock collector, a special list of rock and mineral museums that are open to the public is appended. The list is arranged alphabetically according to state and city, and the reader will find one or more within easy reach from almost any locality. Although museum specimens, because they are exceptional, seldom represent rocks and minerals as they are found *in situ,* they do serve as a primary starting point for becoming acquainted with Mother Nature's mineralizations. Such museums and their staffs can serve one well in helping him become acquainted with their regional rocks, minerals, and gem stones, in addition to providing directions to the more easily reached collecting areas.

Other distinctive features of this book include a brief description of most of the important minerals likely to be found in the many localities outlined in Part Two. Of the more than 1500 known minerals, it is not likely that over 10% to 20% will appear in any average collection. The rest are either extremely rare, laboratory curiosities, or subvarieties of the better-known types.

A special chapter is devoted to the technique of reading a geologic map as it is done by the professional prospector. These maps, used in conjunction with standard topographic maps such as are available for most areas of the country, lead the mineral and gem stone prospector on to the discovery of new and unexplored collecting fields. Rock formations may differ greatly in surface appearance, but those of a similar age (containing similar mineral substances) have common attributes. Geologic maps are available for most of the United States, and can readily be obtained from the U.S. Geological Survey or regional land offices.

For many persons with the time to take life easy, rock collecting has become something of a way of life in itself, a phenomenon of the mid-twentieth century. Not infrequently, the amateur becomes professional and earns his way by supplying mineral dealers with quality rocks. This field guide to prospecting is, therefore, a guideroad to retirement. It is also a highroad to a fascinating pastime which is attracting an ever-increasing coterie of adherents.

JAY ELLIS RANSOM

*Los Angeles, California*
*June 1961*

# PART ONE

# CHAPTER I

# *Introduction to Rock Collecting*

/\\/\\/\\/\\/\\/\\/\\/\\/\\/\\/\\/\\/\\/\\/\\/\\/\\/\\/\\/\\/\\/

## OUR WORLD OF MINERALS

Our world is truly a planet of rocks and minerals. Not only do all life forms require a considerable variety for nourishment, but our whole social order depends on their availability and distribution. The very foundation stones of civilization—copper, tin, iron—are but extractions from colorful ore minerals. Uranium, the desperately sought after strategic element of the heady 1950's, is certainly the most recent in a lengthy role of minerals which have helped to raise mankind from the Stone Age to the Atomic Era.

We all recognize the importance which minerals (including the elemental metals) play in war and conquest. But this is by no means the whole story. Different civilizations have placed different emphases on the various segments of the mineral kingdom, and the whole story of prospecting coincides with the social and religious overtones to cultural evolution. Modern man's prosperity depends largely upon the natural resources at his disposal and, in the twentieth century, minerals literally spell energy, tools, communication, and manufacturing. Indeed, mining is one of the four basic industries (the others being

3

agriculture, fishing, and lumbering) that produce raw wealth. Hence, the prospector, whether for ore minerals or for gem stones for decorative purposes, is no less important now than he has always been since the dawn of Mankind.

## ROCK HUNTING DOWN THE AGES

There is no documentable beginning to rock collecting or prospecting. In every continent prehistoric graves reveal that gem stones and colorful minerals were used for ornamental or ceremonial purposes. Certainly, when you start out on a week-end holiday to hunt rocks, you are following an age-old urge to get out into the open and to bring back mementos of your trip. Ancient midden heaps in all parts of the Old World reveal that, twenty to thirty thousand years ago, our ancestors sought much the same kinds of minerals which nineteenth-century American Indian tribes used in their own primitive Stone Age economy.

Such refuse pits show that pretty pebbles and crystals were also collected "for fun" as well as for religious and magical purposes. Rocks have always had intrinsic value, some for ornamental or practical purposes and others for their supposed medicinal properties or magical powers to ward off evil or to invite romance. Both the most ancient Egyptian burials and modern American Indian graves have yielded to the archaeologist great quantities of amulets, necklaces, or other talismanic or decorative objects fashioned from agate, carnelian, jade, rock crystal, turquoise, and hammered native copper or gold. Anthropologists consider that probably Magdalenian and Solutrian peoples of prehistoric Ice Age Europe used rutilated quartz crystals as magical devices for warding off the evil spirits of sickness, just as the Apache and Navajo medicine men of the last century did, and as some still do.

The art of prospecting for minerals and gem stones goes far back into antiquity. For more than 2000 years, the Pharaohs of Egypt sent organized prospecting and mining expeditions into the Arabian Desert, the Sinai Peninsula, and the Sudan after turquoise and emeralds, both decorative stones possessing magical properties. A British archaeologist found one of the earliest references to prospecting on an Egyptian memorial stone, or stele, dating to the seventh king of the Third Dynasty in about

3000 B.C. The hieroglyphics recorded how 754 slaves had ar-rived in the Sinai Peninsula mines to dig out turquoise "by order of the Pharaoh." The names of the supervisory staff and their positions were included. Chief among these technologists was the "Diviner of Minerals," that is, the prospector—he who seeks out minerals.

Evidently those turquoise mines played out, because in 1830 B.C. a certain Captain Harurre, whom we might call a geologist today, was dispatched on a prospecting expedition to the same Sinai-area mines to explore for new veins of the sky-blue tur-quoise. He must have had his troubles, because after three months of fruitless prospecting, Harurre nearly succumbed to despair. Finally, invoking the aid of Hathor, the goddess of mines and minerals, he was rewarded by a "strike," and recorded his gratitude in imperishable stone hieroglyphics on another stele set upright in the ground: THE DESERT WAS HOT AS A FURNACE, THE HILLTOP SEEMED ON FIRE, AND THE VEIN OF ORE WAS EXHAUSTED. THE ANSWER CAME: "THERE IS TURQUOISE TO ALL ETERNITY," AND AT THAT MOMENT THE VEIN APPEARED.

## JASON AND THE GOLDEN FLEECE

Shipbuilding and navigation may have been outgrowths of prospecting. In 1250 B.C., Jason and his comrades sailed from Greece in the ship *Argo* (whence the word "argonaut") on the heels of a rumor that gold had been discovered on the flanks of the Caucasus Mountains in the land of Colchis, which is now Soviet Georgia.

In the heroic Greek legend, Jason represents youth and ad-venture, while his betrothed, Medea, daughter of King Aeetes who ruled Colchis, provided the scientific, i.e., geologic, knowl-edge which enabled Jason to find his Golden Fleece in the gold-bearing gravels of the streams which descended the lofty Cau-casus Mountains to the plains of Ares, or Mars. The legend has much of fancy, but the simple truth of the matter is that Jason and his hardy adventurers were bona fide prospectors, not unlike the hordes who sailed from Seattle, Washington, for the Klondike and Alaska in the great gold rush of 1898.

More than 2500 years ago the Greeks were already prospect-ing the stream gravels of the Italian Peninsula and Sicily for agate, one of the most revered and decorative gem stones of all time. Grecian tombs have yielded tens of thousands of carved and polished agate ornaments, showing that this "magic rock" was as highly thought of then as it continues to be today by modern lapidaries.

## EARLY ROCK CLASSIFICATIONS

The world's first rock collectors were probably early Pleistocene ape men, such as Peking man and Java man of a million years ago. Artifacts from Southeast and East Asia reveal that these humanoids had learned by trial and error how to use and roughly shape stones for hand axes. Subhuman Neanderthals of Europe 100,000 years ago left many varieties of chipped-stone tools in their graves. These Old Stone Age (Paleolithic) primitive species of man collected rocks for practical purposes, their choices running to agate, chert, flint, quartzite, and obsidian—all rocks eagerly sought by today's rockhounds.

The earliest metals found in Old World burials were very likely picked up by primitive men in stream gravels as raw, shiny chunks of copper and gold. We know that Cro-Magnon man, 25,000 years ago, used gold as an ornamental mineral, and that copper was being hammered into bracelets in Egypt as early as 12,000 B.C. Throughout most of Europe by 4000 B.C., our ancestors were fashioning copper and its tin alloy, bronze, into useful utensils and often into deadly weapons. The very earliest finds indicate to us that trading took place among diverse bands or tribes of Proto-Man, because agate, amber, chert, flint, jade, obsidian, ochers, and salt (halite) are found in graves scattered at great distances from their possible places of origin. Therefore, we cannot say just when the "ultramodern" practice of collecting and trading rocks really began.

Prehistoric man learned slowly which types of stone lent themselves to specific useful purposes. We do not know how he classified rocks and minerals, but it was probably not unlike the simple categories into which modern American Indian rock hunters placed the whole mineral kingdom. It goes like this: (1) rocks that can be chipped, i.e., glassy substances such as the various members of the quartz family minerals; (2) stones that can be ground, shaped, or carved, such as basalt,

dolomite, granite, jade, jadeite, limestone, marble, and nephrite; (3) earths that can be used for paint, i.e., metallic ochers,
such as cinnabar (red), azurite (blue), limonite (yellow), and
malachite (green); (4) crystals to drive out evil spirits, such as
quartz, topaz, tourmaline; and (5) rocks that are good for
nothing.

At least 5000 years ago, a beginning had been made in understanding the basic geology and the origin of ores. But 50 cen-
turies were to elapse before any systematic body of knowledge
would be accumulated and classified regarding rocks and minerals, ores and mining, and gem stone properties as we know it
today.

## GEM STONES OF THE ANCIENTS

Modern rock collectors usually seek for gem stones rather
than for metallic ores, which were the primary goal of prospectors during the last century. The old definition of prospecting was more or less limited to the search for commercially
valuable sources of gold, silver, copper, lead, zinc, or other
metal. Hence, until recently, prospecting to the average man
was almost a lost art.

During the world scramble for atomic-energy minerals in
the hectic 1950's when uranium was temporarily king, amateurs
from all sorts of mundane city occupations bought Geiger coun-
ters, studied up on uranium mineralogy and geology, and became acquainted with old-fashioned and ultramodern prospecting techniques. All this was very helpful to Uncle Sam,
and many a so-called amateur brought embarrassed blushes to
the cheeks of professional prospectors working for the Atomic
Energy Commission.

Today, the prospecting boom is as active as ever, but not for
strategic metals. Most of the amateurs who got their boots dusty
and their necks sunburned in the rush after atomic wealth have
switched to the search for gemmy mineral substances and have
built up impressive personal collections. Their new knowledge
turned them to the oldest known hobby of man—the search
for decorative minerals, in other words, gem stones.

Gem stones rank among the most valued of all substances
and, in a multitude of forms, have been prized since the dawn

of human existence. In contrast to the hundreds of lovely minerals gathered by modern collectors, Stone Age man gathered only thirteen basic types of rock. These included amber (fossil resin), calcite, fluorspar, jadeite, pyrite, quartz family minerals (agate, carnelian, chalcedony, chert, flint, jasp-agate, jasper, quartzite, rock crystal), serpentine, and steatite (massive talc) as well as basalt, granite, limestone, marble, and the clay minerals for baking into ceramics and pottery.

At a time when Neolithic man was picking up gold and copper nuggets to be hammered into ornaments (20,000-14,000 B.C.), he was already using nephrite (massive jade), sillimanite (prismatic water-worn crystals of aluminum silicate found as clear blue gemmy pebbles), and turquoise. About 2000 B.C., the first true emeralds appear in the graves; by 500 B.C. sapphires and rubies were included in the burial vestments. The very earliest diamond dates back only to 480 B.C.

Cuneiform-inscribed clay tablets baked by the Sumerians 6000 years ago indicate that they were the earliest people to appreciate the intrinsic value of gems and gem stones. These first inhabitants of Mesopotamia were also the first to develop the art of stone cutting and polishing, laboriously carving agate, carnelian, and lapis lazuli into cylinder seals, signet rings, beads, and lavalieres. Great quantities of these decorative objects were gathered from the ruins of Kish by the Field Museum— Oxford University Joint Expedition to Mesopotamia. The ancient lapidaries used the cryptocrystalline quartz minerals for seals because the hot wax used for sealing papyrus or parchment documents does not stick to these polished, cool stones.

## AGATE EXTRAORDINARY

Perhaps the most loved and widely used gem stone of all, both in antiquity and in modern times, is agate. There are many varieties of this microcrystalline form of quartz ($SiO_2$), such as banded, dendritic, fortification, moss, and sagenitic, but all are equally hard (7) and wear extremely well. All are translucent, and most have intricate and colorful inner designs which bring out the best in the imagination—hence, their talismanic charm. Modern rock collectors gather a greater gross tonnage of this lovely gem stone mineral than of all other gem stones put to-

gether, mainly because there is more of it. On a purely commercial valuation standard, agate ranks very high in dollars
and cents. In variety and attractiveness, agate exceeds all other
gem stones.

As long ago as 500 B.C., the Greeks and Sicilians were scrab-
bling for agates among the gravel bars of the river Achates, now
called Drillo, which flows through the Val de Noto in Sicily.
So highly valued was this mossy form of cryptocrystalline
quartz, that it was in great demand around all the shores of the
Mediterranean. The first known writer on rocks and minerals,
Theophrastus (372-287 B.C.), observed in his book on *Stones*
that "agate is a colorful stone, usually sold at high prices." It
was also Theophrastus who derived the name "agate" from the
name of the Sicilian stream.

One of the rewards vouchsafed to the modern rock collector
echoes the old Greek philosopher's observation. Once you have
tumbled, or otherwise cut and polished the agates you bring
home from the great outdoors, you will find a ready market
for them. That is, if indeed you can bring yourself to part
with their loveliness!

## PLEASURES AND REWARDS IN ROCK COLLECTING

Prospecting for minerals and gem stones has many rewards
beyond the cash value of the stones brought home. The solitary
hobbyist is almost as dead as the dodo bird. Rock hunting, unlike prospecting for ores, has become largely a family project
or a group enterprise which brings people of all ages and back-
grounds into an "outdoor togetherness" that many times leads
to new and lasting friendships.

Of the tens of thousands of rock enthusiasts who take to the
trails and byroads on weekends or during vacations, not a few
keep their weather eyes peeled for a likely vein of commercially
valuable mineral. Such individuals are true prospectors, dif-
fering from the lone-wolf professional in that they are not dedi-
cated to the search for ores. A seam of colorful agate will do
just as well, thank you. And more than likely it will be far
more valuable on the gem stone market than any similar exposure of gold ore would be. Even the big copper-mining com-
panies of Arizona and Utah recognize that the copper-rich

minerals, chrysocolla and malachite, are worth much more per pound as gem stone materials for cutting and polishing than as sources of refined metallic copper.

Where gold ore is considered "high grade" if it averages $35.00 a ton (one ounce of gold), a good outcrop of seam agate may run 50 cents a pound on the rockhound market. In tumbled form—that is, when broken into fragments suitable for mounting into bracelets, earrings, and necklaces and polished in a rotating, barrel-like "tumbler"—even poor-grade agate will bring several dollars per pound. Good quality moss agate, such as "Montana moss" from the gravel bars of the Yellowstone River, brings extremely high prices, polished or not. Then there is "Wyoming jade" and California's "Monterey jade," available to all who sniff the breezes in those two widely separated areas, with rough-stone prices mounting into the thousands of dollars for top-quality "finds." Such crassly commercial pricing does not, of course, include the simple pleasures of getting out into the sunlight and winds of far places, vacationing while collecting rocks. The best of the gold-rush days had nothing on present-day gem stone prospecting. Indeed, it could not offer nearly as many tangible or intangible rewards to the average prospector as hunting agates does to the modern gemologist.

## ROCK-HUNTING AS A LIFELONG HOBBY

While the lure of fascinating gem stone discoveries may provide an attractive incentive for prospecting, it is seldom the real goal. In this complex world of crowded city living, the whole business of hunting and collecting rocks seems strangely keyed to our need for physical exercise and a return to a more natural world.

Collecting rocks is ridiculously easy; in fact, children grow up with almost an instinct for garnering pocket-loads of pretty rocks. The mineral kingdom starts in your own back yard, or nearly so, and extends outward therefrom as widely as your ability to travel. It is limited only by geography, weather, or your mountain-climbing agility in areas, like Colorado or Utah, where prize crystals of kunzite, spodumene, and topaz crop out of pegmatite granites on the bony crests of towering peaks.

Many rock collectors actually began their hobby as children. Your own offspring will be your most enthusiastic supporters for field trips, especially if you start them out with visits to a mineral museum where rocks are displayed at their loveliest. When you and your children have had your eyes opened to the beauties within an unpretentious stone, you are well started on a hobby that has no limitations.

Then, too, the art of the lapidary is so simple that amateurs from eight to eighty regularly turn out their own lovely jewelry at home, far excelling with the inexpensive power machines available in any rock shop the artisans of ancient Egypt and Mesopotamia. The dollar pair of cheap plastic earrings sold in the local dime store is worth fifty times as much when made at home out of moss agate, carnelian, or Wyoming jade, which you have gathered yourself and fashioned into exactly the same design. As you develop this hobby, you learn that the innumerable decorative items seen in any rock dealer's shop—offered usually at high prices—you can make at home for virtually nothing and, at the same time, enjoy the creativeness which your own ingenuity brings to their production. Most commonly, you will probably want to slab, cut, and polish your rocks into attractive ring sets ("cabochons"), earrings, lavalieres, bookends (from massively occurring gem stone minerals, like howlite), necklace mountings, belt-buckle settings, and the countless variations of costume jewelry embracing true gem stones instead of plastic.

It may seem absurd, although it isn't, but cutting and polishing hard-rock gem stones is actually simpler, less expensive, and in the long run more rewarding than painting, sculpturing, woodworking, or photography. It must be so, because so many machinists, cabinetmakers, carpenters, bricklayers, plumbers, photographers, electronics engineers, lawyers, and physicians have taken up rock collecting and lapidary work as a combination outdoor-indoor way of life that leads to a pleasurable and useful retirement.

CHAPTER **II**

# *Preparation for Rock Hunting*
ΛΛΛΛΛΛΛΛΛΛΛΛΛΛΛΛΛΛΛΛΛΛΛΛΛΛ

To leave for a vacation with only a vague notion about doing a little rock hunting along the way is like asking the plumber to repair a leak in your piping system. Very likely, he will have to go back to his shop for some special tools, and he will charge you accordingly. Miles from home, you may suddenly become aware that you have reached a worthwhile rock collecting locality. Think how chagrined you might be at not having suitable implements along to enable you to dig out the lovely gem stones or minerals others all around you are ohing and ahing about.

**THE ROCKHOUND'S WORKING TOOLS**

A city "sidewalk superintendent" needs no more equipment than his two sharp eyes and his two sets of fingers to pick an interesting crystal out of an excavation for a new building, if he can talk the foreman into letting him inside the barricade to get it. In the field, however, you will need some sort of collecting sack and tools for hammering, prying, digging, or chipping off pieces of rock. One thing you will never need is dynamite!

It is no news to parents that their youngsters load their pock-

12

ets with everything from beach pebbles to tree toads, but a pocket is just not big enough for a bona fide rock collector. There are two easily acquired alternatives to pocket-loading: the Boy Scout type of knapsack or packboard worn over the shoulders, or an empty ten-pound flour sack draped from the belt. The latter is the more common for field explorations in search of float, the small bits and pieces of gemmy minerals that may lead you to an outcrop of the stuff. Then, when you have located a substantial deposit of "rock," you may find that additional digging-out tools and back-packing facilities are necessary.

*The Prospector's Hammer and the Cold Chisel.* Chief among all implements useful to the prospector and rock collector is the specially constructed *prospector's hammer,* or hand pick, available in almost any hardware store at moderate cost. Once you are on location, it doesn't take long for you to realize that the hammer is a rockhound's best friend. With one end square, for pounding, and the other long, tapered, and extremely hard, for prying, this versatile tool soon feels like a natural extension of your arm. More than any other implement, the prospector's pick is the hallmark of all who look for rocks, whether ore minerals or gem stones.

Frequently, the prospector's hammer is used in conjunction with a second, most useful tool—the *cold chisel.* Taken together, these two implements may be considered an absolute minimum supply of tools needed to give you your tenderfoot badge in rock hunting. Thus, you may be able to remove many beautiful crystals from crevices, vugs, or from beneath surfaces that would otherwise prevent your getting them out intact.

*Additional Special Tools.* For the more advanced collector with one eye cocked toward the finer things in life, the ingenious use of a number of discarded dentist's, carpenter's, or stonemason's tools can do wonders in helping you separate a delicate gemmy crystal or fibrous crust from a resistant matrix or mine-tunnel wall. An ordinary *pocket knife* and a small *steel file* will also prove quite valuable. If you hope to do some gold prospecting, then a *gold pan* is required because of its peculiar shape and slope to the sides. Naturally, you will find a light *sledge hammer* very helpful in breaking up big rocks into smaller ones for easier transport over the hill by back-pack to your car.

In one side pocket with your loose change you can easily carry a dime-store *horseshoe magnet* to help you distinguish between magnetite and chromite and similarly appearing ilmenite or rutile. A small magnifying glass, preferably one with two or three lenses to give magnifications from 5 to 20 times, materially aids in visualizing very small drusy-type crystallizations that need identifying. It also helps you distinguish between flecks of pure gold and "fool's gold," i.e., pyrite or marcasite—a laudable distinction that quickly separates the rank amateur from the semiprofessional.

For even more positive identification of minerals, a *streak plate,* or a small square of tile with one side rough, is a must. Almost every mineral has its characteristic streak, made by rubbing it against a rough, hard surface. This streak is remarkably consistent, irrespective of great differences in outward appearance of field specimens, and it is one of the primary bases for mineral identification. Every handbook of mineral identification lists the characteristic streak colors.

## CAMPING AND FIELD-PROSPECTING EQUIPMENT

Perhaps you will want to spend your entire vacation prospecting and living out in the field, the way a professional prospector does. Then you will need to go equipped with enough additional items to load your car, jeep, station wagon, or pickup truck to the gunwales. The following list of equipment is by no means complete, but you can use it as a basic guide to the organization of your camping or prospecting equipment.

| *Camping Equipment* | *Prospecting Equipment* |
|---|---|
| Ax, for cutting wood or stakes | Black light (ultraviolet lamp) |
| Bad-weather clothing, hat | Canvas specimen bags, sieve |
| Bucket for hauling water | Chemical field-test kit, acids |
| Clothes: work, relaxation | Compass and tripod |
| Coleman stove | Geiger or scintillation counter |
| Cooking, eating utensils | Knapsack or packboard |
| First-aid kit | Location notices, stakes |
| Folding card table, chairs | Map portfolio, detailed maps |

| *Camping Equipment* | *Prospecting Equipment* |
|---|---|
| Food, enough to last | Portable drawing board |
| Gasoline lantern, candles | Rifle, revolver, ammunition |
| Gasoline or water can | Shovel, mattock, pry bar, rake |
| Reading materials, books | Sledge hammer, wedges |
| Rope, chain, cable | Snake-bite kit |
| Sheath knife (6-inch) | Surveying instruments |
| Sleeping bag, blankets, tarp | Water canteen (2-quart) |
| Tent, camp trailer | Writing instruments, notepaper |

## BLACK-LIGHT PROSPECTING

Strangely enough, nighttime prospecting with a "black light," or ultraviolet-ray lamp, can be extremely rewarding. Many minerals with an unattractive daytime appearance fluoresce brilliantly in all colors of the rainbow when exposed to ultraviolet light. In the blackness of a moonless night the fluorescent minerals, of which there are a great many, wink back at you like the glowing eyes of a cat caught in the head-lights of your car. And yet you yourself are barely able to see the lamplight at all! A well-chosen collection of fluorescent minerals displayed in a black-light cabinet, entirely enclosed away from daylight, will add unusual interest to your over-all collection.

An inexpensive ultraviolet lamp producing the necessary short wavelengths is usually used for laboratory research and for mineral prospecting. It is particularly useful in scouring the earth's surface the easy way for sheelite, from which comes the highly strategic tungsten, since this mineral fluoresces a brilliant blue-white. It has been estimated that amateur and professional prospectors have used the black light to discover more than $100,000,000 worth of sheelite since the end of World War II.

You will find that nighttime prospecting is a lot of fun; colorful surprises lie everywhere over the earth's surface when seen by black light. But beware! A desert scorpion, as poisonous as a rattlesnake, fluoresces the most beautiful yellow-green you ever saw, not unlike the various uranium-bearing minerals. You are not apt to die from a scorpion sting, but it can make you deathly sick.

## CLOTHING AND FIRST-AID SUPPLIES

Certainly your clothing should be suitable to the area you prospect and its climate. At almost any time of year, you will wear different clothing in northern New England from what you might put on in the desert Southwest. But in all areas you will find that leather hightop boots or stout hiking shoes give you the most protection from brambles, cacti, sharp rocks, barbed wire, or snakes. Rock collecting terrain is generally pretty hard on shoe leather, so composition soles are not only more practical but give you better footing on steep slopes.

A hat to shade your eyes and a water canteen to quench your inevitable thirst also contribute to your comfort and safety. Women should avoid high heels, fluffy skirts, and floppy hats at all costs. Wearing bluejeans, capris, or matador pants and low-heeled hiking shoes, women who accompany their prospector husbands should be prepared to face wind, dust, insects, and a broiling sun in summer.

Although it is an excellent precaution to carry a small snake-bite kit along in the glove compartment of your car, the danger from rattlers, scorpions, Gila monsters, or other unpleasant creatures including an occasional tarantula, is practically nil. They are all more afraid of you than you are of them, and they are perfectly happy to stay out of your way. However, an evening campfire will draw scorpions and sidewinders; hence, in the southwestern deserts, at least, it is good practice to shake out your bedroll before retiring and, certainly, to sleep off the ground on army cots.

A much greater annoyance that can lead to serious infections throughout the West, from Canada to Mexico and the Sierra Nevada to the Great Plains, is cactus, especially Arizona's cholla, perhaps most beautiful in its spring chartreuse when back-lighted by the golden sunshine. Cactus spines are tipped with tiny spurs that allow them to work forward into sensitive flesh. A pair of pocket pliers makes possible the painful but sometimes necessary experience of de-spining an unwary hand or bottom. The most frequent victims are young children and dogs. *Caution*: It is always best, for obvious reasons, to leave pets at home. Not only does this protect them from physical injury, but it is a consideration for the feelings of others who may not enjoy pets of any description!

## WRAPPING AND LABELING ROCKS AND MINERALS

Whether you use a flour sack or a packboard, you will find it expedient to carry a supply of soft tissue or cotton for wrapping particularly delicate specimens before putting them into your bag. Old newspapers are excellent for coarser specimens. Some collectors prefer to use a small paper or cloth bag for each sample and to enclose pertinent information on a scrap of paper, later transferring these data to a catalogue file card.

A good system for a beginner is to label each specimen immediately when found before putting it into his sack, using small squares of adhesive tape pasted on and numbered consecutively for the day's finds. The numbers can be jotted down in a pocket notebook as to date, possible identification, common name, geologic formation where found, location, or any other pertinent information. At any collecting locality you are sure to find others, perhaps more experienced, who will be pleased to help you identify your discoveries.

Permanent labels can be applied at home after you have cleaned your specimens. A popular field practice is the number-and-notebook system mentioned above. Then, at home when preparing the best specimens for your collection, you substitute a small square of white paint or enamel for the adhesive tape and protect the India-ink numbers with a coating of lacquer, plastic, or ordinary fingernail polish.

Long ago, Dana in his book *System of Mineralogy* which was brought up to date in the Seventh Edition, presented a standardized numbering system that is used today by all professional mineralogists. You may want to apply his system, with personal adaptations, to your own collection. For example, *pyrite,* which is one of the commonest minerals you will encounter and is often known as "fool's gold," carries the Dana number 2911. Your first find would be labeled 2911—1, your second 2911—2, and so on in consecutive order. Your card-catalogue file would then contain your field notes under the general heading SULPHIDES, Pyrite, $FeS_2$, worked up and neatly transferred to the appropriate card.

## PLANNING YOUR DISPLAY

In planning your display of rocks and minerals, strive for some coherent organization and a definite arrangement. This can be done by putting all similar minerals, such as the sulphides, together in one group. Crystals and aggregates of crystals make a lovely shelf display; so do particularly colorful ore minerals. Petrified wood, especially Wyoming's "Eden Valley wood," can be displayed as a unit. Sliced and polished thundereggs from various parts of the volcanic West belong together, as do the tremendous variety of fossils. Sometimes, you might place all the minerals and gem stones from one locality together, to show what a particular area, like San Diego County, has to offer.

You will find it impossible and inadvisable to try to compete with the massive collections found in mineral museums. Therefore, you may wish to specialize in one or another category of the mineral kingdom—perhaps only crystals, or petrified woods, or thundereggs, or fossils. In fact, most collectors come to view the whole, varied mineral kingdom through eyes focused on some particular aspect of peculiar interest to themselves.

Such specialized collections often exceed in interest and variety the best which museum collections afford. It takes time, surely, and organization to build up a worthwhile collection, but the rewards reach far beyond the cash value assigned to it as part of your "estate." However you approach the fascinating and wonderful hobby of gem stone and mineral collecting, you will find that you have greatly increased your awareness and delight in the world around you.

## SAMPLE RECORD FORMS

Keeping records of your finds may seem unimportant. Nevertheless, if you use your field notebook constantly and acquire the habit of recording your observations systematically, you will find that it adds greatly to the interest and value of your rock collection.

The following outline forms can serve as a guide to the organization of your collection. In practice, you should keep your

forms as simple as possible, yet include all pertinent information. Forms may be dittoed or mimeographed inexpensively,
and varied according to your particular needs and as your experience dictates.

The first form is for information gathered in the field and
jotted down in your field notebook.

## MINERAL FIELD LABEL

Specimen No._____Local name_____Date_____
Species_____Variety_____Color_____
Associated Minerals_____
Locality _____
Geologic Occurrence_____

Remarks _____

Collected by_____Associates_____

The next card should be prepared with care, reduced in
size, neatly typed, printed, or hand-lettered. It is designed to
be included along with your prize specimens in your museum
case for the edification of your viewers.

## MUSEUM DATA CARD

No._____Species_____Variety_____Dana No.____
Composition _____Formula_____
Associated Minerals_____
Locality _____Occurrence_____
Geologic Age_____Collector_____

### NOTE-TAKING PRACTICE

The habit of jotting everything down methodically in your
notebook will pay dividends in the long run. You cannot rely
on your memory; therefore, your field notes should be as full
and accurate as possible. Write down all your impressions and
your observations, particularly including precise distances and
directions for reaching each collecting locality.

Professional geologists make a practice of writing on only every other page of their notebooks in order to leave plenty of space for future additions, corrections, drawings, photographs, or maps sketched in the field. You will do well to sketch in all significant geologic structures and geographc features (see Chapter VI), such as ridges, mountain ranges, watercourses, and man-made objects that will help you locate yourself accurately on a topographic map.

Wherever possible, you might take photographs and include them, separately catalogued, along with your enumerated rock and mineral specimens on the last pages of your notebook. For each photograph or sketch, you should record a number, the locality, name, direction or angle of shot, and any remarks as to time of day, light value, length of exposure, diaphragm, and focus.

Finally, it is a useful habit to mention whatever else may seem significant to you, as, for example, under "Remarks": brief description of the terrain (slopes, vegetation, etc.); nearby camping facilities, including water and fuel supply; condition of road or trails; any special equipment that would aid in securing specimens; and any later references to articles or books dealing with the site.

By leaving nothing to chance or memory, you will find that rock collecting can be hugely satisfying. Your records and field notes will make you an authority as far as your own collection is concerned. At the same time, you will have the added satisfaction of knowing that others, who view your collection, will recognize it as a competent job and respect you for your industry.

CHAPTER **III**

# Your Mineral Collection
ΛΛΛΛΛΛΛΛΛΛΛΛΛΛΛΛΛΛΛΛΛ

Undoubtedly, a collection of rocks and minerals represents one of the easiest, most practicable, and interesting approaches to the study of the world around us, for the mineral kingdom is everywhere. Unlike flowers which fade after mounting, insect study or taxidermy which destroys life, and many other varieties of nature which deteriorate when gathered into cabinets, the infinitely varied and beautiful forms which rock takes improve with organization and display. Moreover, the intrinsic value of such a collection only increases with time. Then when, at the end of a long and interesting life of building up your collection, you present it to a museum or to a school—some may even buy it, although most educational institutions are financially limited—its educational value lives on indefinitely.

## GETTING ACQUAINTED WITH MINERALS

So that you will quickly become acquainted with the many lovely species of mineral, you will probably want to make your initial collection one of a general nature. In this way, you become gradually acquainted with the basic principles of mineralogy and develop your techniques for labeling, mounting, and display. Later, as your particular interests develop, you may wish to specialize in one or two fields of this varied hobby.

Almost every prospector brings home far more minerals and gemmy stones than he can ever possibly use without going into the rock-dealing business. In fact, many an amateur rock collector retired into dealership and a comfortable income. Many an amateur lapidary, creating jewelry at home, suddenly discovered that the most interesting way to display his (usually her) product was to sell them "at high prices." In any case, field-trip explorations into the back country invariably result in a tremendous overflow of rocks.

One well-known California rockologist wag, speaking before a Los Angeles mineral society, suggested that all the best gem stone and mineral-hunting localities left in America are in the basements and backyards of the rock collectors! He suggested further that it might well profit the hobby if each person took all his excess rocks back to the deserts and mountains and strewed them along the roads for others to pick up, rather than permitting them to become trash eventually to be dumped into the sea. He had a point there!

Most collectors build up their rock displays in multiples. Every time you cut a rock into halves in order to see what is inside, there is one half for you and the other half to trade. Larger specimens may be slabbed into several attractive slices on a diamond saw. Hence, nearly all rockhounds eagerly trade around for unusual specimens to add to their own collections. Mineral societies encourage trading, when summer vacation trips are but pleasant memories of sun, sky, and earth made imperishable by the colorful gem stones brought home.

You will also find that an occasional purchase from a roadside rock shop helps build an interesting collection. No one can expect personally to visit all the rock fields in the world or, for that matter, in his own state. There are entirely too many. However, dealers in most communities acquire large stocks of minerals through commercial channels, including lovely gem stones from all parts of the globe, and so constitute legitimate sources for beautiful specimens.

Your rock collection is the tangible evidence of your field trips and vacations, attesting to your inner sense of beauty and your powers of observation. Each specimen carries a story far more important to you than the fact that it is simply a certain species of rock, like apatite.

A visitor viewing your specimens usually wants to know more about them than their technical names; he can always determine these for himself. More impressive than the name on an identifying card is the locality information, for your friend may want to go there to find his own specimens, and something about its geologic history. Without a complete label, even the most beautiful crystal aggregate is "just another rock," having only slight intrinsic value. Spotting its location on a large-scale topographic map hung on an nearby wall also adds interest.

## PREPARING YOUR SPECIMENS

In order to achieve a satisfactory display, many rock enthusiasts limit the size of their specimens to about two inches in maximum diameter, reserving separate storage space for large or complex pieces. Each display specimen should be pure and typical of its species; its identifying characteristics should be easily visible. Since some minerals alter on exposure to air, these should be displayed in such a way that the inner, or unexposed surface is shown. Large specimens may be impressive, but they confuse the viewer, while smaller samples lose interesting detail.

Trimming a specimen can be done with light hammer blows in the field, and it can be finished by careful chisel and hammer work at home. Unwanted rock matrix is usually knocked off, with the exception of a suitable sample surrounding a crystal to show how it grew. The matrix, otherwise known as the "country rock" which encases a mineral, adds to the value of a crystal by telling something of its geologic origin.

For example, clear quartz rock crystal may occur as cavity growths in light-colored rhyolite, as at Quartzite, Arizona, or in chocolate-brown basalt, as found in the Bradshaw Mountains of west-central Arizona. Also, a cluster of crystals has greater interest than if they were broken apart and displayed separately.

All minerals, except the unusually delicate and velvetlike, should be thoroughly cleaned with ordinary soap and water, using a toothbrush for scrubbing crevices. Lukewarm water is best, because hot water may crack or damage some minerals.

Others, like native sulphur, will crack in cold water; you learn by experience what unknown minerals might do. Hence, be cautious! Rocks are not everlasting and, once removed from their natural occurrences, are subject to change in a different environment. Many minerals must be coated with lacquer, plastic, or ordinary fingernail polish to prevent oxidation and discoloration.

Good solid specimens can withstand severe scrubbing, even with a wire brush. Those stained with unwanted minerals, like the red iron stain often found on water-clear quartz crystals, may require treatment with oxalic or other acid. Acetic acid is particularly good and gives a brilliant luster to many crystals. Hydrochloric acid, while often used, is more dangerous, and damages or dissolves some minerals.

Where water might dissolve a mineral such as halite (rock salt), alcohol or cleaning fluid can be used. Where no liquids or scrubbing can be applied, because of the extreme delicacy of the mineral, dusting with a syringe or a soft camel's-hair brush will improve the specimen before mounting, especially if it is an intricately grown and fragile needlelike or fibrous crystal.

## UNSTABLE MINERAL SPECIMENS

You will find that certain colorful, attractive minerals change their appearance remarkably after a while. Although seemingly unalterable and imperishable when you find them, they are not stable under the conditions of your collection. After all, you have changed their environment. Like all manifestations of nature, rocks too must make a readjustment to changed conditions of moisture, heat, gases in the air, and handling (perspiration acids). All minerals are chemicals; hence, they react to other chemicals, slowly or rapidly according to the nature of the change and its intensity.

A few, like pyrite and marcasite, sulphides of iron, oxidize and lose their glister; silver tarnishes badly and is usually found dark gray to black in nature, or becomes so on the influence of sulphur gases in the air. A city's atmosphere with its smog ingredients represents a very different chemical atmosphere from the clean outdoor air to which a mineral had become accustomed.

Unstable minerals may be preserved by applying a coating of transparent lacquer, as mentioned above. Other minerals that occur as anhydrides, that is, without possessing water of crystallization, such as rock salt, may absorb moisture from the air and actually melt away. Some minerals, like the southwestern desert borax compounds, which are rich in water of crystallization, may dry out on exposure to the air and simply crumble to a powder. Such mineral specimens need to be kept in airtight containers, with moisture-absorbent species protected by inclusion of a drying agent.

Since careless handling may destroy delicate crystals and hair-like crustal growths, it is never wise to allow visitors to handle prized or rare specimens. Even the most well-intentioned friend, through ignorance or ineptitude, may so damage a lovely mineral or gem stone that its very real dollar value is irrevocably destroyed.

## STORAGE AND DISPLAY

You will need space for storage and display. Many collectors invest in a glass showcase and make their own arrangements of colored minerals or crystals. China cabinets and bookcases may be dusted and the shelves covered with black, velvety material. Both beginners and old-timers resort to cigar boxes, egg cartons, old dresser drawers, shoe boxes—partitioned with cardboard.

For jewel-like crystals or cut and polished gem stones, regular jewelry cases, cufflink boxes, or ring cases come in very handy.

Lighting with separate bulbs or with fluorescent tubes, combined with the skillful use of mirrors to double or magnify your display, add to its interest and brilliance. Often, the artistry of some family member helps to create unusual combinations of colorful materials that will bring out the best in each specimen.

When your finest pieces have been assembled in a cabinet and labeled, you will want to exclude all dust so as not to dull their glowing beauty. Indeed, the veteran collector is meticulous about keeping his specimens as scrupulously clean as possible.

## YOUR CONTRIBUTION TO MINERALOGY

Finally, it will pay you rich dividends to join a local mineral or gemological society and to add your enthusiasm to their meetings. Their organized field trips are family affairs, and the more experienced rock collectors are eager to help beginners become acquainted with the regional minerals, rocks, and geologic formations.

Encourage others to join you in this satisfying branch of natural history, especially children who will love you for it. From their ranks will come the mineralogists, geologists, adventurers, and scientists of tomorrow. Participate, rather than sitting back and merely observing what others are doing, and your own enjoyment in life will increase immeasurably.

Remember, you will get as much out of your experiences as you invest in them, and no more. Study some one phase of mineralogy and know it well. Often, you will be called upon to speak to groups on your specialty, to give talks about your field-trip adventures, and to display your "bragging stones." If you enjoy photography, you have unlimited opportunity to take color slides with which to illustrate your talks, enlivening your mineral display with color shots of the finest museum specimens found in the nation's treasure chests.

Mineral conventions will be well worth your attendance. Every state, and many counties, hold rock conventions at regular intervals with extremely interesting exhibits from all over. Sooner or later, most enthusiastic rock collectors pay the small display fee and install their own table of prize rocks as well as any rocks they wish to offer for sale. More often than not, there is a handsome profit as a result, and you can plow it right back into your next field trip to that new gem stone bonanza you heard about somewhere beyond the blue horizon.

## THE CHEMICAL CLASSES OF MINERALS

Although there are some 1500 recognized minerals, you are not likely to include more than 10 to 20 per cent in your collection, even a large one. However, except for the few naturally occurring elements like copper, gold, platinum, and silver, nearly all the minerals and gem stones you will find can be classified according to specific chemical families.

Various approaches toward classifications were tried in the past, obvious ones such as attempting to arrange them by their crystal structures. But arranging them according to chemical composition has proved to be not only most convenient, but the most scientific, for it has withstood the test of time.

The properties of the elements in the natural chemical compounds give the minerals their immediately recognizable characteristics of *hardness, luster, crystal form, color, streak, fracture,* and *cleavage.* While an expert field man often guesses correctly the chemical group to which a particular specimen belongs, he can check it at home by simple chemical tests in order to be certain exactly to which family it applies. Such elementary tests are described in most manuals of mineralogy listed in the Bibliography.

With the exception of such organic gem stones as amber, coral, jet, and pearl, all true gems and gem stones can also be classed as minerals of definite chemical composition in which the arrangement of atoms of the contributing elements never varies. In some subfamilies, like the garnets, there can be an interchange of metallic elements so that several varieties occur, distinguishable mainly by color and transparency, but all having the dominant crystal shape. Although many gem stone minerals do have a relatively simple and easily remembered chemical formula, most minerals have rather complicated chemical symbolic representations.

Long, unwieldy formulas result from the chemical analysis of typical examples and represent percentages by weight of the various contributing elements. For all practical purposes, you need use only a simple field determination to recognize the most commonly occurring rocks and minerals. (See Chapter V).

### Dana's System of Mineral Classification

In his *System of Mineralogy* Dana classified the minerals according to the following chemical compounds and in the order shown:

ELEMENTS. The naturally occurring native elements, or primitive uncombined units of matter are few in number. Of the

98 natural elements, the nonmetallic solids include only *carbon* (C) in its two forms of diamond and graphite and *sulphur* (S). Among the metals, the prospector cannot find more than *copper* (Cu), *gold* (Au), *platinum* (Pt), and *silver* (Ag, rare).

SULPHIDES, SULPHOSALTS. This class of mineral represents combinations of metals with sulphur, such as *pyrite* ($FeS_2$), *marcasite* (identical formula but different appearance), and *sphalerite* (ZnS). Most minerals of this type look metallic; they are relatively soft, usually brittle, and their crystals when crushed reveal a usually dark to black powder. Thus, *pyrite* ("fool's gold") can be easily shattered by a hammer blow, whereas true gold, which *pyrite* or *marcasite* so closely resembles, merely flattens out because it is malleable.

OXIDES, HYDROXIDES. Since the gaseous element *oxygen* is not only the most abundant element on earth but one of the most chemically active, it is to be expected that it would be a major constituent of many minerals. Indeed, the end-product of weathering is the conversion of other classes of mineral into the oxides, which represent the most stable natural form. Consequently, there are many very unlike minerals that fall into this class, including heavy-ore minerals. Some are extremely hard and resistant, such as *corundum* (ruby, sapphire) with the simple formula of aluminum oxide ($Al_2O_3$), and ordinary *rock crystal* (quartz, $SiO_2$). The majority of oxygen-containing minerals have more complex formulas and may be included in other categories.

HALIDES. This class of compounds of metals with any of the halogen elements, usually *fluorine* or *chlorine* although salts dissolved in ocean water include *bromine* and *iodine,* includes only one gem stone, *fluorite* ($CaF_2$). In the field the prospector is likely to find only one other commonly crystallized halogen mineral, *halite* (rock salt, NaCl), and this only in extremely dry regions. Most halides are very soluble and their crystal forms, usually cubic, are laboratory preparations.

CARBONATES. Many minor gem-stone minerals occur in this category of metals in combination with *carbon* and *oxygen*.

Their crystal forms are often translucent to transparent. None are hard enough to resist abrasion, and all readily dissolve in acids. *Calcite* ($CaCO_3$) is frequently met with in the field as clear crystals, while *rhodochrosite* ($MnCO_3$) appears in metamorphic manganese deposits and ore veins as deep rose-pink rhombohedrons.

NITRATES, BORATES. With the exception of a few, very rare borates occurring in pegmatite granite as remarkably hard minerals, the members of this category are all too soluable to be found in nature. In the dry lake beds of the western states one will find a few borax minerals, such as *howlite* ($Ca_2SiB_5O_9$ $(OH)_5$), which can be used as a gem stone material for making into bookends.

SULPHATES. The salts of metals in combination with *sulphur* and *oxygen* belong here. One class is very soluble and seldom encountered in the field, and the other is quite insoluble. Both types occur deep in the oxidized portions of sulphide ore veins. The prospector is most likely to find *gypsum* crystals ($CaSO_4 \cdot 2H_2O$) in clay beds and limestone cavities.

PHOSPHATES. A typical primary mineral of gem-stone quality is *apatite* ($Ca_5 (Cl, F)(PO_4)_3$), found in pegmatite dikes, ore veins, plutonic rocks, and often in sedimentary deposits. Many secondary minerals of metals combined with *phosphorous* and *oxygen,* often highly colored, belong in this category.

VANADATES, ARSENATES. Metals combined with *oxygen* and either *vanadium* or *arsenic* belong to this group. They are secondary, usually highly colored, zone-of-oxidation minerals found around ore bodies which have undergone extensive weathering. These minerals often make attractive cabinet specimens rather than gem stones that can be cut and polished.

TUNGSTATES, MOLYBDATES, URANATES. This mixed group of ore minerals, often highly colored, lends itself mainly to cabinet-specimen use. Individual minerals are easily identified, and all are heavy and soft.

SILICATES. Taken all together, this group contains more than 50 per cent of all known minerals and by far the largest number and variety of gem stones. The silicates usually have a glassy luster and are variously colored, so that they make into excellent gems because of their extreme hardness and resistance to solution in acids. Most silicates occur as primary minerals rather than as products of weathering; they occur as components of rocks, as segregations in rocks, or as crystal druses lining the insides of rock cavities.

## FIELD IDENTIFICATION

It is important that you be able to separate the various minerals found in the field according to hardness. Minerals with a hardness of 6 or above comprise gems and gem stones which can be sawed, faceted, and polished. Those below 6 are too soft to resist wear, but may make colorful cabinet specimens. A few minerals show different degrees of hardness, according to their axes as, for example, kyanite which has a hardness of 7 across the prism but only 5 along its length. A knife can be made to scratch it along its length, but not across it.

### Mohs Hardness Scale

The Table on pages 32 and 33 lists the most commonly occurring gem stones and minerals according to the simplest field test of all—*hardness*. It is based on the Mohs scale, named after the mineralogist who selected the mineral indices, and the scale can easily be memorized. With 1 representing the softest mineral and 10 the hardest, the scale is as follows:

1. TALC. A mineral very easily scratched by the fingernail; it is the base for common talcum powder. Minerals of this degree of hardness are often slippery to the touch.

2. GYPSUM. A mineral that can be less easily scratched by the fingernail than talc, used for making plaster. *Note*: the fingernail has a hardness of about $2\frac{1}{2}$ and cannot scratch the next representative mineral.

3. CALCITE. A mineral easily scratched by a knife point, used for making cement; it is often associated with common rock limestone.

4. FLUORITE. Used as a flux in blast furnaces, this mineral is

scratched by a knifepoint with some difficulty.

5. APATITE. A mineral very difficult to scratch with a knifepoint because steel has a hardness of about 5½. It is an important source-rock for phosphate fertilizer.

6. FELDSPAR. This may be *orthoclase, microcline,* or *plagioclase;* it cannot be scratched by steel, but can be by quartz.

7. QUARTZ. The hardest common mineral, quartz resists weathering and provides a large family of gem stone minerals; it easily scratches steel and glass.

8. TOPAZ. This gem stone scratches quartz with difficulty, requiring considerable pressure, and it cannot be scratched by quartz, but only by the next two minerals.

9. CORUNDUM. Known more familiarly as *ruby* or *sapphire,* this gemmy mineral can be scratched only by a diamond. Ordinary corundum makes into grinding powders, exceeded as an abrasive only by diamond bort.

10. DIAMOND. One diamond can be scratched only by another diamond. Although about five times harder than corundum, this pure, crystallized form of *carbon* is brittle and it burns easily. It is the only mineral of this degree of hardness.

### Heft and Streak

Prospectors of experience *heft* a specimen of rock in one hand to get the "feel" of its weight in comparison with that of a known variety of mineral, size for size. For example, jade is dense and its heft is heavy; so also are galena and garnet, whereas gypsum and opal feel very lightweight. Field identification by heft comes with experience, and it serves primarily to denote the general category, or chemical family to which a specimen belongs.

The appearance of a mineral powder made by rubbing a sample across the surface of a piece of unglazed porcelain is a surer method of identifying a mineral in the field than is heft. The powder is called the *streak,* and only a freshly broken piece of the mineral should be used.

### Color, Luster, Cleavage, Fracture

These are identifying characteristics of minerals found in the field; they are included with minerals described in Part Two.

## MINERALS ACCORDING TO HARDNESS

| 2-3 | 3-4 | 4-5 | 5-6 | 6-7 | 7-8 | 8-9 |
|---|---|---|---|---|---|---|
| Argentite | Alunite | Apophyllite | Actinolite | Acmite | Andalusite | Adamantine spar |
| Autunite | Anglesite | Augelite | Amblygonite | Amazonite | Aquamarine | Chrysoberyl |
| Bauxite | Anhydrite | Chabazite | Analcite | Amazonstone | Beryl | Corundum |
| Biotite | Antlerite | Colemanite | Anatase | Axinite | Cordierite | Emery |
| Borax | Aragonite | Fluorite | Anthophyllite | Benitoite | Euclase | Ruby |
| Bournonite | Azurite | Hematite | Apatite | Bertrandite | Golden beryl | Sapphire |
| Brucite | Barite | Hemimorphite | Arsenopyrite | Bixbyite | Morganite | |
| Caledonite | Bornite | Heterosite | Augite | Bloodstone | Phenakite | |
| Chalcanthite | Brochantite | Iron (meteoritic) | Beryllonite | Cassiterite | Spinel | |
| Chalcocite | Calcite | Lithiophilite | Brookite | Chrysoprase | Staurolite | |
| Chlorite | Celestite | Manganite | Chlorastrolite | Columbite | Topaz | |
| Cinnabar | Cerussite | Platinum | Chromite | Danburite | Tourmaline | |
| Copiapite | Chalcopyrite | Pyrrhotite | Cristobalite | Dumortierite | Zircon | |
| Copper | Chrysocolla | Scheelite | Datolite | Epidote | | |
| Crocoite | Cuprite | Triphylite | Dioptase | Feldspar | | |
| Epsomite | Descloizite | Variscite | Enstatite | Garnet | | |
| Galena | Dolomite | Wolframite | Eosphorite | Jade | | |
| Glauberite | Dufrenite | Wollastonite | Goethite | Jadeite | | |
| Gold | Enargite | Zincite | Hedenbergite | Jasper | | |
| Gummite | Greenockite | | Herderite | Magnetite | | |
| Gypsum | Heulandite | | Hornblende | Marcasite | | |
| Halite | Howlite | | Hypersthene | Microcline | | |
| Hydrozincite | Kernite | | Ilmenite | Moonstone | | |
| Jamesonite | Lepidolite | | Kyanite | Olivine | | |
| Jarosite | Magnesite | | Lapis lazuli | Orthoclase | | |
| | | | | Pet. Wood | | |

| 2-3 | 3-4 | 5-6 | 6-7 |
|---|---|---|---|
| Leadhillite | Malachite | Lazulite | Plagioclase |
| Linarite | Margarite | Leucite | Plasma |
| Muscovite | Millerite | Limonite | Prehnite |
| Phlogopite | Polyhalite | Microlite | Pyrite |
| Phosgenite | Powellite | Monazite | Pyrolusite |
| Pyrargyrite | Pyromorphite | Natrolite | Quartz family |
| Silver | Rhodochrosite | Nepheline | Rutile |
| Stibnite | Scorodite | Niccolite | Sillimanite |
| Sulphur | Serpentine | Obsidian | Spodumene |
| Thenardite | Siderite | Opal | Tiger Eye |
| Torbernite | Sphalerite | Pectolite | Turquoise |
| Tungstite | Stilbite | Psilomelane | Vesuvianite |
| Vanadinite | Strontianite | Rhodonite | (Idocrase) |
| Wolfenite | Tetrahedrite | Samarskite | Zoisite |
| | Travertine | Smithsonite | |
| | Wavellite | Sodalite | |
| | Witherite | Sphene | |
| | | Thomsonite | |
| | | Titanite | |
| | | Tremolite | |
| | | Uraninite | |
| | | Wardite | |
| | | Willemite | |

CHAPTER IV

# The Geologic Timetable
/\.V\.V\.V\.V\.V\.V\.V\.V\.V\.V\.V\.V\.V\/

As you drive across the face of America, you are constantly aware of the changing scene. From the coastal Atlantic plains, you pass through the Appalachian Mountains and the rolling country south of the Great Lakes. You may find the central states flat and monotonous, even as the land rises slowly westward to the Great Plains. Then come the awesomely scenic Rocky Mountains beyond which are arid deserts, high-timbered plateaus, hundreds of short, jagged mountains interspersed by barren valleys, all of which trend north and south, and many dry lakes known locally as playas. Finally, you reach the Sierra Nevada-Cascade mountain system, one more great valley that you can see across on a clear day, the Coast Range, and the Pacific Ocean.

All that you view through your car windows is scenery, formed through agencies of erosion, uplift, and diastrophic (deep earth) forces that made the mountains or caused their volcanoes to spew forth ash and lava, and created the basins, sinks, and plateaus. To the prospector and gem stone hunter, these evidences of geologic unrest are also the clues to the minerals contained in the different rock formations brought

34

forth to view. In order to interpret the scenery through which
you travel, you need some appreciation of its age and the forces
which brought it into being.

## THE GEOLOGIC TIMETABLE

Since geology often deals with yardsticks measured in millions of years, most of us think of them, if at all, as something
abstract and mathematical. In reality, each horizon is a link
in a cause-and-effect chain going back to the very beginnings
of the universe an unknowable time ago. Every gem or mineral
that you gather into your collection came into existence
through some geologic force acting through some definite
period of time. Just as each one of us represents the summation
of all the genes of all of our forefathers, so also does the immediate and transitory scenery around us, the rocks and minerals which its formations contain, and the fossil remains of
past life forms that appear here and there represent the summation of all the cause-and-effect geologic changes of previous
ages. As James Hutton, pioneer geologist of Edinburgh, Scot-
land, wrote in 1785: "We find no vestige of a beginning, no
prospect of an end." We can only speculate where the earth
itself came from; all that we can be sure about is that the
endless past is constantly with us, and that the scenery we
drive through today is vastly different from the vistas that
preceded our Quaternary Period.

Strangely enough, when we drive across America, our ribbon
of pavement lies most often on the beds of ancient sea bottoms,
even when traversing mountain passes 12,000 feet high. Where
the old sea beds have been tilted, domed, pierced, inverted,
thrust-faulted or broken, we see folds, mountains, gaps, canyons, ridges, and plateaus. These we can understand, for they
seem permanent although they are not, really. For example, the
slippage along the California San Andreas fault, which has
been going on for millions of years, amounts to one to two
inches a year; it is estimated that in another ten million years
Los Angeles could be facing San Francisco across the fault
line. Old Mother Earth is still very much alive and kicking,
as numerous earthquakes tell us each year.

We have no way of knowing exactly the age of the earth.

The present estimate of six billion years is indicative only, based on laboratory experiments. Radioactive measurements reveal that the oldest known crystalline rocks of the Canadian Pre-Cambrian Shield are about two billion years old.

## FOSSIL BASES FOR AGE-DATING ROCKS

We cannot say much about how the earth looked in the first blush of the geologic dawn, save that its surface was made up of nothing but oceans and rocks—raw, jagged, chocolate-brown to black congealed lavas known as basalt, or dreary, gray mountain ranges of granite. It is not until life forms had developed sufficiently to leave fossil reminders behind in the sedimentary rocks that geologists were able to read the story of the earth's unstable crust. Because every fossil type of plant or animal life grew by slow, step-by-step modifications of earlier forms, it was possible to arrive at a consistent and fairly reliable system of dating geologic events during the last half billion years, further verifiable through uranium-disintegration dating.

In tracing back fossil remains, we find no evidence that life existed in the earliest part of the Pre-Cambrian. We necessarily infer that, by the time the first life forms had developed sufficiently hard shells or bony skeletons to withstand fossilization, there must have been an extremely long prior age of evolution from a single-celled origin. Soft-bodied animals could not leave fossils, although fossil imprints of algae have been dated to the end of the Archeozoic Era.

By late Proterozoic time, however, there were several varieties of marine invertebrates and many other very simple forms of living protoplasm. Caught in flows of mud or covered by sand, they were preserved through the eons of time as the sediments were converted by pressure into hard rock. As each life form advanced out of the one before it, some were fossilized. Geologists have linked them together, as the gradual evolution of plant and animal life unfolded, and assigned a specific era or period name to each time division during which a particular fossil form was characteristic and most abundant.

The Table on pages 38 and 39 presents this geologic evolutionary column, with approximate ages in millions of years assigned to the different eras, periods, series, or epochs. Each division shown in the Table is comprised of rock formations containing characteristic minerals and fossils, often widely spread. While the indicated ages are of little importance in themselves, except for mathematical interest, it is the succession of periods, the younger always overlying the older as dramatically revealed in sedimentary bedding exposures, that carries real meaning to the prospector. It is important for you to become familiar with the geologic timetable, especially if you use the geologic map technique, described in Chapter VI, as an aid in ferreting out new and promising mineral or gem stone localities.

## MINERAL ENVIRONMENTS

The earth's crust is built up of many minerals. The nature of any rock specimen indicates something of its formation and denotes the region in which it was found. In visiting the various parts of the United States, you will see that the nation is broadly divided by sections on the basis of geologic boundaries and the types of rock that occur in each area.

The variety of rocks and minerals you can collect in your immediate part of the country depends on where you live. Mineral distribution is sporadic, at best, and very few areas other than New England, New Jersey, North Carolina, or San Diego County, California afford any great variety of minerals. The Midwesterner finds himself severely limited to the species found only in sedimentary rocks, since these constitute the scenery of mid-continental America.

The eastern portion of the United States is dominated by the Appalachian Mountain chain. Here, very ancient sedimentary rocks derived from still older mountains during Ordovician, Silurian, and Devonian eras have been compressed and squeezed into great arches, called anticlines, and into downfolds or troughs, called synclines. The total amount of compression is equivalent to lessening the circumference of the globe by several hundred miles.

Outcropping here and there are intrusions of granite from deeply buried batholiths, or "magmatic" reservoirs of molten rock. During the final stages of cooling, many pegmatite dikes (extremely coarse granite) were formed. Outcropping through many parts of New England, New Jersey, Virginia, and North

# GEOLOGIC TIMETABLE*

Major Stratigraphic Divisions in Use by the U.S. Geological Survey

| ERA and PERIOD | Series, or Epoch | Characteristics | Length in Millions of Years | Began Years Ago, Approximately |
|---|---|---|---|---|
| **CENOZOIC ERA** — QUATERNARY | Recent | Modern Man | | 15,000 |
| | Pleistocene | Glaciers, Mammoths Neanderdthal Man | 1.5 | 1,500,000 |
| | Alps, Cascades, Sierra Nevadas, Second Rocky Mountains | | | |
| TERTIARY | Pliocene | Modern Mammals | 10 | 12,000,000 |
| | Miocene | Anthropoids Volcanism | 13 | 25,000,000 |
| | Oligocene | Carnivores | 15 | 40,000,000 |
| | Eocene | 3-toed Horse | 20 | 60,000,000 |
| | Paleocene | Marsupials | 10 | 70,000,000 |

Himalayas, First Rocky Mountains, South American Andes, Appalachian Re-Uplift

| **MESOZOIC** | | | | |
|---|---|---|---|---|
| CRETACEOUS | Upper | Flowering trees | 35 | 105,000,000 |
| | Lower | Birds, Chalk | 20 | 125,000,000 |
| JURASSIC | Upper | Ginkgo Forests | | |
| | Middle | Cycad trees | 25 | 150,000,000 |
| | Lower | Dinosaurs | | |
| TRIASSIC | Upper | Reptiles | | |
| | Middle | Pine forests | 30 | 180,000,000 |
| | Lower | Ammonites | | |

Appalachian Revolution, Laurentian (Canadian Shield) Uplift, Wichita Mountains

**GEOLOGIC TIMETABLE** (Cont'd.)

Major Stratigraphic Divisions in Use by the U.S. Geological Survey

| | | | | | |
|---|---|---|---|---|---|
| | PERMIAN | | Red desert beds, Potash, Conifers | 25 | 205,000,000 |
| PALEOZOIC ERA | CARBONIFEROUS | | | | |
| | Pennsylvanian | Upper<br>Middle<br>Lower | Coal forests<br>Amphibians<br>Insectivora | 30 | 235,000,000 |
| | Mississippian | Upper<br>Lower | Coal forests<br>Limestone | 20 | 255,000,000 |
| | DEVONIAN | Upper<br>Middle<br>Lower | Ferns, Horsetails<br>Fish (Lung)<br>Shale formations | 60 | 315,000,000 |
| | SILURIAN | Upper<br>Middle<br>Lower | Crinoids<br>Salt beds | 25 | 340,000,000 |
| | ORDOVICIAN | Upper<br>Middle<br>Lower | Graptolites<br>Invertebrates<br>Sediments | 80 | 420,000,000 |
| | CAMBRIAN | Upper<br>Middle<br>Lower | Trilobites<br>Snails<br>Sponges | 80 | 500,000,000 |
| | Killarney Revolution | | | | |
| | PRE-CAMBRIAN | Proter-ozoic<br>Archae-ozoic | Algae, multicell<br>Unicell life<br>No life forms | 1000<br>? | 1,500,000,000<br>4 to 6 Billion |

* O. D. von Engelen and Caster, Kenneth E, *Geology*, McGraw-Hill Book Company, Inc., New York, 1952, p. 419. Also Emmons, W. H., Thiel, George A., Stauffer, Clinton R., and Allison, Ira S., *Geology, Principles and Processes*, McGraw-Hill Book Company, Inc., New York, 1955, p. 621.

Carolina, these pegmatites have provided great quantities of the finest gem stones found anywhere, matched only, perhaps, by similar dikes crisscrossing San Diego County, California.

Between the Appalachian Plateau and the Rocky Mountain system, the underlying plutonic rocks are deeply buried beneath sedimentary deposits. These are the erosional debris from many mountain ranges, some so old that they are gone entirely and their granite roots covered by thousands of feet of sediments. Only here and there in mid-America—for example, in Arkansas, Minnesota, the Black Hills, and the Ozarks—do the basal crystalline rocks reach worn and wrinkled knuckles above this great mantle of sediments. Since continental seas repeatedly covered the low heartland of the North American continent, we find enormously widespread regions of limestone and chalk as well as sandstone, in which collectible minerals or gem stones occur but sparingly.

From the Rocky Mountain chain to the Pacific Ocean, a distance of nearly one thousand miles, we find an extremely interesting and varied topography, literally a rock collector's paradise. Quite new by geologic timetable standards, volcanoes and fissure flows of lava everywhere give evidence of how the world was made. Rich in silica, the associated magmatic waters have created a wonderland of quartz-family minerals and gem stones as well as whole stone forests of agatized and opalized wood.

Volcanism was much more limited in the Southwest, although still important geologically. Here, earth forces raised up vast areas of sea-laid sandstone and limestone into level plateaus many thousands of feet above sea level. In these Permian, Triassic, and Jurassic sediments the rock collector will find a wealth of silicified wood, quartz-family minerals, uranium ores, jasperized dinosaur bones, and gizzard stones (gastroliths) —all magnificent, highly colored specimen and gem stone materials.

## CLASSIFICATIONS OF ROCKS

If we were to define what rocks are, we might say that they are extensive mineral bodies, composed of one or more minerals in varying proportions, which make up the earth's crust.

In the beginning, one rather common theory suggests, as the crust formed, all rocks were of *igneous* origin, i.e., "fire-formed." Crustal contractions and thermal changes within the body of the earth forced the original igneous rocks into mountain ranges. Weathering, which includes the chemical changes brought about by such elements as oxygen, sulphur, and the halogens (fluorine, chlorine, bromine, iodine), plus erosion converted those mountains into *sediments* and distributed them as debris over the earth's surface—a process that continues to go relentlessly on. The sediments piled up to great depths in areas of sinking troughs, or geosynclines, once more building up enormous pressures and heat. Again, chemical and physical alteration occurred so that, many times, it is impossible to identify the original type of sediment in these *metamorphic* rocks. As earth forces maneuvered, the deeply buried metamorphics were once again brought to the surface or pushed upward into towering ranges of mountains where weather could reduce them once more to sediments. And so the process endlessly repeats itself, age on age.

Every geologic period has produced rocks of each of these three types, and in each classification the gem stone and mineral collector will find characteristic species of mineral. By learning to recognize these three fundamental rock classifications and knowing what to look for in each one, you will materially increase your prospecting abilities.

# CHAPTER V

# Classified Rocks and Field Determination of Common Minerals

The magmas which underlie the earth's crust vary in chemical composition. When such bodies of molten lava are volcanically thrust out onto the earth's surface to cool rapidly, their textures and grain size vary greatly from magma which has cooled slowly deep within the earth. Thus volcanic rocks can be differentiated from plutonic rocks, even though their compositions may be identical. In either case, the solidified rocks constitute the first rock classification—*igneous*, that is, formed from fire.

## COMPOSITION OF IGNEOUS ROCKS

A rigid classification of igneous rocks is not possible, because many types intergrade so closely into one another that separation by type is often difficult to determine. The Table on page 44 shows that most fire-formed rocks are mineralogically composed of feldspars, micas, amphiboles, pyroxenes, olivine, and quartz. The light-colored rocks are usually acidic, i.e., silicic because of their high content of the acidic constituent—$SiO_2$, and of relatively low specific gravity. Thus the primary example, granite, constitutes the core of most mountain ranges because it "floats" higher on the plastic substratum than do the basalts.

Basic rocks, like basalt, contain a preponderance of iron, lime, and magnesia; hence, they are usually heavier and dark-colored (brown to black, and dark green). The deep ocean floor is primarily basalt, and this volcanic rock underlies all the continents. Between these two extreme rock types, there is an unbroken series of intermediate rocks with their silica content running from 40 to 80 per cent, so that some are neither acidic nor basic.

*Collector's Stones Found in Volcanic Areas.* Magmas from the earth's deep interior often contain the chemical constituents that go into the making of lovely crystals, gem stones, gems, and commercially valuable ore minerals. Brought to the earth's surface where cooling takes place from the top down, a form of "magmatic separation" occurs, so that each mineral type tends to crystallize out as its point of supersaturation is reached.

In their order of abundance, the elements which make up the igneous rocks are: oxygen, silicon, aluminum, iron, calcium, magnesium, sodium, and potassium. These elements actively combine into various compounds to form the minerals. Some crystallize out earlier than others, so that in most igneous rocks there is shown a definite order of crystallization. Minerals poor in silica, and therefore *basic,* appear first; those rich in silica, being *acidic,* form last. Taken in the usual order for the commoner rock-forming minerals, we find that the accessory minerals, such as zircon, rutile, hematite, ilmenite, and magnetite come first. These are followed by such ferromagnesian minerals as the pyroxenes and amphiboles, and these in turn by the plagioclase feldspars, orthoclase, and quartz.

*The Collector's Potpourri.* The following minerals and gem stones are found associated with igneous rocks in volcanic areas: agate, alunite, apache tears, chalcedony, datolite, epidote, gold, jasper, kimberlite, leucite, nepheline, obsidian, olivine, opal, peridot, perlite, pitchstone, prehnite, pumice, quartz, sodalite, sulphur, thundereggs (nodules), topaz, tridymite-crystobalite, zeolites.

# VARIETIES OF IGNEOUS ROCKS

| | | Name | Color | Texture | Mineral Content | Identification |
|---|---|---|---|---|---|---|
| **COARSE GRAIN** | Volcanic | Andesite | Light | Porphyritic | Feldspar phenocrysts | Absence of quartz |
| | | Peridotite | Dark | Porphyritic | Hornblende, olivine, pyroxenes | Dark green to black color |
| | Plutonic | Diorite | Dark | Grainy | Hornblende, pyroxenes | Absence of quartz |
| | | Gabbro | Dark | Grainy | Hornblende, olivine, pyroxenes | Presence of olivine |
| | | Granite | Light | Grainy | Quartz, feldspar, mica; speckled | Presence of quartz |
| | | Pegmatite | Light | Giant grains | Large crystals of mica, feldspar | Extraordinary crystal size |
| | | Syenite | Light | Grainy | Feldspar, mica; speckled | A granite without quartz |
| **FINE GRAIN** | Plutonic | Basalt | Black | Aphanitic | Olivine, pyroxene, plagioclase | Jointed, vesicular; color |
| | | Felsites | Light | Felsitic (flinty) | Silicic magma | Compactness; flinty surfaces |
| | | Porphyries | Light, dark | Porphyritic (frozen mush) | Phenocrysts of feldspar, quartz, pyroxenes, olivine | Presence of phenocrysts |
| | | Rhyolite | Light | Porphyritic | Quartz phenocrysts | Quartz |
| **GLASSY** | Volcanic | Pitchstone | Dull | Resinous | Altered obsidian | Pitchy luster |
| | | Obsidian | Black, red | Glassy | Silicic glass | Conchoidal fracture |
| | | Perlite | Black | Frothy | Obsidian | Lightweight |
| | | Pumice | White | Vesicular | Frothy obsidian | Rock froth |
| **FRAGMENTAL** | Volcanic | Breccia | Light | Granular | Consolidated fragments of rock | Cemented by ash or dust |
| | | Tuff | Light | Loose | Consolidated volcanic ash and dust | Lightweight; may contain fossils |

Descriptions of these minerals and gem stones are included in Chapter VIII.

## THE PEGMATITE MINERALS

Pegmatite is a coarsely crystalline form of granite, and therefore to be included under the igneous rocks, but separately. It represents the final closing stages of rock formation, in which all the volatiles and most of the still uncombined, rare elements have been concentrated in a small, residual liquid phase. Owing to the presence of such dissolved rare gases as fluorine and chlorine, as well as superheated steam, this liquid is very fluid. The rock-making minerals like feldspar, quartz, biotite and muscovite mica have a chance to crystallize out in coarse, often interlacing masses frequently associated with many rare minerals.

During the high-temperature phase, while the congealing granite stock is still largely molten, this residual fluid cleans out nearly all the simpler minerals from the bulk of the granite. Under great pressure, the fluid is squeezed into fissures and cracks in the sedimentary overburden, or "cover," where final congealing takes place as the temperature drops. Eventually, erosion removes the overburden and the pegmatite granites are revealed as "dikes" which outcrop in short or long lines running straight across country or branching into many concentric arcs surrounding the major granite dome.

Rock collectors easily learn to recognize this peculiar, extremely coarse form of granite which also bears the apt title, "giant granite," because of the large crystals of feldspar, quartz, mica, and often beryl. Individual crystals of purest gem quality range from a fraction of an inch to such colossal structures as one microcline feldspar crystal from a Maine pegmatite that was 20 feet across! A South Dakota Black Hills crystal of spodumene, from the Etta mine near Keystone, was 42 feet long and weighed 90 tons. Monstrous crystals of clear, sparkling blue beryl from both New England and the Black Hills have measured from 18 to 27 feet in length. But these are exceptions, of course; nor are such giants the best quality gem material, being flawed and sometimes impure.

Although ordinary pegmatites are chiefly composed of the

granite minerals, many carry lovely crystals of rubellite (pink tourmaline), schorl (black tourmaline), and apatite. A particularly attractive pegmatite granite, which does not incorporate gemmy substances, is graphic granite. Quarried for artistic building stone, this odd-appearing granite contains microcline feldspar and quartz interlocked in an angular pattern curiously reminiscent of old Teutonic runic inscriptions of the third century A.D. It is, indeed, often referred to as "runic granite."

*The Rock Collector's Hope Chest.* The following pegmatite gem stones and minerals, described in Chapter VIII, will interest many rock collectors: alexandrite, amblygonite, apatite, aquamarine, arsenopyrite, autunite, beryl, beryllonite, biotite, cassiterite, cat's-eye, crysoberyl, columbite-tantalite, corundum, cryolite, dufrenite, dumortierite, emerald, epidote, esophorite, fluorite, gahnite, garnet, gummite, herderite, heterosite-purpurite, hiddenite, ilmenite, kaolin, kunzite, lazulite-scorzalite, lepidolite, magnetite, microcline, microlite, molybdenite, monazite, morganite, muscovite, orthoclase, phenacite, phosphuranylite, quartz crystals, ruby, samarskite, sapphire, siderite, spinel, spodumene, topaz, torbernite, tourmaline, triphylite-lithiophilite, urininite, uranophane, wardite, zircon.

## ROCKS THAT LIE IN BEDS (STRATIFIED ROCKS)

Most surface rocks were formed by the action of weather on pre-existing granites, basalts, and other igneous intermediates harking back to the fiery origins of the earth. Probably all deeply buried igneous rocks will eventually be uncovered by erosion. They, in turn, will be weathered away and transported by wind, water, gravity, or glaciers to be deposited as bedded layers of sediments like the pages in a book. When geologic forces have converted the soft clays, sands, marls, muds, and gravels into solid rock, we have the second great class of rocks known as the *sedimentaries.*

Approximately 58 per cent of continental sediments are shales, that is, hardened muds and clays. Sandstone and conglomerates, the latter being gravelly masses hardened into solid rock, constitute 22 per cent. Nearly 20 per cent more are limestones, originally deposited under shallow "epicontinental" seas. A modest 1 per cent of all rock debris is made up of gypsum, salt, phosphate rock, chert, flint, agate, and coal. Although it is estimated that the earth's outer crust is 95 per cent igneous rock and only 5 per cent sedimentaries, it is further estimated that approximately 75 per cent of all the earth's land areas are blanketed with a superficial layer of sedimentary rocks immediately beneath the soil (which is not a sediment, but a chemical alteration of the topmost layer of rock). These sedimentary deposits range from a few inches in thickness to 40,000 feet deep and attest to a great variation in geologic time and climatic conditions.

### Classes of Sediments

The most common end-products of weathering are: (1) sand, composed mainly of pulverized quartz; (2) clay, from decomposed feldspars and the kaolin minerals; and (3) precipitates, from soluble minerals that include mainly colloidal silica (agate, chalcedony, chert, flint, jasp-agate, jasper, etc.) and the carbonate and phosphate minerals. Lime, calcite, and the phosphates make up the bulk of the precipitates, forming immense beds spread over wide areas where the earth's surface was anciently covered by shallow seas, especially throughout the Midwest and the southeastern and southwestern states. Other minor sediments include the clastic (volcanic ash, bombs, lapilli, and cinders), meteoritic (dust and fragments from outer space), and magmatic (hot-springs deposits).

Of special importance to scientists and rock collectors is the wealth of fossils found in nearly all sediments. These may be casts of plant parts or cell-for-cell replacements (volume-for-volume substitution) by minerals of life forms that died and became embedded in muds and limey deposits, or were covered by volcanic debris, and preserved from the oxidation processes of decay until mineralization could take place from percolating waters. Sediments laid down under the seas contain marine molluscs principally. Fresh water sediments are often rich in petrified woods, impressions, and casts of leaves or other plant units (trunks, limbs, twigs, nuts, cones), and a wide assortment of fossilized animal bones. Petrified wood, often beautifully colored and of gem-stone hardness 7, occurs in every state and in almost every county. The woods occur in rocks of every geologic age from the Silurian to the Recent. Of these, the rock collector is primarily interested in agatized, opalized, and silicified types, colorfully stained by trace impurities.

## The Bedded Rock Formations

Leaving the high, barren peaks to their primary erosion, as we travel toward the mouth of a river, we find that each successive sedimentary bed contains a concentration of like-sized particles. Beneath the bottom-most bed, we almost always find the old crystalline igneous rocks that reveal the original crust of the earth. As an illustration, the Pre-Cambrian schists at the bottom of Arizona's Grand Canyon underlie all the thousands of feet of sedimentary formations above, and in the walls of the canyon itself we read much of the history of the earth as it pertains to the Southwest.

Sedimentary rocks occur in the following major categories, most of which are easily recognizable and distinguishable from one another. All contain interesting mineral specimens.

*Arkose*—a conglomerate rich in quartz and feldspar grains resulting from the fragmentation of granite by alternate freezing and thawing plus chemical weathering.*

*Bentonite*—a very fine-grained, bluish-white clay derived from volcanic ash by chemical alteration.

*Bog Iron Ore*—a precipitated sediment, usually in fresh-water bogs, rich in iron oxide derived from weathering.**

*Breccia*—fragmented, angular rocks cemented together; it includes fault and friction breccias, volcanic breccias, tuff, brecciated marble (New England), agglomerates, and others.

*Chalk*—fine-grained limestone composed generally of shells and shell fragments, principally foraminifera, or resulting from calcium carbonate precipitation.

*Coal*—an organic bog or swamp sediment derived from the decomposition of ancient forest vegetation.

*Conglomerate*—gravels of water-rounded pebbles firmly cemented together; it is sometimes called "puddingstone."

---

* Authority for this statement is Pough, Frederick H., *A Field Guide to Rocks and Minerals*, p. 21, (Houghton-Mifflin, 1953); and Dana, E. S., and C. S. Hurlbut, *Manual of Mineralogy*, 15th Ed., p. 366, (John Wiley & Sons, 1952).

** Pough, Frederick H., *A Field Guide to Rocks and Minerals*, p. 140, lines 14-15: "It is deposited as 'bog iron ore,' and forms residual brown iron ores in the southwestern United States, in Missouri, and in Cuba."

*Coquina*—limestone composed of loosely assembled shells and shell fragments, like a shell heap cemented together.

*Diatomaceous Earth*—sediments made up of the fossil siliceous external skeletons of microscopic plants called diatoms.

*Dolomite*—massive bedded limestone in which the original calcium (of the carbonate) has been replaced by magnesium. It is harder than limestone, and also less effervescent in acid.

*Evaporites*—a group name for deposits of anhydrite, gypsum, salt, etc., resulting from evaporation of their solutions.

*Greensand*—a sandstone rich in the green grains of glauconite.

*Gypsum*—commonly occurring hydrous calcium sulphate deposited in ancient sea beds as rock gypsum, alabaster, gypsite, selenite, or satin spar, left behind by evaporation of the sea.

*Limestone*—marine-deposited calcium carbonate occurring widely, and frequently containing marine fossils.

*Loess*—fine-grained, wind-transported dust, sometimes deposited hundreds of feet deep as in China and Iowa.

*Marl*—porous masses of shells and shell fragments in deposits on lake bottoms or around margins of shallow seas; also a lime mud not containing organic remains.

*Oölite*—resembling cemented fish roe, this rock may be calcareous, ferruginous, phosphatic, or siliceous; it is built up of concentrically layered small spheres, each one containing a grain of sand or a fragment of shell.

*Phosphate Rock*—derived from apatite-containing minerals, this calcium phosphate sediment is widely distributed.

*Salt*—known mineralogically as halite, sodium chloride deposits occur very widely, often associated with beds of gypsum.

*Sandstone*—most interesting, colorful, and varied of clastic sediments, sandstone is composed of loose sand firmly cemented together, its color depending on the cementing agent. Quartzite, often highly colored, is sandstone cemented together by silica forming extremely weather-resistant rock.

*Shale*—this is the end-product of weathering and is the finest grained and usually most thinly bedded, having been transported the farthest by water.

*Siliceous Sinter*—hot water precipitate of silica jelly, dried and hardened; found around geyser basins and as hot-springs deposits.

*Tillite*—an unassorted conglomeration of rocks, boulders, breccias, pebbles, clay, and sand particles dropped from glacial ice and later cemented together; found only in Ice Age areas.

*Travertine and Tufa*—light-colored calcareous deposits of earthy, spongy, or porous material from hot mineralized springs.

*Volcanic Ash*—blown by tremendous explosive force from active volcanoes, volcanic ash is simply pulverized lava; in the West it occurs in thick beds over widespread areas and is the source material for bentonite.

### Minerals and Gemstones in Sedimentary Formations

In various cycles of erosion, deposition, consolidation, uplift, and re-erosion, unusually heavy or resistant minerals like quartz, diamond, tin, platinum, gold, topaz, tourmaline, and zircon may lag behind and become concentrated in "residual" economic deposits. Gem stones like topaz, tourmaline, and zircon, which originally were formed in pegmatite granites, may actually weather through several cycles and gradually be worn down to sand grains only to be recrystallized from concentrated sands during a period of metamorphism. Such new crystals are often well formed and of high gem quality.

Minerals and gem stones to be found in uplifted and eroded sedimentary formations include the following: agate, apatite, aragonite, barite, bauxite, borax, calcite, carnotite, celestite, chalcedony, chert, colemanite, concretions, coral, diamond, dolomite crystals, flint, fluorite, fossils, fulgarites, galena, geodes, gypsum, halite, hematite, howlite, jasp-agate, jasper, kaolin, kernite, limonite, magnesite, marcasite, millerite, opal, opalite, platinum, polyhalite, pyrite, quartz crystals, septarian nodules, siderite, soda niter, strontianite, sulphur, sylvite, thenardite, ulexite.

### THE METAMORPHIC ROCKS

All types of rocks must constantly undergo alteration to conform with a changing environment. Every rock form is the product of a definite environment, whether formed by heat, pressure, chemically active "juices," gases, or vapors. As geologic processes bring about new and different environments, rocks which were in stable equilibrium under the original conditions must modify or alter their internal structure, texture, and sometimes even color in order to arrive at a new mineralogical equilibrium. This adjustment to new conditions we call *metamorphism* (Greek *meta*, change, and *morphe*, form). All transformed rocks belong to the third and last great class of rocks, the *metamorphics*.

Thus, when you mold a handful of moist, gray clay into a brick and bake it to the hardness of stone at 3000° F, you are metamorphosing original sedimentary minerals into something very different in color and texture. Rocks most responsive to a new environment are, quite naturally, the sedimentaries. Because igneous rocks were originally formed under great heat and pressure, they are least affected by new applications of either. Also, earlier metamorphics resist subsequent changes. But, again, all rocks will eventually change their natures as one geologic age follows another.

At least five easily recognized metamorphic rock types come from original sediments. Their importance to geology and mineralogy is great, for under the impact of massive subterranean intrusions of magma into the sedimentary overburden, regional metamorphism may cover thousands of square miles and result in many rich bonanzas of mineable ores and minerals. The Table on page 52 indicates the progressive alteration that takes place when unconsolidated sediments undergo compaction, heat, and pressure.

When sediments accumulate to great depths, their weight naturally develops enormous pressures on the bottom layers. At the same time there is a build-up of heat, some of which may come from radioactivity. The metamorphic process is hastened greatly, however, when intruding bodies of magma from the earth's bowels penetrate the sediments and thrust and tilt them into high mountain ranges. The fringes are areas of "contact metamorphism," i.e., lines of contact between the molten lavas and the cold overburden. Along such lines extensive mineralization takes place, and the world's greatest ore bodies as well as valuable gems and gem stone minerals, are found in such zones.

### METAMORPHOSED SEDIMENTARY EQUIVALENTS

| Unconsolidated Sediments | Consolidated Rock | Metamorphic Alteration |
| --- | --- | --- |
| Gravel | Conglomerate | Conglomerate schist Conglomerate gneiss |
| Sand, Silicates | Sandstone | Quartzite, Hornfels Schists, Serpentine |
| Clay, Mud, Silt | Shale, Argillite | Slate, Phyllite, Mica schist, Gneiss |
| Calcareous ooze | Limestone, Dolomite | Calcareous schist Marble |
| Peat, Carbon | Lignite, or Bituminous coal | Graphite, or Anthracite coal |

## Metamorphic Rock Types

The metamorphic rock types encountered most commonly can be quite easily recognized, as follows:

*Gneiss* (pronounced "nice")—banded, coarsely textured, granitelike rock in which each band is made up of but a single variety of crystalline mineral; it is often called "banded granite."

*Marble*—very minute calcite crystals, formed from the original unorganized carbonates by low heat and pressure, give the broken surface a "sugary" texture; it has no cleavage.

*Metamorphosed Coal*—as the pressure of accumulating sediments on a body of carbonaceous matter increases, it forms a progressive series of organic fuels: peat, lignite, bituminous coal, anthracite coal, and finally graphite; each member successively contains more pure carbon and less water, oils, and gases; the end-product is pure elemental carbon.

*Phyllite*—micaceous, banded, or foliated rock of uniform composition, phyllite is formed from clay under more intensive metamorphism than that which creates slate.

*Quartzite*—under intense heat and pressure cemented sandstone becomes smooth, glassy (all silica), and dense; it is just as hard as quartz, 7, and can be split, or "cleaved" through the individual sand grains instead of around them as in the original sandstone; often highly colored by iron.

*Schist*—most representative of metamorphic rocks, the various schists (mica, hornblende, quartz, limestone, etc.) are composed of definite, grainy minerals; they are recognizable by their thin, wavy leaves or "foliations."

*Slate*—dense, usually dark-colored, slate is familiar as the "blackboard" in a school room; it splits easily into sheets.

### Collectible Metamorphic Minerals

The heat and pressure of the metamorphic process causes secondary or "weathered" minerals to revert to the high-temperature minerals. The results are lovely gem stones, crystals, enriched metallic ores, as well as rock-forming minerals. During contact-metamorphism, many new minerals are created through new chemical combinations.

Widespread regional metamorphism usually reveals rocks rich in mica as well as containing other minerals that show an elongated or flattened shape. Often, as new magmas invade a previously metamorphosed series of rocks, hot corrosive fluids containing rare elements introduce further changes in the cold metamorphic minerals through enrichment, i.e., addition, of silica, boron, magnesia, chlorine, fluorine, tantalum and other rare-earth elements. Thus, a second series of rare contact-metamorphic minerals can be recognized as characterizing the newest environment in the geologic series.

Minerals most commonly found in contact-metamorphic zones include many valuable ores, metal sulphides, and hornfels. In addition, the following "high-temperature" gem stones and minerals occur in the metamorphic rocks: actinolite-tremolite, andalusite (chiastolite), anthophyllite, axinite, bixbyite, brucite, calcite, chalcopyrite, chlorite, crysotile (asbestos), cobaltite, cordierite, corundum, danburite, diopside, dumortierite, epidote, garnet, graphite, hornblende, idocrase (vesuvianite), ilmenite, jade, jadeite, kyanite, lapis lazuli, lazulite-scorzalite, lazurite, magnetite, marialite-meionite, mica, nephrite, orthoclase, pyrite, pyrophyllite, pyrrhotite, rhodochrosite, rhodonite, rutile, scheelite, serpentine, sillimanite, sphene (titanite), spinel, staurolite, tourmaline, wollastonite, zircon.

## FIELD DETERMINATION
## OF COMMON MINERALS

Although many rock collectors are not accustomed to identifying ordinary rocks, except in the most general terms, the well-informed mineral and gem stone prospector should know the common minerals. These are often guides to specimen material as well as to commercially valuable ores that might be worth staking out as a mining claim.

### IDENTIFYING CHARACTERISTICS

*Color* and *hardness* constitute quick, field-identifying characteristics, along with *heft*. Most of the common rocks may also be divided easily into *light-colored* versus *dark-colored nonmetallics*. These may further be subdivided into *hard* and *soft*, those which show *cleavage* when struck by a hammer, and those which develop only *fracture*. Metallic, colored minerals are distinguished on the basis of *color* and *streak*, rather than by hardness.

The Table on pages 55-56 provides a handy reference for quickly identifying commonly occurring rocks and minerals in the field, using only a coin, a knife blade, or the rocks themselves to ascertain "scratchability," or relative degrees of hardness. If one mineral can scratch another, the one that does the grooving is, naturally, the harder. Two minerals of equal hardness will either scratch each other or, more likely, fail to make any impression either way.

*Cleavage.* Cleavage is the property a crystal has of breaking at any place along one of a series of parallel planes that will reflect light as a mirror does. Some minerals have no cleavage; some have only one direction, some two or more. When there are two or three directions of cleavage, it is important to note whether they are perpendicular or oblique to each other. Cleavage can be said to be good, fair, poor, or none. Perfect cleavage occurs in mica books, which separate like the pages of a book.

*Fracture.* Any break not a cleavage is a fracture. The most important fracture for purposes of identification is the "conchoidal" fracture, a smooth curving break with sharp edges like

## FIELD DETERMINATION OF COMMON MINERALS
a break in thick glass. Other fracture types are: *rough, splintery, even, uneven,* and *subconchoidal* (not quite conchoidal). *Miscellaneous Properties.* Further identification can be made by noting whether a mineral is *transparent, translucent,* or *opaque.* Some minerals have *smell* or *odor,* or a *slippery feel.* Others are *flexible* (can be bent only) or *elastic* (return to original shape). A few minerals are *sectile* (can be cut), *malleable* (can be hammered into other shapes or dented because they are not *brittle*). A very few of the metallic minerals are *magnetic.*

### FIELD CHECK OF MINERALS

#### NONMETALLIC, LIGHT-COLORED

*Hard, Cleavage* — Hardness

| | | Hardness |
|---|---|---|
| Pink to flesh-colored, blocky cleavage | Orthoclase | 6 |
| Grayish, lathlike, smooth (94°) | Plagioclase | 6 |
| Green, columnar, prismatic | Actinolite | 5-6 |
| Gray to red, greasy, soluble | Nepheline | 5½-6 |

*Hard, Fracture*

| | | |
|---|---|---|
| Green, glassy, granular | Olivine | 6½-7 |
| Glassy, variously colored | Quartz | 7 |
| Isometric, garnetlike, dark matrix | Leucite | 5½-6 |

*Soft, Cleavage*

| | | |
|---|---|---|
| Salty taste, cubic crystals | Halite | 2½-3 |
| Colorless, rhombohedron | Calcite | 3 |
| | Dolomite | 3½-4 |
| Flexible plates | Gypsum | 2 |
| Rectangular cleavage | Anhydrite | 3½ |
| Soapy feel, greasy, micaceous | Talc | 1 |
| Elastic, flaky, glistening | Muscovite | 2-2½ |
| Fibrous, brittle | Zeolite | 3½-5½ |
| Fibrous, flexible | Asbestos | 2-5 |
| Green, greasy, fibrous, little cleavage | Serpentine | 2-5 |

*Soft, Fracture*

| | | |
|---|---|---|
| Yellow, burns blue, suffocating odor | Sulphur | 2 |
| Earthy | Kaolinite | 2-2½ |

#### NONMETALLIC, DARK-COLORED

*Hard, Cleavage*

| | | |
|---|---|---|
| Black, prismatic (87–93°), glossy | Augite | 5-6 |
| Green to black, prismatic (56°, 124°) | Hornblende | 5-6 |
| Dark green, basal, glossy | Epidote | 6-7 |

*Hard, Fracture*

| | | |
|---|---|---|
| Brownish-green, uneven, glossy | Epidote | 6-7 |
| Dark brown, orthorhombic, glossy | Staurolite | 7-7½ |
| Red, green, yellow, glassy, 12-sided | Garnet | 6-7½ |
| Black, columnar, hexagonal | Tourmaline (schorl) | 7-7½ |
| Pink, green, columnar, hexagonal | Tourmaline | 7-7½ |
| Variously colored, waxy, conchoidal | Agate, chalcedony, chert, jasper, quartzite | 7 |
| Black, mottled, red, green, glassy | Obsidian | 7 |
| Dark, crystalline, foliated | Schist | 5-7 |

*Soft, Cleavage*

| | | |
|---|---|---|
| Brown to black, elastic, flaky | Biotite | 2 |
| Green to black, micaceous, flexible | Chlorite | 2-2½ |
| Brown rhombohedrons, pearly | Siderite | 3½-4 |

METALLIC, COLORED

*Black*

| | | |
|---|---|---|
| Black streak | Magnetite, Ilmenite | 6 |
| Black streak | Coal, Graphite | 1-3 |
| Red streak | Hematite | 1-6½ |
| Yellow streak | Limonite | 1-5½ |

*Red*

| | | |
|---|---|---|
| Metallic, fracture jagged | Copper | 2½-3 |
| Earthy | Hematite | 1-6½ |

*Yellow, Brown*

| | | |
|---|---|---|
| Metallic, black streak | Pyrite | 6-6½ |
| Earthy, yellow streak, brown cubes | Limonite | 1½-5 |

CHAPTER **VI**

# *The Geologic Map**
AAAAAAAAAAAAAAAAA

Many mineral or gem stone collecting fields become worked out, except for float, after a period of intensive collecting. However, each occurrence of desirable materials can be considered as a particular geological exposure, and you can expect that similar outcroppings must occur at other, possibly widely spaced locations.

The geologic map is probably one of the most useful field aids in helping both the amateur and the professional mineral and gem stone prospector find his way to new and more promising areas in which to prospect. The better-known, and certainly the most exploited rockhound fields are those most easily reached by automobile. Additional mineralized areas may often be found in the surrounding region, and you can get to them on foot simply by following the indications shown on a geologic map of the area. Such maps are commonly available at very modest cost (see page 67).

Scientific prospecting is not easy, and following a hunch hardly practical. The earth's thin rocky outer layer cannot be turned

---

* Adapted from "The Geologic Map" by Quintin O. Aune, *Mineral Information Service*, State of California Division of Mines, Vol. 13, No. 8, August 1960.

inside out for detailed study. Moreover, its basic proportions are so vast as not readily to be visualized in the field. Far more materials are still locked inside the earth—often very close to the surface—than were ever dug out, and only a tiny glimpse here or there gives us any clue to their whereabouts.

It is from these modest clues that sharp-eyed geologists have fashioned their detailed maps. Commercial prospectors use these aids constantly in their search for metals, minerals, and fuels. Although rarely indicative of the type of minerals and gem stones prized by amateur collectors, the same maps can be used in pursuit of cutting materials.

By skillful interpretation of the lines, colors, and symbols on the geologic map, the prospector learns where to explore for metallic ores or to drill for oil, even though these natural resources may be buried deep below the surface. Similarly, the nongeologist or amateur gem stone hunter may use the map to select promising areas in which to seek for new collecting fields equal to, or better than, gem stone deposits he already knows.

## HOW THE GEOLOGIC MAP IS MADE

*The Base Map.* The base for most modern geologic maps is a topographic contour map, particularly valuable for making satisfactory measurements of height, slope, and distance. A little practice reveals the astonishing detail with which the natural features of the earth's surface are shown, such as rivers, mountains, valleys, and plains by means of contour lines, labels, or symbols. These maps also clearly indicate such man-made features as roads, dams, bridges, towns, canals, individual barns and houses as well as civil boundaries, property outlines, township-and-range grid systems, parallels of latitude, and meridians of longitude. It is very easy to orient yourself exactly on this base map with its pinpointed reference points and lines if its scale is reasonably large. Once oriented, you can readily identify nearby outcrops and any other geologic notations added to the basemap.

*The Geologic Map.* Most geologic maps are made squarely on top of existing topographic maps, simply by adding a variety of lines and symbols that were adopted and standardized in the eighteenth century. The lines, called "contact lines" or simply "contacts," mark out the line of junction or contact between adjacent bodies of different types of rock. If the contact is clear-cut and can be precisely located, it is drawn with a *solid line*. If it is not clear-cut, or merely inferred (an educated guess), a *broken line* is used. A *dotted line* indicates the probable line of contact where it has been buried under later deposits.

Early map-making geologists soon learned to correlate separated exposures of the same type of rock. Where the separate exposures were numerous enough to make a map seem exceedingly complex, they resorted to the use of color to simplify things by painting all the isolated outcrops of a given type of rock with the same color. Thus colors on a modern geologic map were arbitrarily selected to identify rock units by reference to a legend at the edge of the map.

*Mapping Symbols.* The custom of age-dating sedimentary layers according to the fossils they contain also provides the symbols used in conjunction with color to show different varieties of rocks. Thus, Quarternary (Q) rocks are usually shown as yellow, Tertiary (T) sediments as orange, and Jurassic (J) deposits as green. The color used has no relation to the actual appearance of the formations in the field. For instance, most Jurassic sandstones, particularly in southwestern America, are stained red with iron oxide. Tertiary sediments may be any color, but browns, grays, and blacks predominate—the colors of ordinary dirt and clay. The Table on page 60 illustrates the common map-color units and the symbols and names used for the different ages to which the time units have been loosely attached.

Note that primary age-symbols are the capital initial letters, whereas the rock type or, on more detailed maps, the specific rock formation is shown by small letters following the age-symbol. Thus: "Pc" represents *Pliocene continental*, i.e., non-marine rocks of Pliocene age, or 12,000,000 years ago; "Tm" stands for Tertiary (Monterey formation); and "KJf" is Cretaceous-Jurassic (Franciscan formation).

All symbols used on a particular map are summarized with their meanings in the margin.

Sometimes, a geologic feature is not marked directly onto a map, but is indicated by simple trigonometric principles, i.e.,

## HOW TO READ A GEOLOGIC MAP

| Conventional Map Colors* | Symbol and Period | | Estimated Ages of Time Boundaries in Years | Characteristic Fossil Types |
|---|---|---|---|---|
| Yellow | Q | Quaternary | 1,500,000 | All present forms of life and a few extinct species of mammal |
| Orange | T | Tertiary | 68,000,000 | Mammals, flowering plants, marine snails, clams, oysters |
| | P | Pliocene | (12,000,000) | |
| | M | Miocene | (25,000,000) | Horse (four genera), grass |
| | O | Oligocene | (40,000,000) | Titanotheres, flowering plants |
| | E | Eocene | (60,000,000) | Creodonts, Eohippus, birds |
| | Ep | Paleocene | (70,000,000) | Small five-toed quadrupeds |
| Yellow-Green | K | Cretaceous | 130,000,000 | Reptiles, dinosaurs, snails, ammonites; conifers, Sequoia |
| Green | J | Jurassic | | |
| Blue-Green | Tr | Triassic | 180,000,000 | Ammonites, dinosaurs, flying reptiles, cycads, amphibians, pine forests |
| Blue | P | Permian | 185,000,000 | Primitive land plants; corals, clamlike marine animals, tree ferns |
| | CP | Pennsylvanian | | |
| | CM | Mississippian | 265,000,000 | |
| Blue-Purple | D | Devonian | | Fish, crablike animals (trilobites); Simple invertebrate animals |
| Purple | S | Silurian | | |
| | O | Ordovician | | |
| Terra Cotta | C | Cambrian | 500,000,000 | Trilobites |
| Gray-Brown | pC | Pre-Cambrian | 4½-6 billion | Marine algae and spongelike forms |

* The map color usually used for igneous rocks, such as granite, is pink or red in order to differentiate them from sedimentary rocks. No fossils occur in igneous rocks.

by symbols for direction and distance from some visible landmark that also appears on the base map. *Direction* is indicated
as a horizontal angle between the line from one place to another
and a standard north-south line measured by magnetic compass.
*Distances* may be paced by foot, measured by tape, or obtained
by plane surveying. A little practice in interpreting these elementary symbols will pay you rich dividends in leading you to
untouched mineral fields, especially in all the states west
of the Mississippi River.

## READING THE GEOLOGIC MAP

Reading a geologic map with comprehension takes some practice, but it is not difficult. To begin with, it is probably easiest
to select a geologic map of an area well known to you before-
hand, preferably close to home. It should be as detailed as possible, with an accurate topographic base and a clearly defined
geology. The latter should include symbols to indicate the geologic structures and, perhaps, fossil localities. If a geologic road
log (a form of geologic map and description that follows along
a given road or highway) is also available for your area, so
much the better.

A brief study of the base map features, such as roads, streams,
towns, prominent landmarks, etc., and their orientation with
respect to the indicated geologic features should help you to
become scientifically familiar with the area. You should then
travel through it and take particular note of the cultural and
geologic features shown on the map. An inexpensive hand compass will further help you to orient yourself with the map and
to determine attitudes of any bedded rocks that crop out above
the surrounding land surface.

Finally, it would be advisable to study the map's geologic
features closely. Choose an area within the map where good
exposures of flat-lying, or only slightly deformed sedimentary
rocks are indicated by the appropriate symbols. Examine the
actual rocks to familiarize yourself with them and with their
map representation by color and symbol.

*Sedimentary, or Layered Rocks.* Rock units depicted on a
geologic map commonly include layered rocks that were once
deposited as sediments, since, by and large, these are the most

frequently encountered rocks found on continental land masses. Although the most extensive geologic formations of sedimentary origin were originally formed flat on the ocean floor, features that illustrate many of the basic principles of deposition may be observed along stream channels and around lake shores. In some regions the sedimentary features of ancient stream channels are abundantly exposed in quarries and road cuts—excellent places to prospect for gem stones.

Recent marine deposits may be exposed on the cliffs bordering ocean beaches. Ancient sea-laid sediments which have been raised high into dry land, often as great mountain ranges of extraordinary scenery like those in Glacier National Park, are usually tilted one way or another from the center of uplift. The fact that their layers appear superimposed on one another indicates that, indeed, they were once laid down by deposition on the level floor of an ancient sea. The angle of tilt is included on the map as a "dip-strike" symbol.

As you enter the area covered by a geologic map, you should pay particular attention to stream-cut and road-cut exposures of the various geologic units shown on the map. You should also look on your map for contacts between formations, and seek out exposures where such contacts may be observed.

If a line of contact is exposed, try to compare its description in the related text with its appearance on the map and how it actually looks as a landscape feature. Is the bedding observable as described? Does the younger (upper) unit lie in normal stratigraphic position over the older (lower) unit? Check the unit's detailed description in the text, or "geologic column," with its actual appearance in the outcrop with respect to color, grain size, and internal textures. Does the measured attitude, i.e., the direction and degree of slope of the bedding planes at this outcrop, agree with that shown on the map?

If there seem to be discrepancies in the answers to the above questions, you should check to be certain that you have correctly interpreted the bedding plane, allowed for magnetic compass declination, and avoided any nearby piece of iron or steel that might throw your compass reading off.

*Note:* It is important to understand the nature of folding in the area being investigated. By projection of the folded bed, you may be able to follow a layer of mineral or gem stone bearing rock to locate new or unexplored localities for concentrated exploration.

*Use of Dip-Strike Symbols.* Wherever outcrops of the bedded rocks permit the necessary measurements to be made, their attitude or slope is indicated by the dip-strike symbol—⊥. "Dip" stands for the slope and "strike" for the angle which it makes with a north-south line. Strike directions are readily determined by a simple magnetic compass with an attached level, and indicated on the geologic map by straight lines of appropriate direction.

Dip is an angle in a vertical plane and is always measured *downward* from the horizontal plane, or horizon. Its direction is perpendicular to the strike, which is the direction of the intersection of the surface with any horizontal plane. Taken together, dip and strike determine the position or *attitude* of a surface with respect to horizontality and to compass directions. Sometimes, the direction of dip is shown by an arrow and its magnitude by adding a figure in degrees, e.g., 15°.

Since dip and strike are always taken together at an outcrop, they are shown on the map by the combined symbol. The exact location of the outcrop reading is at the intersection of the two perpendicular lines on the symbol, which on your map may be slanted in any direction to conform with the locality, as: north 45° east, dip 20° southeast. From even a relatively small number of such symbols on a map, it becomes possible to visualize underlying fold structures, even in areas where outcrops are few and far between.

### FAULTS

Fault lines which are indicated on a geologic map are not always easy to see, except in the comparatively rare instances when you might be fortunate enough to find the fault exposed in a road cut or streambank. Major fault zones are commonly subdued, poorly exposed features—a result of long weathering and overgrowths of vegetation. They may be visible only as a shallow trough or as a number of notches along a hillside. California's infamous San Andreas fault, which caused the great San Francisco earthquake of 1906, is a noted fault zone which occupies a marked trough, or "topographic depression," visible in many places along its more than 700-mile length.

Questions to ask yourself in the field are: Can any faults be recognized by the offsetting or disruption of bedding planes along a straight line or zone of rubble in any streambank or road cut? Can the same bed be identified on both sides of the offset? Is this fault shown on the geologic map? Does the map show different rock formations on opposite sides of the fault zone? If so, a closer look at any nearby outcrops might prove very interesting.

Note whether the mapped fault zone is marked or not by foreign rock fragments in the soil, which resemble neither of the adjoining formations in color or texture. If present, these fragments may be "fault gouge," i.e., ground-up, altered, commonly stained rock fragments. Or, they may be fragments of an older, underlying rock formation which have been dragged to the surface along the plane of fault movement. Such fragments provide concrete indications of minerals or gem stones which may be buried somewhere below the surface.

A trip over any of the passes that cross a mountain range, or along any rugged, mountainous seacoast that is characterized by rocky headlands and deep indentations, should reveal outcrops which will illustrate some or all of the answers to the foregoing questions.

## FOLDS

When you have learned to recognize faults in the field, and the various features which indicate rock slippage, you are ready to look at the folded rocks. Folds small enough to be visible are frequently exposed in stream channels, ocean cliffs, and road cuts, especially in the relatively young, still rising West Coast mountain ranges. Folds too small to show on a standard geologic map may often be recognized in a single road cut.

Larger folds may be recognized by studying the dip of the bedding planes. For example, as you progress through mountainous country, the strata exposed in a road cut may all dip toward the west. As you drive eastward from road cut to road cut, the dip of the beds gradually diminishes in steepness from one exposure to another. Finally, the beds appear to flatten out, and you find yourself at the top of an anticlinal (inverted-U) fold.

Still farther to the east, the beds begin to dip slightly, then more steeply, but this time toward the east. In this case, you have just crossed the crest of a north-trending *anticline*, or archlike fold. The Appalachian Mountains are particularly noted for this type of rock folding, but it should be further noted that most of their crests have been cleanly planed off, and only the side dips remain.

Anticlinal crests are well developed in the mountain systems of western America. A simpler although somewhat rarer structure is a *homocline*, i.e., a monotonous geologic structure in which the beds all dip in the same direction. These are well exposed along the east front of the California coast ranges west of Red Bluff, and along the sea coast in the Santa Barbara-Gaviota area.

## INTERPRETATION OF GEOLOGIC MAPS

If you are to make good use of geologic maps to help you locate new fields of gem stones and minerals, you must learn how to interpret the colors, lines, and symbols of a map sheet, for these represent the distribution and structural features of widespread formations that may be exposed only here and there above the earth's surface. If an isolated outcrop shows the presence of zircon, for instance, you can be rather certain that this gem stone occurs throughout the formation. If collectors before you have cleaned out the specimens from the known outcrop, naturally your problem is to "discover" similar outcrops farther on as shown on your map. Your reward will be many prize examples, well worth the time it took you to learn how to "prospect" on paper.

After a good deal of practice, the experienced map reader is able to perceive, instead of a physical two-dimensional image of brown contour lines on a map, a three-dimensional mental image of the land surface portrayed, not unlike looking through glass. This image will include ridges, valleys, mountains and plains, *and their underlying structures*. This ability is most helpful, because topographic variations may also reflect differences in rock types. They may even reflect the attitudes of layered sediments or the relative ages of different rock units.

For instance, a gently tilted hillside may be the resistant topside of a hard-rock formation; float may indicate that the hill is actually made of quartzite. Likewise, the relative age of two mountain peaks may sometimes be inferred from the contours on a topographic map, which reflect the relative degree of weathering and dissection the mountains have suffered because of erosion or glaciation. The more ridged and dissected, the older the mountain.

With the familiarity that comes only from practice, the conventional map colors evoke the proper mental images. You easily picture granite intrusions into sediments and note that the green areas on your map mean rocks of Mesozoic age, and in these rocks you may discover dinosaur bones. The trained interpreter "sees" tilted, folded, faulted, and sheared rocks instead of merely dip, strike, and shear symbols. You "see" in your mind's eye rock strata crossing a hill, or offset along a stream, rather than a colorful patchwork of lines on a sheet of paper.

The time that it takes for you to become familiar with these aspects of interpretation is time well spent in rock hunting. Its rewards and dividends make for exciting, profitable field trips.

### HOW TO USE A GEOLOGIC MAP IN PROSPECTING

A few simple rules can be set down by which you can follow a geologic map to new collecting fields.

1. Check the index map of the U.S. Geological Survey for quadrangle sheets. Check county and state offices for their maps and for information relating to prospecting. Then send for the particular quadrangle maps that cover known rock-hunting locations of special interest to you.

2. Visit any well-known rock collecting field, such as one of those listed in Part Two and, map in hand, locate yourself exactly with respect to the map's contour lines.

3. Note the type of rock formation from which the known gem stones or minerals originate, by color and symbol. Determine from the map where this mineralized formation trends. Pay attention to distances, outcrops, canyon breaks, and folds. Use a compass bearing to indicate routes of surface travel that cross the formation which has proved by its one known locality to be rich in the desired minerals.

4. Explore this formation as far as your time permits, check-

ing outcrops, talus slopes, draws, and canyon or stream beds for float. Continue to orient yourself in accordance with the features shown on the geologic map.

5. Be sure to carry a canteen of water. You are likely to get very thirsty if the weather is warm.

Many dealers in gem stone materials use this method for locating new fields which, for the most part, they keep scrupulously secret until they have removed the most commercially valuable specimens. By that time, little of worth is left for the amateur who, if he desires good cutting material, must then purchase it from the dealers.

## WHERE TO OBTAIN GEOLOGIC MAPS

For states west of the Mississippi River, geologic maps may be ordered from the *Distribution Section, U.S. Geological Survey, Federal Center, Denver, Colorado*. Indexes of map coverage and prices for individual maps will be supplied upon request.

For areas east of the Mississippi, indexes and maps can be ordered directly from the *U.S. Geological Survey, Washington 25, D.C.*

State and county maps may be purchased from private firms advertising in the regional rockhound publications listed in Appendix I, or directly from the various seats of government. Many governmental agencies have published unclassified reports which are available to the public either as printed copies at modest cost or in open file for public inspection.

These reports, usually found in the major public libraries, may contain valuable geologic information, maps, and diagrams. Most include descriptions of rocks, gem stones, and minerals that are helpful in prospecting and exploration for amateur and professional alike.

## ACTUAL STEPS IN PROSPECTING FOR NEW LOCALITIES

Whether one is after gem stone materials or commercially valuable minerals, the serious prospector will consider the acquisition of a supply of geologic maps only one step in the over-all preparation for a satisfying field trip. There are five additional steps to consider.

*Step 1.* When entering a new area, it is advisable to go to the nearest public library in order to study all the available literature and maps relating to that part of the state. County and state road maps are always available from automobile clubs or the various gasoline stations servicing an area. A little inquiry will reveal where forest-service maps, state and federal geologic and topographic maps, and local mining maps can be studied. Look up or obtain all copies available on geologic reports, published and unpublished, by federal, state, or private organizations.

*Step 2.* Nearly all of America has been photographed scientifically from the air. Look up or obtain by purchase all available aerial photographs of the area you would like to explore. These are particularly important in regions where the literature indicates there may be promising mineralizations. A good technique to use is to place an acetate overlay sheet over the photograph and mark onto it with grease pencil notes or symbols that will help you orient yourself in the field. You can then lay the acetate sheet over your map for field study.

*Step 3.* Make your first, or reconnaissance trip into the area by whatever means is available. If you have time to travel far off the beaten track, going in by horseback or jeep is the usual practice. En route, you should visit every area of geologic interest, every old gopher prospect hole, abandoned mine, or unusual outcropping, especially if a pegmatite dike. You should continually reorient yourself with respect to the geologic map and record notes on everything of interest. Keep close track of time and distance, if you are in rough country, to facilitate a return at a later date.

*Step 4.* Trust nothing to memory! Make notes of any investigations, particularly if they are of old mines, and try to relate them to your maps. You will probably not have time to investigate all likely prospects thoroughly on any one trip, but you may want to return for a follow-up hunt.

*Step 5.* When you have obtained a general picture of the total area and fixed it in your mind, select a particular section for more thorough investigation. Note routes into it and which portions are easy to prospect by foot or from horseback. Make sketches and rough maps in a notebook and add any observations that seem pertinent to a possible return trip some day. Take both area-wide photographs and detailed, close-up shots of promising exposures, and gather plenty of representative mineral samples as you proceed.

Remember that as your experience increases more and more of what you read on the geology of the area will stay in your mind. Even though you may not fully understand everything you find in print, you will certainly absorb a good deal of it. And every little bit added to your knowledge will help you in your next prospecting trip.

# PART TWO

# CHAPTER VII

# Where to Find Rocks and Minerals
/\/\/\/\/\/\/\/\/\/\/\/\/\/\/\/\/\/\/\/\/\/\/\/\/\/\/\/\/

In a book of this size, it is almost impossible to list all of the known rock-hunting localities. The Bibliography given in Appendix I enumerates various regional field publications which detail specific areas, usually with mileage maps. Even these are by no means complete. Almost every experienced rock collector knows of localities which have never been named in print, many of which he found himself and which he will reveal only to close friends.

Chapter VI has presented the technique for scientifically prospecting for new rock-hunting fields, starting from any of the well-known localities. In this section, the most important mineral and gem stone areas are described, arranged alphabetically by state and county. You will discover that desirable minerals are not evenly distributed over the earth's surface, and that there are few areas in which all types of rocks meet. The number and variety of your collection will depend not only on where you live, but also on the amount of vacation travel you can devote to ferreting out strange and interesting mineral specimens. Appendix II lists alphabetically by state and city all the most important rock museums. These are wonderful places to start from, providing you with a background of regional geology and helping you to recognize the rocks and minerals to be found in the surrounding countryside.

New Englanders are fortunate in being surrounded by an extremely broad and rich rock-hunting region. So are residents of southern California and Oregon. But Midwesterners are narrowly limited to sedimentary rocks and the few minerals they contain (see Chapter V). Nearly all mountainous districts are sure to offer a wide variety of mineral substances, often colorful ores where mines have been developed. In any case, almost every state does have at least a few localities you will find worth investigating. Here they are, as follows:

## ALABAMA

Alabama comprises two geologic regions and few gem stone areas. The northeast section is rather mountainous and constitutes the southern end of the Cumberland Plateau. Here, limestone caverns yield calcium minerals hard enough to cut and polish. The rest of the state is a rolling plain averaging about 500 feet above sea level in which the Tuscaloosa Formation disgorges chert.

BIBB COUNTY: Centreville area, 5 mi. N along Highway 5 —*barite crystals, chalcedony, chert, siliceous oölite.*

BLOUNT CO.: Blountsville, 1 mi. W—*agate, chalcedony, chert.*

CALHOUN CO.: limestone and dolomite quarries—*barite.*

CHEROKEE CO.: Centre, Miocene outcrops—*tektites.*

CLAY CO.: pegmatite outcrops—*beryl, feldspar, mica, quartz.* Erin, see Jefferson Co.

COOSA CO.: Bradford area pegmatites—*beryl, corundum, feldspar, quartz, sapphire.* Hissop, 1 mi. NE and 3/4 mi. SW— *golden beryl.* Rockford—*aquamarine, golden beryl, quartz.*

JACKSON CO.: Gurley, SE—*agate, chert.*

JEFFERSON CO.: Idaho—*turquoise* in copper prospects. Also south of Pleasant Grove Church and in RR cut 2½ mi. N of the church near Erin in Clay Co.

LEE CO.: sandstone quarries—*itacolumite* (flexible sandstone).

MARENGO CO.: Barton's Bluff—*calcite crystals.*

RANDOLPH CO.: Pinetucky, Pat Ayers Prospect No. 2 Mica Mine, 2¼ mi. NE—*aquamarine.*

SHELBY CO.: Birmingham—*diamond.*
ST. CLAIR CO.: Brompton, 1¼ mi. E at Prescott Siding—*diamond.*
STONE HILL COPPER MINE—*azurite, malachite.*
TALLADEGA CO.: limestone caves—*stalagmites.*
TALLAPOOSA CO.: Nonspecified areas—*sapphire.*

## ALASKA

Alaska comprises four major districts: Southeastern—rugged coastal mountains, fjords, and many timbered islands; Aleutians —volcanically active island chain; Interior—sea-level tundras and many placer-gold streams; Arctic Coast—plains region between the Brooks Range and the Arctic Ocean. Travel and communication is everywhere difficult and expensive. In most areas mining is or has been of major importance. Except for jade in the extreme northwest portion, the ore minerals dominate the gem stones.

ADAK ISLAND: beach gravels yield *jasper.*
ADMIRALTY ISLAND: Gambier Bay to Wilson Cove, and near Point Gardner—*agate, chalcedony, jasper.*
ATTU ISLAND: SE beach gravels—*chalcedony, jasper.*
BARANOF ISLAND: Red Bluff Bay—*serpentine.* Head of Silver Bay, SE of Sitka—*rhodonite.*
CHICAGOF ISLAND: Iyoukeen Cove—*alabaster.*
JUNEAU INDIAN RESERVATION: Copper River—*star sapphire.*
KOBUK RIVER DISTRICT: Jade Mountain and Jade Hills, 30 mi. W of Kobuk and in all regional stream gravels; also Shungnak River bars—*asbestos, nephrite, serpentine.*
KOTZEBUE SOUND: area mountains—*pectolite.*
KUPREANOF ISLAND: Glacier Bay and Hamilton Bay— *agate, jasper, petrified wood.*
POINT BARROW: mountains to the south—*pectolite.*
PRINCE OF WALES ISLAND: Sulzer; Green Monster Copper Mine—*chalcopyrite, epidote, grossularite garnet, rock crystal.*
SHUMAGIN ISLANDS: Sand Point—*agate, carnelian, chalcedony, jasper.*
TANAGA ISLAND: *agate, jaspers.*
UNALASKA ISLAND: beach gravels—*agate, chalcedony,*

*jasper, plasma agate.* Mt. Makushin back of Dutch Harbor—*obsidian, sulphur.*

WRANGELL DISTRICT: Stikine River mouth 1¾ mi. SE of Sergief Island along Garnet Creek—*almandine garnet.*

ZAREMBO ISLAND: beach gravels of Kuiu Island and Saginaw Bay—*agate, jasper, petrified wood.*

## ARIZONA

Often known as the "Copper State," Arizona ranks among the most heavily mineralized regions of the world. In nearly every district are old and new mines affording colorful mineral specimens. The northern portion is part of the Colorado Plateau with arid plains and high, timbered plateaus with elevations ranging from 4000 to 10,000 feet. This great plateau breaks in a vast escarpment stretching across central Arizona and known as the Tonto and Mongollon Rims. Southern Arizona, where the Gila River flows across the entire state, is a land of hot desert plains broken by north-south ranges of dry, severely eroded mountains. It is an immense, empty land of contrast between arid cactus deserts and snow-capped mountains still relatively unexplored for any minerals other than gold, silver, and copper.

APACHE CO.: Beautiful Valley (between Chinle and Ganado), and N of Chinle—*petrified wood.* Cedar Ridge, Echo Cliffs (Chinle formation)—*agate, jasper.* Concho area, and W of St. Johns—*agate, agate* (dendritic), *chalcedony, chert, petrified wood;* also on both sides of the road between Highway 666 and Navajo and in a wide area embracing Sanders and Witch Well. Ganado (SW)—*agatized wood.* Mexican Water, 5 mi. W at Garnet Ridge—*pyrope garnet* ("Arizona rubies"); also in the Moses Rock field, 10 mi. N of Mexican Water in San Juan Co., Utah. Round Rock, 12 mi. WSW of village of same name—*petrified wood.* SW of Tanner Springs in Tanner Wash, and N of Pinto Siding (Santa Fe RR)—*silicified wood.*

COCHISE CO.: Bisbee area copper mines—*azurite, bornite, brochantite, chalcanthite, chalcocite, chalcopyrite, chalcotrichite, chrysocolla, cuprite, malachite, native copper, shattuckite.* Chiricahua Mountains—*agate, chalcedony, jasper, petrified wood.* Courtland, ¾ mi. NW at Turquoise Ridge—*limonite, turquoise.*

COCONINO CO.: Flagstaff, Brown Onyx Quarry—*onyx*. Lees Ferry on Colorado River near mouth of Paria River; Moenkopi, 9 mi. NW around Willow Springs and in Nokai Creek Canyon 10 mi. E of Dunns—*silicified wood*.

GILA CO.: Apache Indian Reservation, Altar Mountains near Globe—*andesine, andesine-sunstone*. Cherry Creek Wash, 15 mi. NE of east end of Roosevelt Reservoir—*agate, jasper*. Chrysotile-Cienega-Salt River Canyon asbestos mines—*asbestos, chrysotile serpentine*. Globe district, 6½ mi. W at Keystone and Live Oak Mines—*chrysocolla, chrysocolla-stained chalcedony, copper minerals, malachite, rock crystal*. Miami, 5 mi. W at Castle Dome Mine—*chrysocolla, chrysoprase, clay minerals, copper minerals, crocidolite, sericite, turquoise*. San Carlos, 2½ mi. SW at Peridot Mesa—*peridot*. San Carlos Reservoir, S bank of Gila River below Coolidge Dam—*agate, garnets, native copper*.

GRAHAM CO.: San Carlos Indian Reservation—*black hypersthene, peridots*. Stanley district, SE by dirt road that leaves Highway 70 about 8 mi. E of Coolidge Dam, Stanley Buttes (Crystal Peak, Limestone Mountain, Quartzite Mountain)—*andradite garnet*. Stanley's Deer Creek Basin and south side of Copper Reef Mountain—*agate, chalcedony, jasper*.

GREENLEE CO.: Most areas yield *agate, chalcedony, jasper, petrified wood* to casual prospecting. Ash Spring Mountain and Ash Spring Canyon—*agate, jasper*. Clifton area, (1) both sides of Highway 75 between Clifton and Duncan—*petrified wood*; (2) Limestone Canyon along the San Francisco River 7 mi. NE of Clifton—*purple agate*; (3) Mulligan Peak and Ward Canyon, 15 mi. E of Clifton—*red agate*; (4) Mule Creek Road, 14 mi. SE of Clifton—*chalcedony geodes*; and (5) York, 15 mi. S of Clifton—*agate* (banded, fire), *carnelian, jasper*. Both sides of Highway 666 between Guthrie and Safford—*cryptocrystalline quartz gem stones*. Morenci, Detroit and Manganese Blue mines —*azurite, chalcotrichite, malachite*. Peloncillo Mountains— *agate* (pastel), *chalcedony, jasper*.

MARICOPA CO.: Aguila, washes to west along Highway 60-70—*Apache tears* (*obsidian*). Alama Mountain—*variscite*. Aztec Mountain—*chrysoprase*. Camp Creek, 18.6 mi. N of Cave Creek on road to Seven Springs—*orbicular* ("*Cave Creek*") *jasper*. Canyon Lake Reservoir, 1½ mi. S of Port of Phoenix—

*chalcedony geodes.* Cave Creek area, along road between Cave Creek and New River, 4 mi. SW—*agate, gold, orbicular jasper, quartz.* Four Peaks, 45 mi. ENE of Phoenix and 9¾ mi. W of Roosevelt Dam, on flanks of 2nd peak from the south—*amethyst.* Gila Canyon—*chrysoprase, garnet.* Rock Springs, Agua Fria River, New River, and Skunk Creek gravels between Phoenix and Prescott—*agate, chalcedony, jasper.* Saddle Mountain, 22 mi. NW of Hassayampa—*fire agate.* Seven Springs, 3 mi. N—*onyx.*

MOHAVE CO.: Big Sandy River gravels, 22 mi. N of Wikieup—*onyx.* Burro Creek crossing of Highway 93 about 47 mi. NW of Congress Junction; also 6½ mi. NW of Burro Creek Bridge—*agate, amethystine chalcedony, chalcedony roses, chert, jasper, obsidian.* Cabezas Mountains, Cohen Mine—*scheelite crystals.* Kingman area, SW side of Cerbat Range, 15 mi. NW of Kingman to SE of Mineral Park—*kaolin minerals, turquoise.* Colorado River gravels, E side alluvial terraces and foothills (from Lake Meade southward)—*agate, chalcedony, chalcedony roses, jasper, petrified wood* (ironwood, palm, cycad). Hualpai Mountains, Boriana Mine—*scheelite crystals.* Mineral Park area, (1) Ithaca Peak, 1 mi. E of Mineral Park; (2) Aztec Mountain, 1 mi. S of Ithaca Peak; (3) at end of range of hills ⅓ mi. SSW of Mineral Park; and (4) on a mountain 4/5 mi. SSE of Mineral Park—*clay minerals, turquoise.* Oatman-Topoc District, (1) between Kingman and Goldroad; (2) Meadow Creek Pass; and (3) Sitgreaves Pass—*agate* (fire, grape), *chalcedony, chalcedony roses, jasper.* Schaeffer's Springs—*chalcedony.* Topoc, 7½ mi. N—*agate, chalcedony, jasper.*

NAVAJO CO.: This broad region of Triassic and Jurassic sediments, particularly southeast of Holbrook, is noted for its *petrified wood,* such as *Araucarioxylon arizonicum, Podozamites arizonica* (cycad type), and *Woodworthia arizonica.* In addition, some 35 other species of flora including, cycads, ferns, fungi, gingko trees, and horsetail rushes are found petrified. The larger tree trunks contain cavities that yield *amethyst, quartz crystals,* and related *cryptocrystalline quartz minerals.*

PIMA CO.: Ajo copper mines—*azurite, chrysocolla, malachite, shattuckite.* Arivaca-Ruby-Twin Buttes area—*azurite, bornite, chalcopyrite, covellite, cuprite, native copper, tetrahedrite.* Cortaro, hill surfaces SW—*agate* (banded, moss, plume). Tiger, Mammoth Mine—*cerrusite, dioptase, leadhillite, malachite, willemite, wulfenite*.

PINAL CO.: Florence, head of Martinez Canyon, NE—*agate, jasper*. Superior, perlite mines, SW—*Apache tears (obsidian)*.

SANTA CRUZ CO.: Helvetia-Rosemont mining district—*copper minerals*. Patagonia mining district (Duquesene, Harshaw, Red Mountain, Washington)—*actinolite, arsenic, chalcocite, chalcopyrite, diopside, epidote, galena, garnet, gedrite, hedenbergite, hornblende, magnetite, pyrite, pyrrhotite, tourmaline, tremolite, wollastonite*.

YAVAPAI CO.: Castle Hot Springs, 24 mi. NE of Morristown—*agate*, (gray, blue, fortification), *agate nodules, chalcedony roses, drusy quartz geodes, dumortierite, jasp-agate, jasper, manganese in quartzite, quartz crystals* (many with inclusions), *rose quartz, schorl (black tourmaline)*. Congress Junction, Date Creek, NW—*agate, garnet, jasper, limonite pseudomorphs after pyrite, quartz crystals*. Chino Valley—*agate, chalcedony, jasper*. Constellation area—*amethyst, jasper, quartz crystals*. Jerome, Perkinsville road, 9 mi. out—*agate* (varicolored), *jasper*. Mayer, on Highway 69 SE of Prescott and across Big Bug Creek—*"paisley shawl" onyx*.

YUMA CO.: Castle Dome Mountains—*opal, turquoise*. Brenda, S on Highway 60-70—*jasper*. Cibola road, 4½ mi. W of junction with Highway 95—*opalite*. Crystal Peak, in Plumosa Mountains 9 mi. S of Quartzite and 7.2 mi. E on poor dirt road —*limonite pseudomorphs after pyrite, quartz crystals* (chatoyant), *quartzite, rock crystals*; also in various washes for several miles eastward. Muggins Mountains, 6 mi. NW of Wellton and 6 mi. NE of Ligurta—*agate* (moss, plume), *jasper*. Yuma, Colorado River benchlands and sand hills, northward—*jasper, petrified wood* (cycad, ironwood, palm root), *roses (chalcedony)*.

## ARKANSAS

Northwestern Arkansas is mountainous and strongly mineralized. The important mountain ranges are the Boston and Ozark Mountains, really part of the segmented Ozark Plateau, and the Ouachita Mountains which are the roots of a very ancient range. To the south and east stretch broad, fertile plains.

GARLAND CO.: Chance, 2 mi. W—*quartz crystals* (large,

clear). Jessieville area—*quartz crystals, smoky quartz.* Miller Mountains, 9 mi. W of Chance—*quartz crystals, variscite.*
HOT SPRINGS CO.: Gifford area RR cuts—*amber.* Magnet Cove—*quartz crystals, sunstone.* Novaculite Mountains—*chalcedony, novaculite ("Arkansas Stone"), quartz crystals.*
MADISON CO.: Delaney—*quartz crystals.*
MARION CO.: Yellville area lead and zinc mines, especially the Morning Star Mine—*smithsonite* ("turkey fat").
MONTGOMERY CO.: Crystal Mountain—*quartz crystals.* Fisher Mountain, S of Mount Ida—*rock crystal, smoky quartz.*
PIKE CO.: Murfreesboro, Prairie Creek, 2½ mi. SSE—*amethyst, diopside, epidote, garnet, hematite, peridote, pyrite, quartz crystals.* Trinity formation of Cretaceous rocks intruded into Carboniferous formations—*diamond* (mines), *peridotite.*
POLK CO.: Mena, 7 mi. SE—clear *quartz crystals.*
SALINE CO.: Bauxite (30 mi. SW of Little Rock) quarries yield gem *bauxite (heliotrope bauxite).* Paron, 6-mi. radius—*quartz* (crystals, milky, smoky). broad area extending into Montgomery Co., i.e., from Paron to a point 5 mi. SW of Mount Ida—*calcite, chert, chlorite, feldspar, milky quartz, quartz crystals,* mostly found along the mountain and ridge crests.
SCOTT CO.: Blue Ball—*peridotite.*
WHITE CO.: Searcy—*peridotite, diamond.*

## CALIFORNIA

Second largest state of the continental United States, California has a diversified topography and complicated geological history. A series of mountain ranges extend along the 1200-mile coast, and behind them are relatively dry alluvial valleys (Sacramento and San Joaquin). In the south lie vast, arid deserts (Colorado, Mojave), and rising east of the great central valleys is the almost impenetrable granite barrier of the Sierra Nevada Range. Not only is California noted for its Mother Lode gold mines, but it ranks among the leading gem stone regions of the world. In fact, the Mother Lode counties of Butte, Calaveras, El Dorado, Mariposa, Nevada, Placer, Sierra, Tolumne, and Yuba were once noted for their gem quality *gold quartz,* formerly a prize collector's mineral.
ALPINE CO.: Markleeville, Loope district, S—*jasper.* Sonora Pass, along Highway 108—*agate, chalcedony, jasper.*

AMADORE CO.: Indian Gulch (near Fiddletown), Jackass Gulch and Rancheria (near Volcano), and Loafer Hill (near Oleta and Plymouth)—*diamond, gold.* Oleta and Volcano stream gravels—*amethyst, rock crystal, rose quartz.*

BUTTE CO.: Cherokee—*diamond* in stream gravels. Cherokee Flat—*diamond, gold.* Oroville area, (1) Thompson's Flat—*diamond, gold;* (2) west bank of Feather River, 1 mi. N—*diamond;* (3) Feather River gravels near Yankee Hill—*axinite,* and at Yankee Hill—*diamond, gold.* Pulga, north side of Feather River ½ mi. NE of Big Bar Station—*californite, grossularite garnet, serpentine.*

CALAVERAS CO.: Garnet Hill—*andradite garnet.* Mokelumne Hill district, (1) 2½ mi. S of the hill, and (2) Eclipse, i.e., Infernal Mine 3 mi. S, and other area mines—*gold, rock crystal.*

COLUSA CO.: Stonyford Creek gravels N of Ladoga—*jasper, nephrite, serpentine.* Sulphur Creek—*onyx.*

CONTRA COSTA CO.: Berkeley Hills, E of Berkeley, road cuts along Skyline Boulevard N of Fish Ranch Road in Moraga Formation—*chalcedony.*

DEL NORTE CO.: Crescent City, Pacific Ocean beaches—*agate, chalcedony, jasper, moonstones, petrified wood.* Smith River gravels—*diamond.*

EL DORADO CO.: Georgetown, 2½ mi. SSE at Traverse Creek—*californite* (massive), *garnet, idocrase.* Placerville, (1) area gold placers—*phantom quartz crystals, rock crystals* (many with inclusions); (2) American River, 5.6 mi. NE of Placerville—*nephrite;* and (3) Cedar Ravine, Forest Hill, Smith's Flat, Webber Hill, and White Rock Canyon—*diamond, gold.*

FRESNO CO.: Chowchilla River gravels—*turquoise.* Coalinga, Jacolito Canyon 3½ mi. S—*orbicular chert.* East side of Watts Valley, 1½ mi. S of Hawkins Schoolhouse and 700 feet above Watts Creek—*californite, garnet, serpentine.*

HUMBOLDT CO.: Trinity River gravels—*diamond.* Van Dusen River gravels—*agate, jade, jasper.*

IMPERIAL CO.: Cargo Muchacho and Chocolate Mountains—*agate, chalcedony, dumortierite, quartz crystals*—also 10 to 12 mi. N of Ogilby on either side of Indian Pass, with *petrified palm root.* Coyote Wells, to N—*fossil clams, fossil oysters.* Midway Well, 2 mi. E on road to True Friend and

Silver Mom mines on east flanks of Chocolate Mountains—
*opal, turquoise.* Wiley Well area, Hauser geode beds—*agate,
jasper, geodes, nodules.*
INYO CO.: Ballarat—*cerussite, wulfenite.* Cerro Gordo district mines—*brochantite, caledonite, copper carbonate ores,
linarite, smithsonite.* Furnace Creek Wash borax mine—*colemanite*—also in Gower Gulch and in the Ryan district outside
of Death Valley. Little Lake—*sanidine.* Mount Blanco district
borax mines—*howlite.* Owens Valley mine dumps—*azurite,
chalcopyrite, chrysocolla, cuprite, malachite, tellurides.* San
Carlos Mine—*lapis lazuli, opal.*
KERN CO.: Bakersfield, schist outcrops along Walker's
Creek, SE—*chiastolite crystals.* Castle Butte foothills, SE side,
but N of Highway 466—*agate, chalcedony, chert, jasper, petrified wood.* Greenhorn Mountains, (1) Huckaby and Little
Acorn mines—*epidote, quartz crystals, scheelite*; (2) scheelite
mine dumps—*epidote, scheelite crystals, smoky quartz crystals*
with *epidote inclusions.* Horse Canyon, (1) 7 mi. up the canyon
and 3 mi. SW of Cache Peak—*agate* ("Horse Canyon," moss,
lace, and tube); (2) Cache Creek Canyon, 2 mi. E of Monolith
on Highway 466—*"Horse Canyon" agate* varieties. Kramer
district, 35 mi. SE of Mojave and just N of Boron—*howlite.*
Mint Canyon—*howlite.* Red Rock Canyon, 18 mi. N of Mojave
—*precious opal.*
LAKE CO.: Clear Lake and Lower Clear Lake area, especially along Cole Creek—*dolomite crystals, obsidian.* Great
Western and Mirabel mercury mines, off Highway 29—*actinolite, chert, cinnabar, jamesonite, metacinnabar, millerite,
opalite, stibnite, tiemannite.* Middletown, 1½ mi. E on road to
Lower Lake—*pectolite, serpentine.*
LOS ANGELES CO.: Acton, hills and washes S and SW—
*agate, chalcedony, jasper, quartz.* Calabasas, 8 mi. N of Malibu
Beach on Highway 101—*agate, jasper, natrolite, sagenite agate.*
Escondido Canyon, between Acton and Agua Dulce Canyon—
*agate* (banded, green moss, sagenitic), *amethyst geodes, jasper.*
Palos Verdes, quarries and road cuts SW of Los Angeles—
*barite crystals, fossil shellfish, whale bones.* Redondo Beach to
El Segundo, low-tide ocean gravels—*moonstones.* Rosamond
area, (1) Gem Hill—*agate, chalcedony, jasper, plasma, uraninite*; (2) Portal Ridge—*rhodonite*; and (3) Wheeler Springs—

*jasper, obsidian, arrowheads.* San Gabriel Canyon, site of old Eldoradoville 20 mi. NNE of Glendora—*gold nuggets.* Tick Canyon, off Mint Canyon—*howlite.* Tujunga Canyon—*gold nuggets.* Zuma Beach—*fossil sharks' teeth.*

MADERA CO.: Chowchilla River, near Chowchilla Crossing on Fort Miller road—micaceous schists yield *chiastolite crystals.* Coarse Gold, (1) 2 mi. N, and (2) 5 mi. NE—*axinite, byssolite* (fibrous *actinolite*), *gold, quartz crystals, sphene.* Dalton, ½ mi. W at Dalton Copper Mine—*chiastolite crystals.* Ritter Range, west side—*lazulite.* Near Springerville—*axinite, byssolite.*

MARIN CO.: Eel River (North Fork)—*jade.* Petaluma, 5 mi. SW on east flanks of Massa Hill—*nephrite, satelite* (fibrous *serpentine*), *serpentine.* San Francisco Bay area, outcrops of Ingleside chert beds, 530 feet thick, and Sausalito chert beds, 900 feet thick yield a high-silica *chert* in bright colors, locally known as *kinradite*; (1) Point Bonita at foot of Golden Gate Bridge—*kinradite,* and (2) Sausalito, on SE corner of Marine Peninsula—*kinradite.*

MARIPOSA CO.: Moore's Flats metamorphic rocks, and from Hornitos slates, 12 mi. S of Mariposa—*chiastolite.*

MENDOCINO CO.: Eel River gravels—*jadeite, nephrite.* Leach Lake Mountain, both sides below Leach Lake—*jadeite.* Williams Creek gravels, near Mina and Covelo—*jadeite.*

MODOC CO.: *labradorite, sunstone.* Fort Bidwell; (1) pass between Fort Bidwell and Pine Creek—*agate, chalcedony, jasper, quartzite,* (2) east flank of Warner Mountains between Cedarville and Fort Bidwell—*agate, jasper,* Glass Mountain, or Buttes (on Siskyou Co. border)—*obsidian* (banded, black, blue, gold, green, rainbow, red, silver). Goose Lake—*agate, chalcedony, jasper.* Sugarloaf Mountain, 5 mi. E of Davis Creek Ranger Station—*obsidian* (all colors).

MONO CO.: Bodie road, lava beds just N of Mono Lake —*sanidine.* Mono Craters, east of Highway 395—*obsidian* (banded, variously colored). White Mountain, mines on west side—*anadalusite, augelite, dumortierite, lapis lazuli, lazulite, quartz, sillimanite.*

MONTEREY CO.: Cambria Pines area, Salmon and San Simeon creeks—*jade* in beach gravels. Cape San Martin, in low tide gravels—*nephrite, serpentine.* Jade Cove, 1250 feet SE of Plaskett Point and just S of the mouth of Willow Creek about 1200 feet NE of Cape San Martin, reached from State Highway 1—*nephrite, serpentine.* Lime Kiln Creek cove, 8 mi. N of Plaskett Point, on Pacific Ocean—*rhodonite.* Santa Lucia Range, west side stream gravels between Point Sur and Salmon Creek Ranger Station—*jade, nephrite, serpentine.* Stone Canyon, 18 mi NE of Bradley—*brecciated jasper.*

NAPA CO.: Knoxville, 3½ mi. out at Lone Pine chromite mine—common green *opal.* Manhattan Quicksilver Mine—*cinnabar, onyx.*

NEVADA CO.: French Corral—*diamond.* Nevada City area; (·1) Blue Tent Mining Camp, and (2) Sailor Flat—*agate, chalcedony, jasper, opalite, opalized wood, petrified wood.*

PLACER CO.: Shady Run gravels—*garnet, rock crystals* with *chlorite inclusions, serpentine.*

PLUMAS CO.: Genessee Valley, Indian Valley, Peters Mine near Taylorsville—*rhodonite.* Gopher Hill, Nelson Point, Sawpit Flat, Upper Spanish Creek—*diamond, gold.*

RIVERSIDE CO.: Blythe, Floyd Brown Mine—*fluorite.* Box Springs Mountain, 2 mi. E. of Riverside—*aquamarine.* Crestmore quarries, 3 mi. N of Riverside—*californite.* Jensen Quarry, at Crestmore—*idocrase, rose quartz, tourmaline.* Coahuila Mountain mines, particularly the Williamson Mine—*aquamarine, beryl, morganite.* Midland—*spinel.* Mule Mountains, SE of Wiley Well—*agate* (common, fire), *chalcedony, chalcedony roses* with *goethite* overlay (the so-called *fire agate*), *jasper.* Pegmatite outcrops of Lookout Mountain; Red, Little, Coahuila, and Thomas mountains; Rouse Hill—*idocrase, rose quartz, tourmaline.* Thomas Mountains—*amazonite.*

SAN BENITO CO.: Clear Creek gravels, along road between Hernandez and New Idria, and in area around Santa Rita Peak—*albite, analcite, biotite, garnet, jadeite, prehnite, serpentine, sphene, thomsonite.* Headwaters of San Benito River 25 mi. N of Coalinga—*benitoite, joaquinite, natrolite, neptunite, serpentine.*

SAN BERNARDINO CO.: Adelanto, Kramer Hills 30 mi. N along Highway 395—*chalcedony minerals, jasper.* Amboy Crater, S of Bagdad—*jasper, obsidian.* Barstow area; (1) Black Mountains 11 mi. N.—*fossils,* (2) 20 mi. NW at head of Blacks Canyon near Opal Mountain—*opal* (common, precious), (3) Eagle Crags 40 mi. N—*agate (blue) nodules, bentonite, calcite, chalcedony, chalcedonic quartz, chert, jasp-agate, jasper, jasp-opal, opal, opalite, orpiment, siderite, wonderstone,* (4) Goldstone Camp 30 mi. N—*turquoise,* (5) Leadpipe Springs in Eagle Crags district, 1½ mi. NE of springs on N side of steep hill—*agate (blue) nodules, chalcedony, jaspers, opal nodules, precious opal, septarian nodules, thundereggs,* (6) 15 mi. NW of Leadpipe Springs—*agate (blue) nodules, bentonite, clear chalcedony speckled with cinnabar, milk opal, opalite, quartz geodes,* (7) Solo Mining District—*turquoise.* Cady Mountains E of Ludlow; (1) Afton Canyon 10 mi. N of Baker—*agate (purple, sagenitic, tubular), crystal geodes, iron and opal nodules, rhyolite nodules* (agate centers), (2) old mine dumps just E of Ludlow—*agate, chalcedony, chrysocolla, fluorite, jasp-agate, jasper, malachite, psilomelane (calcite), psilomelane (manganese), smithsonite.* Cajon Pass area; (1) Blue Cut—*actinolite, epidote, slickensides,* (2) Lone Pine Canyon—*actinolite,* (3) summit in alluvial fan dropping northward—*rhodonite.* Calico District; (1) borate mines—*colemanite, howlite, ulexite,* (2) west side of Mule Canyon—*"silver" onyx (dendritic travertine),* (3) head of Mule Canyon—*petrified palm,* (4) Wall Canyon—*barite, cerargyrite, chert, embolite, jasper, orpiment.* Cascade Canyon, 12 mi. N of Upland and 5 mi. E by trail up San Antonio Canyon—*diopside, mica, lapis lazuli, quartz crystals.* Cottonwood Siding, Santa Fe RR, Gove Mine 2 mi. W—*turquoise.* Goffs area; (1) Barnwell, 32 mi. N in the New York Mountains—*turquoise,* (2) west of road between Goffs and Lanfair 12 mi. N of Goffs—*agate, chalcedony, jasper, petrified palm.* Hinkley, 18 mi. N off Highway 91/466, on secondary road N—*common opal*—also along both sides of a 6-mi. stretch of road—*agate, chalcedony, geodes, jasper.* Owl's Head Springs, in Owl's Head Canyon—*sagenite agate.* Pisgah Crater, S of Highway 66 and 35 mi. E of Daggett—*agate, chalcedony, chalcedony roses, "Lavic" jasper, obsidian.* Pyramid Peak, W side and E of Highway 190, ¼ mi. E of Death Valley—*onyx.* Sperry Wash, SE of S entrance to Death Valley National Monument—*petrified wood* (cycad, palm). Turquoise Mountains, Manvel District 5½ mi. from Halloran Springs on Highway 91/466, various small mines, especially the Himalay Claims at the head of Riggs Wash 12 mi. ENE of Silver Lake—*turquoise.* Turtle Mountains, Carson Well—*agate (common, moss), chalcedony,*

*chalcedony roses, jasp-agate, jasper, sagenite.* Wingate Canyon
—*sagenite agate.* Yucca Valley, 15 mi. NW and 1 mi. above
Pipes Canyon Public Camp—*onyx.*
   SAN DIEGO CO.: Alpine, Highway 80 about 35 mi. from
San Diego—*dumortierite, orbicular gabbro.* Chihuahua Valley,
N side to Hot Springs Mountain 4 mi. NE of Warner Springs,
many mine dumps, especially Pearson Mine—*tourmaline*
(gem). Escondido, Moosa Canyon—*axinite.* Jacumba; (1) Crystal Mine 8½ mi NW—*beryl,* (2) Dos Cabezas, 8 mi. NNE
alongside RR—*hessonite garnet.* Mesa Grande District, W
of Lake Henshaw near Highway 79, many mine dumps, especially Esmeralda, Himalaya, and Mese Grande mines—*aquamarine, beryl* (massive), *lepidolite, morganite, quartz crystals,
smoky quartz, tourmaline.* Pala District, pegmatite mines on
Hiriart Hill, Pala Chief Mountain, and Tourmaline Queen
Mountain, above San Luis Rey River N and NE of Pala—
*apatite, aquamarine, beryl, cleavelandite, kunzite, lepidolite,
morganite, quart crystals, smoky quartz, spodumene, tourmaline.* Palomar Mountain; (1) E rim of Aguanga Mountain,
Ware Mine—*quartz crystals, topaz, tourmaline,* (2) Mountain
Lily and Pearson mines, also Ware Mine—*beryl, lepidolite,
schorl, smoky quartz crystals, tourmaline.* Pinto Wash, S of
Highway 80, and tributaries—*wonderstone* (banded *rhyolite*).
Ramona District; (1) Hatfield Creek Valley pegmatite outcrops
3½ mi. ENE of Ramona on west side—*aquamarine, morganite,
spessartite garnet, topaz, tourmaline,* (2) Emeralite No. 2
Mine, (J. W. Ware) 3¾ mi. ENE of Ramona—*"emeralite"*
(greenish-blue *tourmaline*), *tourmaline,* (3) many other mines
overlooking Hatfield Creek—*beryl, feldspar, smoky quartz crystals, topaz, tourmaline,* (4) Little Three Mine—*cleavelandite,
schorl, smoky quartz crystals, spessartite garnet*—also farther
NE at Spaulding Mine, (5) in flats below Little Three Mine—
*diamond, gold,* (6) McFall Mine 7½ mi. SE of Ramona—
*epidote, grossularite garnet.* Rincon District, E of Rincon Indian Reservation in upper part of Pauma Valley, many mines
but especially the Clark and Victor mines on SW spur and the
Mack Mine 1½ mi. SSE of Rincon—*aquamarine, beryl, morganite, tourmaline.*
   SAN FRANCISCO CO.: Cliff House at Land's End Promontory, 1 mi. NE—*spherulitic chert.* Coyote Point, South San

Francisco Bay E of San Mateo Junior College and just N of the
yacht harbor—*chert* (brecciated, orbicular), *jasper.*
    SAN LUIS OBISPO CO.: Nipomo area fields and cuts—
*agate* (moss, sagenite), *stibnite, fossil bone, fossil wood, jasper.*
Paso Robles, in creek gravels—*jadeite.* Pozo, 5 mi. S, near Salt
Creek in the Santa Lucia Range 9.7 mi. from Routzahn County
Park—*onyx* (variously colored).
    SAN MATEO CO.: Pescador Beach 45 mi. S of San Francisco
—*orbicular chert.*
    SANTA CLARA CO.: Morgan Hill, 7 mi. NW of Gilroy
near Llagas Creek—*poppy (flowering) jasper ("Morgan Hill"
chert).* New Almaden mercury mines—*chert, cinnabar.*
    SISKIYOU CO.: Agate Flat—*agate, bloodstone, jasper, petri-
fied wood.* 6 mi. S of Berryvale—*onyx.* Chan Jade mine on
Indian Creek—*gold, idocrase, nephrite, serpentine.* Dunsmuir—
*pyrope garnets.* Indian Creek N of Happy Camp—*williamsite*
(noble serpentine). Between East Fork of Indian Creek and
Thompson Creek, 9 mi. N of Happy Camp on E side of
Thompson Mountain—*rhodonite.* South Fork of Indian Creek,
10 mi. NNW of Happy Camp—*californite, grossularite garnet,
idocrase, serpentine.* Jenny Creek NE of Hornbrooke—*agate,
carnelian, petrified wood.* Hundreds of mines occur along a
gold belt extending from Hornbrooke to Salmon Summit.
    SOLANO CO.: between Fairfield (Suisun) and Vacaville,
onyx quarries—*onyx.*
    SONOMA CO.: Calistoga, W—*opalized wood.* Between Glen
Ellen and Kenwood—*precious opal in kaolin.* Near Healdsburg
—*onyx.* Slopes of Mount Kanaktai—*obsidian.* Petaluma, 2½
mi. E along Adobe Creek—*pertified wood.*
    TRINITY CO.: Trinity River and tributaries—*agate, chal-
cedony, gold, jasper, nephrite, petrified wood, serpentine.*
    TULARE CO.: Coso Mountains, E of Little Lake on High-
way 395—*obsidian.* Exeter, Venice Hill mines in NE ¼ Sec.,
8 T., 18 S., R 26 E, Mt. Diablo Meridian—*chrysoprase, opal,
serpentine.* Lemoncove 3 mi. N on N side of a ravine ⅓ mi.
NE of Kaweah River and 1 mi. E of Ward Ranch—*quartzite,
rhodonite.* Lindsay, 1 mi. ESE, pits on N end of a low hill—
*chrysoprase, cryptocrystalline quartz, opal, serpentine.* Porter-
ville; (1) E of Plano and 1½ mi. S of town—*chalcedony, cryso-
pal, chrysoprase, opal* (common), *serpentine,* (2) same minerals

8 mi. E of town and ½ mi. S of Deer Creek. Visalia, S end of Venice Hill 8 mi. E of Visalia—*satelite* (serpentine).

VENTURA CO.: Frazier Mountain, borate mines N of Lockwood Valley—*howlite*.

YUBA CO.: Feather River gravels—*axinite, gold.*

## COLORADO

Eastern Colorado is part of the high Great Plains, and these retain much of their ancient tidal flats nature. Gentle slopes rise to the foothills of the Front Range, and behind this broad north-south barrier lie the great mountain peaks, rich in mineral and gem stone wealth. Western Colorado is a well-watered region of timbered plateaus, and natural amphitheaters, high snow-capped mountain ranges along the Continental Divide, and intermontane valleys. The southwestern region is mostly mesa and canyon, while the northwest embraces the remote canyons of the Green and Yampa rivers. The state's mean elevation is 6800 feet, with 51 peaks more than 14,000 feet high.

BOULDER CO.: Coal beds in the Laramine Formation—*amber.*

CHAFFEE CO.: Buena Vista, Chalk Creek—*sapphire.* Calumet City, ¼ mi. S and 3 mi. W of Turrett, at old Calumet Iron Mine—*deep blue sapphire.* Top of Mount Antero and summit of White Mountain, El. 14,000 feet, both at S end of Sawatch Range 15 mi. NW of Salida or 12 mi. SW of Natrop—*aquamarine, beryl, bertrandite, feldspar, fluorite, limonite, microcline, muscovite, phenakite, quartz crystals, sericite, smoky quartz.* South slopes of Mount Princeton, 5 mi. N of Mount Antero—*aquamarine, beryl, quartz crystals.* Ruby Mountain, E side of Arkansas River opposite Nathrop—*feldspar, quartz crystals, sanidine, spessartite garnet in rhyolite, topaz.* N and SE flanks of Ruby Mountain—*Apache tears (obsidian).*

CLEAR CREEK CO.: Idaho Springs; (1) Silver Creek 6 mi. W, and (2) along Trail Creek 2 mi. NW—*amethyst.* Red Elephant Mountain, Lawson-Dumond mining district—*amethyst.*

CONEJOS CO.: King Mine, on Pinon Mountain 1½ mi. W of Rio Grande River and 10 mi. E of Manassa, or 13 mi. ESE of Lajara—*kaolin, quartz* (stained), *sericite, turquoise.*

DOUGLAS CO.: Devil's Head (Platte Mountain), S of summit on top of a ridge below main access road—*cassiterite, feldspar (microcline), fluorite, hematite, limonite, smoky quartz, topaz.* Larkspur—*jasper.* Parker, 1 mi. S—*petrified wood.* Pine Creek, pegmatite outcrops 11 mi. W of Sedalia—*amazonite, smoky quartz crystals.* Palmer Lake, Front Range foothills 10 mi. NW—*alabaster, gypsum, satin spar.*

EAGLE CO.: Green Mountain zinc mines—*sphalerite.*

ELBERT CO.: Bijou and Kiowa Creek gravels—*petrified wood.* Platte River gravels, especially SE of Elbert—*opalized and silicified wood.*

EL PASO CO.: Laramie Formation coal mines—*jet.* Calumet—*sapphire.* Colorado Springs; (1) 4 mi. NE at Austin Bluffs—*agate, carnelian, chalcedony, jasper,* (2) Eureka Tunnel NE of road summit between Colorado Springs and Rosemont on lower side of road—*zircon,* (3) 7 mi. SW, St. Peter's Dome pegmatites via Gold Camp Road—*kaolinite, mica, quartz, zircon.* Crystal Park, regional pegmatites at base of Cameron Cone, Mount Arthur, and Mount Garfield—*blue topaz.* Peyton area gravel beds—*petrified wood.* St. Peter's Dome, S of Stove Mountain—*amazonite, smoky quartz crystals, topaz.*

FAIRFIELD CO.: Branchville—*kunzite (spodumene).*

FREMONT CO.: Canon City; (1) Felch Creek, 6½ mi. S—*agate nodules, chalcedony, geodes, jasper,* (2) Garden Park, 7 mi. N—*agate, chalcedony, dinosaur bone* (silicified), *jasper*—wherever upper Morrison Formation shales outcrop in hills W of Oil Creek, (3) 12 mi. NW of Canon City and 1 mi. S of Twelvemile Park—*amethyst, quartz crystals.* Royal Gorge, near Canon City—*aquamarine, beryl, tourmaline.* Texas Creek; (1) Amazon Claim, 6½ mi. N in East Gulch—*beryl,* (2) Wild Rose Claim, 6 mi. N and ⅓ mi. W of Echo Canyon-East Gulch junction—*rose quartz.*

GILPIN CO.: Central City, East End Mine—*agate* (moss), *labradorite.*

GRAND CO.: Colorado River, 2 mi. above at Williams Fork—*moss agate.* Hot Sulphur Springs, NW on Willow Creek —*agate* (moss), *chalcedony, fossil wood.* Middle Park area—*agate* (common, moss), *chalcedony, chrysoprase.* Mouth of Williams Fork—variously colored *jaspers.*

GUNNISON CO.: Italian Mountain, west side—*lapis lazuli.*

Quartz Creek district pegmatites between Ohio City and Parlin
—*beryl, lepidolite, mica, monazite, tantalum and columbium
minerals, tourmaline.* Mount Beckwith—*moonstone (feldspar).*
JEFFERSON CO.: Bear Creek, between Golden and Ralston
—*alabaster.* Centennial Cone, 15 mi. W of Golden, on NW
flanks—*aquamarine, beryl, smoky quartz crystals.* Drew Hill—
*chrysoberyl.*

LAKE CO.: Leadville; (1) Alicante mines—*fluorite, quartz
crystals, pyrite, rhodochrosite,* (2) 7 mi. NW at Poor Boy and
Turquoise Chief mines—*turquoise.*

LARIMER CO.: Owl Canyon Store, 2 mi. NE—*alabaster.*
Red Feather Lakes District, Pennoyer Amethyst Mine—*amethyst, quartz crystals.*

LAS ANIMAS CO.: Trinidad, 34 mi. SE, Trinchera Mesa
in Wet Mountain Valley—*jet* in coal seams.

MESA CO.: Black Ridge fossil beds—*dinosaur bone (petrified), gastroliths.* Fruita; (1) 2 mi. S—*gastroliths,* (2) 4 mi.
W at Dinosaur Ridge—*petrified dinosaur bone* from Morrison
Formation exposures, especially *allosaurs* and *brontosaurs,* (3)
gravels and washes S of Fruita—*gastroliths, petrified wood,*
(4) Glade Park and Pinon Mesa—*opal, opalized wood,* (5) Opal
Hill 4 mi. SW of Fruita—*opal* (variously colored and banded),
*opalized wood.* Colorado River Valley and side canyons westward from Grand Junction to Utah border—*agate, chalcedony,
jasper, opal, opalized wood, petrified dinosaur bone.* Good-
man's Point, near Cortez—*petrified dinosaur bone.*

MINERAL CO.: Creede Mining District, on Willow Creek
—*amethyst* (massive), *chalcedony, milky quartz, silver ores,
sphalerite.* Embargo Mining District, Wagon Wheel Gap—
*agate* (banded, moss), *chalcedony, jasper, quartz.* West Willow
Creek gravels between Amethyst and Commodore mines—
*turquoise.* Wolf Creek Pass, 6 mi. W of summit—*agate, chalcedony, jasper.*

MOFFAT CO.: Green and Yampa river gravels—*agate, carnelian, chelcedony, dinosaur bone* (jasperized, silicified), *jasper.*

MONTEZUMA CO.: McElmo Creek Valley sandstones—
*dinosaur bone.*

MONTROSE CO.: near Uncompahgre—*bloodstone.*

OURAY CO.: Mount Sneffels—*andradite garnet.*

PARK Co.: Agate Plateau, Buffey—*agate*. Alma, Sweethome Mine in Buckskin Gulch—*rhodochrosite*. Fairplay, to SW —*agate, jasper*. Guffey, around Guffey and between this community and Hartsel—*agate* (banded, moss), *chalcedony, chert, jasper, quartz*. Hartsel, South Platte River gravels—*agate, jasper*. South Park, near Grand River—*bloodstone, garnet*.

PIKES PEAK: granite outcrops, covering 1000 square miles in several counties are laced with pegmatite dikes—*amazonite, quartz crystals, topaz, tourmaline*.

PROWERS CO.: 18 mi. S of Lamar—*silicified wood*.

RIO GRANDE CO.: Loma, 15 mi. N, Rio Grande River gravels—*agate, amethyst-lined geodes, jasper*. Twin Mountains, E sides NW of Del Norte—*agate* (banded, plume), *chalcedony, chert, geodes, jasper, quartz crystals*.

SAGUACHE CO.: La Garita Creek—*agate, chalcedony* in exposures of volcanic rocks. Villa Grove, 8 mi. NW at Hall Mine—*lazulite, turquoise*.

SAN JUAN CO.: Silverton, N at Eureka—*rhodonite*.

SUMMIT CO.: Kremmling, 16 mi. S at Big Four Mine—*sphalerite*.

TELLER CO.: Florissant area; (1) N of town—*amazonite, smoky quartz crystals, topaz*, (2) 2 mi. N at Crystal Peak—*amazonite, beryl, feldspar, fluorite, goethite, hematite, limonite, muscovite mica, phenakite, pyrite, quartz crystals*, (3) 2 mi. NE of Lake George, in Crystal Peak area and ½ mi. NW of Crystal Peak—*amazonite, quartz, topaz*, (4) Petrified Forest area—*silicified wood*. Manitou Springs, 5 mi. S in Crystal Park at foot of Cameron Cone—*amazonite, smoky quartz crystals, topaz*—also on draws, ridges, and slopes of Bear Creek Canyon to the south. Stove Mountain, 10 mi. SW of Colorado Springs —*amazonite, smoky quartz crystals, topaz*. Woodland Park, 18 mi. N at Devil's Head—*amazonite, quartz* (clear), *smoky quartz crystals, topaz*.

WELD CO.: Kalouse area—*agate, jasper, petrified dinosaur bone, silicified wood*. Stoneham, 3 mi. NE, off Highway 14 in the "Chalk Bluffs"—*barite*.

YUMA CO.: Burlington, 20 mi. N along South Fork of the Republican River—*agate, chalcedony, jasper, opal* (moss, opaque white).

## CONNECTICUT

This 60 by 95 mile state is divided about equally into the eastern and western highlands, separated by the Connecticut River Valley (the central lowlands). The western highland, with its Litchfield Hills and Taconic Mountains, is the higher and more rugged half. A few peaks exceed 2000 feet. Basalt sills outcropping into the Connecticut River Basin yield gem quality *prehnite*.

FAIRFIELD CO.: Monroe—*tourmaline*. Trumbull Twp., Long Hill tungsten mine 1 mi. S of RR station—*calcite, fluorite, pyrite cubes, topaz* (blue).

HARTFORD CO.: East Grandby, Roncari Quarry—*datolite*. Around Farmington—*agate, prehnite*. Meriden, quarries 1½ mi. NW—*amethyst, quartz crystals*.

LITCHFIELD CO.: Branchville, Old Feldspar Quarry—*aventurine, beryl, columbite, mica* (curved), *spodumene (kunzite)*. Litchfield and Southbury mica schists—*staurolite* (fairy crosses) New Milford Twp., 5½ mi. N, 13° W of New Milford at George Roebling or Merryall Mine—*aquamarine, beryl* (golden), *biotite, feldspar, garnet, muscovite, schorl*. Roxbury, Old Iron Mine—*chalcopyrite, galena, pyrite cubes quartz crystals, quartz* (opalescent), *siderite, sphalerite*. Torringford and Woodbury area basalt sills—*agate nodules*.

MIDDLESEX CO.: Brandon, New London, Oneco, and Stony Creek (various quarries)—*apatite, spodumene*. Bolton (mica schists)—*staurolites* (fairy crosses). East Hampton Twp., 3½ mi. SE of East Hampton at Slocum Quarry—*beryl* (golden). Haddam Twp., 5 mi. SSE of Middle Haddam at Gillette Quarry on E bank of Connecticut River—*beryl, chrysoberyl, garnet, quartz crystals, tourmaline*. Middletown Twp., various quarries, but especially ½ mi. W of Benvenue at Riverside Quarry on S bank of Connecticut River—*aquamarine, beryl*. Portland Twp. (1) 1 mi. S of Portland Reservoir at Pelton Quarry—*citrine, quartz* (rose, smoky), *rock crystal*, (2) Strickland Quarry, 2½ mi. NE of Portland on W side of Collins Hill near summit —*apatite, aquamarine, beryl, citrine, morganite, quartz* (rose, smoky), *rock crystal, tourmaline*.

NEW HAVEN CO.: Guilford Twp. (1) around Guilford and East Haven—*agate*, (2) Hungry Horse Hill—*iolite (cordierite)*.

TOLLAND CO.: Schists outcropping around Stafford, Tolland, and Vernon—*quartz crystals, rose quartz, staurolite.*
WINDHAM CO.: Willimantic—*topaz.*

## FLORIDA

This long, sea-level peninsula rises in the north to rolling, pine-clad hills, while the central area abounds in lakes and swamps. In the south the Florida Everglades is a broad region resting on an ancient coral formation.

HILLSBOROUGH CO.: Hillsborough Bay, NE arm of Tampa Bay, at Balast Point and Davis Island—*silicified coral, chalcedony, coral geodes, quartz-crystal lined chalcedony geodes.* Hillsborough River, N of Tampa—*brain coral with agate, finger coral.*

PASCO CO.: Bailey's Bluff, S of New Port Richey—*chalcedony, silicified coral.*

PINELLA CO.: Tarpon Springs area—*chalcedony replacements of coral, chalcedonized fossils, silicified coral.*

POLK CO.: 7 mi. NE of Lakeland—*chalcedony, silicified coral.*

## GEORGIA

This state, heavily wooded with pine, easily divides into three major topographical regions. Mountainous North Georgia includes the Appalachian Plateau, a valley-and-ridge province, and the Blue Ridge province. Embracing about one-third of the state, Middle Georgia consists of the Piedmont Plateau, a sort of bridge between the rugged north and the low coastal plain that occupies the southern half of the state. Most of the northern counties have alluvial deposits in which *diamonds* are found.

BARTOW CO.: Kingston area—*agate* (banded, various colors), *jasper.* Saltpeter Cave area—*jasper.*

BULLOCK CO.: *fire opal.*

CHATHAM CO.: *bloodstone (heliotrope).*

CHEROKEE CO.: Ball Ground; (1) S and W—*staurolite,* (2) between Ball Ground and Canton—*almandine garnet,* (3) E side of Sharp Mountain, 1 mi. W of Fairview Church—*staurolite,* (4) on N side of Bluff Creek, 4½ mi. W of Ball Ground

along Route 1—*staurolite*. Cochran Mine, 2½ mi. N, 78° E of Ball Ground—*agate, beryl, rutilated quartz*.
CLAYTON CO.: Morrow Station, 13 mi. S of Atlanta—*diamond*. Laurel Creek Mine—*aquamarine, beryl, red corundum*.
COBB CO.: Belmont Hills, ¼ mi. SE—*quartz* (milky, rose). Near Marietta—*agate, jasper*.
CRISP CO.: Cordele area—*agate* (moss), *jasp-agate, jasper*.
DODGE CO.: Dubois, Empire, and other county exposures of Miocene rocks—*tektites*.
ELBERT CO.: Antioch Hill, near Deweyrose—*amethyst, aquamarine*—also near Yellow Mine on N side of Little Broad River, 3 mi. from Ogleby.
FANNIN CO.: (1) Regional railroad and road cuts, (2) Blue Ridge, W of Cole's Crossing, and (3) Windy Bluff, NW of Mineral Bluff—*staurolite* (fairy crosses).
FAYETTE CO.: 1 mi. N of Fayetteville—*amethyst*.
FLOYD CO.: Rome area—*rose quartz*.
HALL CO.: Gainesville, Glade Creek—*diamond*.
IRWIN CO.: Regional Miocene rock outcrops—*tektites*.
JONES CO.: Round Oak area—*agate, jasper, petrified wood*.
LUMPKIN CO.: Dahlonega, 9½ mi. NE at Williams Mica Mine which is 2¼ mi. SW of Ward Gap—colorless *topaz*.
MORGAN CO.: 2 mi. E of Buckhead—*amethyst, quartz crystals*.
MURRAY CO.: Fincher Bluff, N of Hooker School—*silicified oölite*—also in road cuts between Sardis and Spring Place.
PAULDING CO.: Dallas area; (1) Little Bob Copper Mine, and (2) a place 6 mi. SE of Dallas—*almandine garnet*.
PICKENS CO.: Tate, 4 mi. W at Cook Farm—*beryl*.
RABUN CO.: Clayton area; (1) Beck Beryl Mine, 7 mi. E—*beryl*, (2) 4 mi. SE—*amethyst* (gem). Rabun Gap, 1 mi. N at Ledbetter Mine on Black Creek—*amethyst*.
SPAULDING CO.: Vaughn 2 mi. E at T. J. Allen Farm—*beryl*.
TOWNE CO.: Hiwasse area amethyst and ruby mines, also Charlie's Creek—*amethysts, quartz crystals*. Lake area—*ruby, sapphire*.
TROUP CO.: La Grange; (1) 8 mi. N at Minerals Processing

Co. Mine, 1 mi. S of Smith's Crossroads on W side of Highway 219—*aquamarine, beryl, muscovite, rose quartz, schorl.* Louise, Chromite Prospect just N of Calloway Airport—*beryl.*

TWIGGS CO.: 11 mi. NE of Macon—*diamond.*

UNION CO.: Garrett Mine, 2 mi. S of Hightower Bald, between Jacks Branch and Shoal Branch—*amethyst, quartz crystals.*

UPSON CO.: Thomaston, 7½ mi. SE at Mitchell Creek Mica Mine—*apatite, muscovite mica.* Yatesville, ¼ mi. E of center of town at Herron Mine—*beryl.*

WASHINGTON CO.: *fire opal.*

WHITE CO.: Horshaw Mine, Racoochee Valley—*diamond.*

WHITFIELD CO.: Dalton area, road cuts along Tarr Creek —*oölitic jasper* (red), *siliceous oölite* (black).

WILKES CO.: Graves Mountain, 11 mi. from Washington— *lazulite, rutile.* Magruder Mine—*azurite, barite, bornite, chalcopyrite, galena, gold, malachite, pyrite, sphalerite.*

## IDAHO

Oddly shaped, Idaho has a varied topography. The central and northern portions are extremely rugged, encompassing the massive Sawtooth and Salmon River mountain systems, with many lakes and peaks rising more than 12,000 feet high. *Copper, gold, lead, silver,* and *zinc* are extensively mined. Southern Idaho is largely arid sagebrush deserts, with unexploited phosphate deposits in the southeast and many mining ghost towns in the southwestern mountains south of Boise. Basalt covers large areas, as part of the 200,000-square-mile Columbia Lava Plateau embracing Idaho, Oregon, and Washington through which the Snake River has carved its deep canyon.

ADA CO.: Many places—*agate, chalcedony, jasper, petrified and opalized wood.* Mussellshell Creek, Snake River—*zircon.*

ADAMS CO.: Copper and gold mine dumps—*azurite, malachite.* Mesa—*opalized wood.* New Meadows, 5 mi. E along Little Goose Creek Canyon—*diamond.* Rock Flat gravels—*diamond, garnet, ruby, sapphire, topaz, zircon.* Weiser Cove, and N of Weiser near Mesa—*opalized wood* in volcanic ash.

BEAR LAKE CO.: Montpelier, Hummingbird Mine in Paris Canyon—*quartz* impregnated with *cuprite* and *malachite.*

**BENEWAH CO.**: Fernwood; (1) Emerald Creek and its East Fork, 5 mi. SE of Fernwood—*almandine garnet*—also (2) Ruby Gulch, 2 mi. S of Fernwood.

**BLAINE CO.**: Arco area, 20 mi. W in Lava Creek District—*tourmaline*. Little Wood River—*agate, chalcedony, jasper*. Muldoon area—*agate*. Pole Creek area, and all other regional Tertiary basalts—*chalcedony geodes* (with *amethyst* linings), *quartz crystal geodes*.

**BOISE CO.**: Most county mine dumps yield *quartz crystals*. Camas Creek—*topaz*. Centerville, N to Garden Valley, pegmatite outcrops—*aquamarine*. Deadwood Gulch—*garnet, gold*. Idaho City, both sides of Moore Creek—*precious opal*.

**CASSIA CO.**: Moulton, 5 mi. NW and just E of Almo—*topaz*.

**CLEARWATER CO.**: Pierce, 11 mi. N near Headquarters —*almandine garnet* (star). Rhodes Creek—*zircon*.

**CUSTER CO.**: Toward head of Big Lost River, as well as all other Tertiary basalts outcropping over a wide area—*chalcedony geodes* with *amethyst* fillings. Stanley Basin gold gravels —*corundum, sapphire*.

**FREMONT CO.**: Crystal Butte, 18 mi. N of St. Anthony and 8 mi. SE of Ivan—*andesine*.

**GEM CO.**: Emmett; (1) Black Canyon Dam—*precious opal*, (2) Squaw Butte, 5 mi. E—*agate* (blue, fortified).

**IDAHO CO.**: Resort—gold placers yield *corundum, zircon*. Salmon River gravels, both sides and in tributaries—*agate, jasper*. Slate and McKinsey Creeks—*agate, jasper*. Warren District—*topaz*.

**KOOTENAI CO.**: Setters—*common opal* (yellow to brown).

**LATAH CO.**: Near Moscow and Whelan, squarely on boundary between Idaho and Washington—*precious opal* in decomposed basalt.

**LEMHI CO.**: Leesburg placers—*gold, petrified wood*. Near May—*massive opal*. Panther Creek Valley 6 mi. below headwaters in porphyry dike extending 1½ mi. along creek—*opal* (common, nodules, precious). Parker Mountain District—*agate, chalcedony*.

**LINCOLN CO.**: Bliss, Clover Creek to E—*opalized wood*.

**NEZ PERCE CO.**: Avon, 7 mi. NW of Deary—*aquamarine*. Cavendish, 4 to 5 mi W—*opal, opalized wood*. Lewiston; (1)

Clearwater River gravels upstream from Lewiston for about 100 mi., but especially between Lewiston and Myrtle—*fibrolite* (gem *sillimanite*), (2) regional gold gravels—*agate, aquamarine, garnet, gold, quartz crystals.* Silcott, basalt bluffs overlooking the Clearwater River opposite Silcott—*precious opal.*

OWYHEE CO.: Bruneau Desert—*agate, chalcedony, jasper.* Cliffs, 40 mi. S of Boise at Brace Brothers Ranch—*precious opal.* Enterprise, 3 mi. W and 2 mi. SW of Sommer Camp in pits and opencuts in *perlitic rhyolite—opal.* Mountain Home, 25 mi. W along Castle Creek—*precious opal.* Nampa area; (1) Graveyard Point, SE—*plume agate,* (2) 8 mi. SW at Squaw Creek Canyon, just below junction of Squaw and Little Squaw Creeks, 3 mi. back of the Snake River—*precious opal* in basalt gas cavitites, *chalcedony* (common, banded), *chalcedony-with-opal, onyx,* (3) Sucker Creek, W—*plume agate.* Oreana, 6 mi. E—*precious opal.* Silver City-De Lamar, scores of great mines, abandoned—*agate, calcite, chalcedony, geodes, jasper, marcasite, pyrite, quartz crystals, silver ore minerals.*

SHOSHONE CO.: S of Avery and around Bathtub Mountain—*staurolite* (fairy crosses).

TWIN FALLS CO.: 3 to 4 mi. N of Nevada line along Highway 93—*chalcedony geodes.*

VALLEY CO.: Yellow Pine District—*opal* (white, spotted with *cinnabar*).

WASHINGTON CO.: Eaton, 5 mi. E, Grouse and Hog creeks—*agate* (banded, iris), *chalcedony.* Meadows, Rock Flat—*corundum, gold, ruby, sapphire.* Weiser 16 mi. NW in Fourth of July Canyon at junction of July and Mann's creeks—*opalized wood* of high quality in volcanic ash 500 feet above creek beds.

## ILLINOIS

Known as the Prairie State, the broad, level lands were smoothed out by Pleistocene glaciers. Beneath the layers of top soil, Illinois boasts great mineral wealth—producing more fluorspar, silica sand, and sandstone than any other state, not to mention bituminous coal. The state is drained by more than 275 rivers, of which the Illinois is the largest.

JEFFERSON CO.: Ashley, 3½ mi. E—*diamond.*

HARDIN and POPE COUNTIES: mines E of Rosiclare and

around Cave-in-Rock, also 4½ mi. NW of latter—*chalcopyrite, cerussite, fluorite, pyrite, smithsonite, witherite.*

HENRY CO.: Mississippi River banks between Cordova, Ill., and Dubuque, Ia.—*agate.* RR siding near Thebes (called Clay), and at Bishop Hill—*agate.*

McDONOUGH CO.: Macomb area—*diamond.*

POPE CO.: *cerussite, chalcopyrite, fluorite, fluorspar, pyrite, smithsonite, witherite.*

WARSAW FORMATION: This formation outcrops in various counties, particularly near Hamilton, Nauvoo, and Warsaw, to yield *amethyst, calcite crystals, chalcedony (botryoidal), dolomite crystals,* and *quartz geodes.*

## INDIANA

The northern part of Indiana, along the Great Lakes, is essentially a glaciated area smoothed by the Pleistocene glaciers. The debris which the ice pushed before it was dropped throughout the central agricultural region. Quite deep in many places, this glacial drift contains rock types, including gems and gem stones, which the ice brought down from unknown deposits far to the north. The southern section of the state, by contrast, is a succession of bottomlands interspersed with knolls, ridges, valleys, and gorges.

ALLEN CO.: Maumee River gravels—*agate, jasp-agate, jasper, petrified wood.*

BROWN CO.: Lick Creek, 15 mi. SE of Martinsville—*diamond.* Salt and Gold creek gravels—*corundum, diamond.* Trevlac area stream gravels, particularly Bear Creek—*quartz-lined geodes.*

LAWRENCE CO.: Heltonsville, Salt Creek gravels—*quartz geodes*—also in stream gravels around Guthrie.

MARION CO.: Indianapolis area stream beds—*feldspar (moonstone).* Williams Creek—*amethyst, quartz crystals.*

MIAMI CO.: Peru—*diamond.*

MORGAN CO.: Highland Creek, 7 mi. NNW of Martinsville—*corundum, diamond, garnet, gold, hematite, ilmenite, magnetite, pyrite, zircon.* Gold Creek—*corundum, diamond, gold, massive sapphire.* Junction of Gold and Sycamore Creeks—*diamond, ruby, sapphire, zircon.* Little Indian Creek—*diamond, gold.*

## IOWA

Except for low hills in the unglaciated northeastern section, Iowa is a prairie state of rich, rolling table lands, interrupted by many streams. For much of the Mesozoic Era, particularly during the Cretaceous Period, Iowa lay underneath broad epicontinental seas, and it is little wonder that this state ranks second in the production of such sedimentary minerals as clay, gravel, gypsum, limestone, and sand. Moreover, as the seas gave way to swamps, luxuriant Cretaceous vegetation produced enough bituminous coal to last an estimated 4000 years. The more ancient Devonian limestones that outcrop around Iowa City and in other parts of the state yield *colony corals* and *stromatopariods* (fossils) which polish into beautiful specimens.

DES MOINES CO.: Burlington area creek beds—*agate, quartz crystals, quartz crystal geodes.*

FREMONT CO.: Devonian limestone outcrops—*fossil corals* and *stromatopariods.*

HENRY CO.: New Lincoln—*agate, jasper.* South edge of Mount Pleasant, in Mississippian limestones—*chert* (colored), *quartz crystal geodes.* Skunk River—*limonite* (brown).

JACKSON CO.: Bellerive gravel pits—*agate, carnelian.*

JOHNSON CO.: Coralville and Iowa City, regional stream gravels—*silicified coral (favosites).*

LEE CO.: Keokuk Geode Beds, outcropping in a broad area around the junction of the Des Moines and Mississippi rivers where the states of Illinois, Iowa, and Missouri come together —*quartz geodes* (filled with clear crystals). Dubuque area— *agate, galena* (cubes and clusters), *jasper, pyrite.*

LINN CO.: Stream gravels yield *silicified coral.*

MUSCATINE CO.: Muscatine, S of town—*agate* ("Lake Superior," moss, sagenitic), *chalcedony, quartz crystals,* in gravel pits.

PALO ALTO CO.: Emmetsburg and Graettinger (stream gravels)—*agate, jasper, petrified wood.*

STORY CO.: Ames—*chalcedony.*

VAN BUREN CO.: Farmington area—*quartz crystal geodes.*

## KANSAS

Containing the geographical center of the United States, the Kansas prairies and plains rise imperceptibly toward the west to an elevation of 3000 feet. The low eastern Mississippian prairies are marked by gently rolling hills and wooded valleys, while the high, western region belongs to the Great Plains, flat and semi-arid. The Ozark Plateau extends into one small corner of the southeast.

The widespread Ogallala Formation (Tertiary) embraces the counties of Clark, Ellis, Logan, Ness, Rawlings, and Wallace. In it one finds *dendritic opal,* white, translucent *opal* as irregular masses or nodules, *opalized bones,* and much *petrified wood.* From the western Cretaceous chalk beds of the counties of Cherokee, Logan, Norton, and Phillips, the collector may gather colorful *chert* (some dendritic with *manganese*), and *jasper.* Anderson, Brown, Chase and Franklin counties yield *barite crystals.* Moreover, the surfaces of draws, washes, and sand hills of western Kansas, as well as the regional creek and stream beds yield *agate, chalcedony, chert, jasper,* and *petrified wood,* especially along Smoky Hill River in Gove, Logan, Trego, and Wallace counties. Regional outcrops of shale produce *selenite.* The Tri-State District (Ozark Plateau extension into Kansas), as well as the counties of Chataqua, Douglas, Elk, and Pleasanton offer the rock collector fine mineral specimens of *barite, calcite, chalcopyrite, cerussite, dolomite crystals, galena, pyrite,* and *sphalerite.*

Thinly covered by Pleistocene and Recent gravels, extensive Pliocene beds cap the monotonous High Plains. Outcrops, cutbanks, and washes of these continental and shallow-lake sediments (mostly from the rising Rocky Mountains farther west) disgorge the fossil bones of camels, elephants, mammoths, mastodons, the first single-toed horse, tigers, wolves, and other fauna of the pre-glacial era two to fifteen million years ago.

BARBER CO.: Along both sides of Medicine Lodge River and in the regional creek beds—*agate, chalcedony, chert, jasper, petrified wood.*

BROWN CO.: Morrill, 4 mi. N at Kanapolis Dam—*celestite.*

CHASE CO.: *chalcopyrite, quartz geodes.*

CHEROKEE CO.: See Tri-State District minerals.

CLARK CO.: Ashland, N near Mount Casino—*agate* (moss), *jasper.*

CLOUD CO.: Republican River gravels—*agate, chalcedony, chert, flint, petrified wood.*

COWLEY CO.: Around community of Rock and along Walnut River—*geodes.*

ELLSWORTH CO.: Carneiro, 5 mi. S along banks of Smoky Hill River—*amber* in lignite exposures.

FRANKLIN CO.: Buffalo area, Ottawa—*barite, fossil bone.*

JEFFERSON CO.: McLouth area in glacial moraines and drift—*"Lake Superior" agate, chalcedony.*

MARSHALL CO.: Big Blue River gravels, tributaries, and on surrounding hillsides and in washes—*agate, chalcedony, chert.*

OTTAWA CO.: Ada, N—*petrified wood.*

RILEY CO.: Bala area, volcanic plug—*magnetite.* Igneous rocks near Stockdale—*pyrope garnet* granules.

TRI-STATE DISTRICT, SE corner of Kansas: Lead and zinc mines—*barite, calcite, cerussite, galena, marcasite, pyrite, sphalerite, smithsonite.*

WALLACE CO.: Wallace, 5 mi. S at road cut—*opal nodules.*

WOODSON CO.: Yates Center, 8 mi. S—*amethyst, quartz crystals.*

WYANDOTTE CO.: Bonner Springs, Lone Star Quarry—*quartz crystals* in *geodes.*

## KENTUCKY

The hardwood-timbered Cumberland Plateau that comprises eastern Kentucky breaks toward the "blue grass" heartland in a series of escarpments and isolated "knobs." To the west is an area of rocky hillsides that denotes a broad region of underground streams which have carved great caverns, *e.g.,* Mammoth Caves, in the limestone substrata. Still farther west, the land is fairly level.

Although extensive mining of coal, fluorspar, sand, and gravel enriches the state commercially, there are few areas that contain rocks or minerals of interest to the collector. However, exposures of black Upper Devonian silt shales sometimes yield petrified wood, such as *Dadoxylon newberryi,* and a 1914 state geological survey report identified silicified tree trunks from the vicinity of Lebanon as *Callixylon oweni.*

ADAIR CO.: Montpelier—*diamond.*

CRITTENDEN CO.: Various mines back of the Ohio River —*fluorite.*

ELLIOT CO.: Ison Creek—*enstatite, garnet* (pyrope), *ilmenite, mica, olivine, peridotite, serpentine.*

RUSSELL CO.: Same stream gravels as in Adair Co.—*diamond.*

## LOUISIANA

This Mississippi-dominated state is basically a low, alluvial plain that rises to a maximum elevation of 500 feet in uplands near Arkansas. All rocks are sedimentary limestones, sands, and silts; there are no gem stone localities, as such. However, Tertiary formations (Eocene and Oligocene) outcrop in nearly every county or parish to produce *petrified wood* (hickory, oak, poplar, palm), particularly large silicified logs in De Sota Parish.

OUACHITA CO.: West Monroe, 12 mi. S in Ouachita River gravels—*banded agate, petrified* and *opalized wood.*

LIVINGSTON, TANGIPAHOA PARISHES: Stream gravels—*carnelian.*

RAPIDES AND VERNON PARISHES: *silicified palm (Palmoxylon).*

## MAINE

Eroded to bedrock by Pleistocene glaciers two miles thick in many places, Maine rests on a very ancient foundation of limestone, sandstone, and shale. The generally mountainous, heavily forested western region slopes northward to the St. John river basin and eastward toward the Penobscot River. Receding glaciers dammed the valleys with long drift ridges to form some 2200 lakes. In the more than 5000 rivers and streams, gravels are productive of many interesting mineral specimens. Where earth forces caused molten granites to intrude the basal sediments and crystallize them, many valuable mineral and gem stone deposits were formed. Perhaps nowhere in the world is there an area of comparable size productive of such an array of quality minerals and gem stones as Oxford County. Here, in particular, the Newry Mines near Rumford and the Mica Mines near Paris are a collector's paradise. Several hundred minerals make up the complete Maine roster.

ANDROSCOGGIN CO.: Auburn Twp., Mount Apatite, 1½ mi. E of Minot—*apatite, beryl, morganite, tourmaline.*

Minot Twp.; (1) Berry Quarry, 1¼ mi. SE of Minot—*tourmaline*, (2) Mount Apatite, 4 mi. W of Auburn—*topaz* (rare), (3) Mount Apatite, 1¼ mi. ENE of Minot—*tourmaline*. Robinson Mountain, Lewiston—*vesuvianite (idocrase)*. CUMBERLAND CO.: Windham, micaceous slates—*staurolites*. HANCOCK CO.: Little Deer Isle—*serpentine* (gemmy). Mount Desert—*amazonite*. KENNEBEC CO.: Litchfield—*zircon*. Litchfield Twp.; (1) 1000 feet N of Spears Corner, and (2) an outcrop 2000 feet SW and 5½ mi. W of Gardiner—*sodalite*. KNOX CO.: Union—*labradorite*. OXFORD CO.: Albany Twp.; (1) Bethel, 6.4 mi. SSE and 1.2 mi. SW of Town House at the Bumpus Quarry—*rose quartz*, (2) French Mountain crest—*aquamarine, rose quartz*, (3) North Waterford Pumping Station, 1 mi. N at Scribner's Ledge Quarry—*rose quartz*, (4) West Paris, 8.8 mi. S 70° W and ½ mi. NE of Flints Mountain at Scribner Mine—*golden beryl*. Andover—*garnet*. Buckfield Twp.; (1) Bennett Quarry, 3 mi. W of Buckfield and ½ mi. N of Bennett Farmhouse—*aquamarine, beryl, feldspar, morganite, tourmaline*, (2) Lewis Mine, 2 mi. SW of Buckfield and at adjoining J. H. Fletcher Mine—*cesium beryl, tourmaline*, (3) 2½ mi. SW of Buckfield and ¼ mi. S of Highway 117—*amblygonite, arsenopyrite, beryl, cassiterite, feldspar, lollingite, mica, pollucite, tourmaline*, (4) 2½ mi. SW of Buckfield at Robinson Dudley Mine—*aquamarine, cesium beryl, pollucite* (rare). Greenwood Twp.; (1) Nobles Corner, 2 mi. NW and ½ mi. E of Mud Pond—*tourmaline*, (2) Tamminen's Quarry at base of Noyes Mountain—*apatite, beryl, moragnite, petalite, pollucite*. Hartford Twp.; (1) Dickvale, 2 mi. SE on S slope of Hedgehog Hill—*aquamarine, golden beryl*, (2) Ragged Jack Mountain, 2 mi. S of south end of Worthley Pond—*chrysoberyl*. Hebron Twp., Mount Rubellite, N end of Greenwood Hill 1½ mi. NE of Hebron and also 2½ mi. N of Hebron—*green tourmaline, pink tourmaline (rubellite)*. Newry Twp.; (1) Plumbago Mountain, Dunton Tourmaline Mine on summit of E spur—*aquamarine, tourmaline*, (2) E spur of Plumbago Mountain 3.9 mi. N 40° W of Rumford Point—*aquamarine*, (3) E knoll of Plumbago Mountain—*albite, amblygonite, beryllonite, eosphorite, her-*

*derite, tourmaline,* (4) Lower Nevel Quarry, NE side of Plumbago Mountain—*spodumene.* Paris Twp., Mount Mica, 1½ mi. E of Paris—*amazonite, cesium beryl, cookeite, feldspar, lepidolite, montmorillonite, morganite, quartz crystals, sagenite, tourmaline.* Peru Twp., Hedgehog Hill, S side—*chrysoberyl.* Rumford Twp., Black Mountain Mica Mine—*spodumene.* Stoneham Twp.; (1) Lord's Hill, ½ mi. SE of Harndon Hill—*autinite, beryl, chalcopyrite, feldspar, fluorite, phenakite, quartz crystals, topaz, tourmaline,* (2) North Lovell, Chapman Hill. 3 mi. N—*blue beryl,* (3) North Lovell, Durgin Mountain, 4 mi. N 30° W, on E side—*beryl* (various colors), (4) base of McKean Mountains, 2¾ mi. WSW of North Lovell—*apatite, beryl, beryllonite, cassiterite, feldspar, mica, quartz crystals* (smoky), *triplite,* (5) Speckled Mountain, 5 mi. N of North Lovell—*yellow beryl,* (6) Sugar Hill—*aquamarine, beryl, beryllonite.* Stow Twp., Deer Hill, 4½ mi. N of Stow or 1¾ mi. ESE of North Chatham, N. H.—*amethyst.*

SAGADAHOC CO.: Phippsburg Twp., Parker Head, 1.3 mi. S 17° W of tide mill at Thoman Feldspar Quarry—*aquamarine, golden beryl.* Topsham Twp.; (1) Brunswick, feldspar quarries overlooking Cathance River to N—*aquamarine, smoky quartz, topaz, tourmaline,* (2) 2½ mi. N of Topsham, a pegmatite dike outcrops on a low hill just N of Cathance River and Fisher Quarry—*albite, cleavelandite, apatite, beryl, cassiterite, columbite, gahnite, herderite, lepidolite, muscovite, topaz, torbernite, tourmaline,* (3) Willes Feldspar Quarry, 2 mi. NW of Cathance Station—*beryl, tourmaline.*

YORK CO.: Newfield Twp., Straw Hill, 4 mi. from Limerick—*sodalite* in boulders and seams.

## MARYLAND

This seaboard state is divided by the great drowned canyon of Chesapeake Bay which, with its indentations and estuaries, clearly distinguishes tidelands from uplands. West and north a rolling piedmont rises to the Blue Ridge and the hills of Pennsylvania.

ALLEGHENY CO.: Frostburg—*barite crystals.*

ANN ARUNDEL CO.: Fort Dorsey and Loper Hall iron mines—*jet.*

BALTIMORE CO.: Bare Hills—*moss agate.* Dyer Quarry—

*serpentine.* Gunpowder River quarries—*aquamarine.* White-marsh—*amethyst.*

BALTIMORE, WASHINGTON, D. C.: (1) numerous out-crops of the Potomac Formation (Lower Cretaceous)—*petrified wood* (cycads), (2) gravel pits SE of Baltimore, and NE at Raspe-burg—*petrified wood*, (3) Delight Serpentine Quarry, 15 mi. NW of Baltimore—*magnesite, serpentine.*

CAPE SABLE: *amber.*

CARROLL CO.: New Windsor—*azurite, malachite.* Be-tween Big Pipe Creek and Middlebury—*chrysocolla.*

CECIL CO.: Boundary with Lancaster Co., Pa., Rocksprings crossroads, 3/4 mi. N—*brucite, chromite, kemmererite* (purple), *magnesite, serpentine, williamsite.*

MONTGOMERY CO.: Rockville, quarry NW near Hunting Hills—*calcite, chlorite, diopside, grossularite garnet* (massive), *idocrase, opal, serpentine.* Kensington Mica Mine—*golden beryl.*

PRINCE GEORGES CO.: Potomac Formation—*petrified wood.*

WASHINGTON CO.: Camp Ritchey—*cuprite, garnet.*

## MASSACHUSETTS

The Connecticut River Valley divides Massachusetts into an eastern coastal plain, marked by short, swift rivers, and uplands which rise westward toward the Berkshire Hills. The latter are but glaciated remnants of an Ordovician mountain building "overthrust" of such magnitude that the whole of New Eng-land was narrowed by several hundred miles. This overthrust raised Cambrian and Ordovician sediments into the Taconic Mountain range in the western part of the state.

DUKES CO.: Gay Head, Martha's Vineyard—*amber.*

ESSEX CO.: Newberry Twp., Newburyport, quarries S—*serpentine* (noble, verde antique). Rockport—*amazonite.* Row-ley—*jasper.*

FRANKLIN CO.: Deerfield, basalt sills—*agate nodules*—also in Deerfield River gravels. East Deerfield, Cheapside Quarry—*amethyst, chalcedony geodes, prehnite.* Northfield—*beryl* (golden), *garnet.*

HAMPDEN CO.: Blandford, and Norwich—*beryl.* Chester, old emery mines—*diaspore, emery* (impure *corundum*), *jasper.*

Lane Quarry, between Springfield and Westfield—*datolite, prehnite.*       . . . . . . .

HAMPSHIRE CO.: Chesterfield Twp.—*staurolite* (fairy crosses). Cummington Twp., Forge Hill, 6 mi. S—*ankerite, garnet, quartz crystals, rhodochrosite, rhodonite.* Goshen, 1½ mi. N 80° W of Goshen, in a pegmatite dike 300 yards N of the north end of Lily Pond—*emerald, goshenite* (colorless to amber *beryl*), *smoky quartz crystals, tourmaline.* Lithia, Barrus Farm—*spodumene.* Pelham asbestos mine—*apatite, asbestos.*

MIDDLESEX CO.: Somerville—*prehnite.* Westford area—*chiastolite crystals.*

WORCESTER CO.: Berkshire Hills—*jasper.* Bolton, 2 mi. E in a limestone quarry—*scapolite* (crystals, massive pink). Lancaster area rocks—*chiastolite crystals.* Royalston, 2½ mi. N 68° E, at Beryl Hill, Reynolds Mine—*beryl, smoky quartz.*

# MICHIGAN

There are two distinct parts to Michigan, separated by Ice Age lake waters. The Upper Peninsula, in the eastern part, has swampy flats and limestone hills along Lake Michigan, while sandstone bluffs rise abruptly above Lake Superior's waters. Many once-great mines attest to the state's mineral deposits and, indeed, in the area of the Keeweenaw Peninsula and Isle Royale at least 60 colorful minerals can be found on the beaches, gravel benches, and mine dumps.

ARENAC CO.: Bayport limestone quarries—*chert nodules.*

BARAGA CO.: Michigamme Mine—*chalcedony, hematite, jaspilite.*

CASS CO.: Dowagiac—*diamond.*

CHARLEVOIX CO.: Norwood; (1) Lake Michigan shores, N—*"petoskey" agates,* (2) Traverse limestone outcrops—colorful *chert.*

CHIPPEWA CO.: Trout Lake, Scott's Quarry, E—*agatized coral, chert, flint.*

EMMET CO.: Traverse limestone outcrops (also statewide) yield *"petoskey agates,"* which are actually *calcite* replacements of *coral.* Especially abundant around Petoskey. Rockport Quarry, 11 mi. NE of Alpena—*pyrite.*

HOUGHTON CO.: Houghton, Quincy Mine across Portage Lake—*datolite, prehnite*—also from Clark, Delaware, and

Iroquois mines. Old Huron Mines—*quartz crystals.* Sheldon-Columbia Mine, on Portage Lake—*algodonite, domeykite.* South Range, Baltic Shaft No. 2—*bornite, chalcocite, chalcopyrite.* Thomsonite Beach, Eagle Harbor, Ahmeek—*agate, thomsonite.*

HURON CO.: Bayport limestone quarries—*chert nodules.*

IOSCO CO.: National City and Alabaster quarries—*alabaster.*

ISLE ROYALE: old workings at Epidote Mining Claim and at Thomsonite Beach—*chlorastrolite (greenstone), datolite nodules, thomsonite.* Head of Siskowit Bay, also on N shore of Tobin Harbor, toward Blake Point, and on adjoining island beaches, and inland on prehistoric lake beaches from McCargo Cove, as well as on most Isle Royale beaches—*agate nodules, carnelian, quartz crystals.* South shore of Siskowit Lake—*chlorastrolite.*

JENT CO.: Grand Rapids, gypsum quarries around Grandville—*alabaster.*

KEEWEENAW CO.: Ahmeek and Mohawk area copper mines—*algodonite, domeykite.* Cliff and Delaware mine dumps—*chlorastrolite.* Allouez Mine in Allouez—*chalcedony, chrysocolla, native copper.*

MACKINAC CO.: Raber area quarries—*silicified coral.* St. Ignace, 10 mi. W at Pointe Aux Chenes—*satin spar.*

MANITOU ISLAND: E of tip of Keeweenaw Peninsula, on Lake Superior beaches around the peninsula, and along N shore of Eagle Harbor and Gratiot, on N shore of Manganese Lake, around shores of Agate and Copper harbors—*"Lake Superior" agates.*

MARQUETTE CO.: Beacon Hill—*amethyst, quartz crystals, tourmaline.* Various mines at Ishpeming, Marquette, Neguanee, and Republic—*jasper, jaspilite.*

ONTONAGON CO.: Mass Mine on Highway 26 out from community of Mass—*datolite, malachite.* Porcupine Mountains—*chalcedony, hematite, jasper, jaspilite, specularite.* Silver City, Gull Point and Ahmeek—*agates.*

SCHOOLCRAFT CO.: Whitedale area quarries—*silicified coral.*

SILICA CO.: Rockwood area—*calcite, celestite geodes.*

## MINNESOTA

This most northerly of all the continental United States was strongly glaciated during Pleistocene times, and more than 11,000 lakes in their ice-scoured basins remain scattered among marshes, moraines, and boulder-strewn hills, drained by three great river systems. Eastern Minnesota is characterized by worn, ancient mountain systems, such as the Cuyuna, Mesabi, and Vermilion ranges rich in iron. South of the iron country, a broad region of rolling hills descends to quiet prairies in the south and west.

COOK CO.: Grand Marais, 14 mi. E, volcanic outcrops near shoreline—"*Lake Superior*" agates. Thomsonite Beach, 5½ mi. SW of Grand Marais on N shore of Lake Superior—*chlorastrolite, lintonite, thomsonite nodules*.

CROW CO.: Cuyuna Range, near Crosby and Ironton—*agate, binghamite, silkstone* (crystalline quartz replacement of fibrous *goethite*).

LAKE CO.: Beaver Bay and Grand Marais—*agate, thomsonite*.

MORRISON CO.: Area gravel pits—*agate nodules*. Blanchard Dam and in Elk Creek gravels near Little Falls—*staurolite* (fairy crosses)—also along both sides of the Mississippi River 3 mi. from Royalton.

PIPESTONE CO.: Old Indian quarries of Pipestone National Monument—*catlinite* (pipestone).

ST. LOUIS CO.: Biwabwik, 1 mi. W at Mary Ellen Mine, and 2 mi. W at Corsica Mine, Sudan Formation outcrops of the Mesabi Range—*agate, algae* (silicified). Duluth area gravels and beaches—*agates*.

## MISSISSIPPI

This low-lying, alluvial state is everywhere characterized by sediments; it lends its name to a 20-million-year depositional period during the Lower Carboniferous era. Few gem stone or mineral collecting localities are known, but *petrified wood* occurs in lignite beds which outcrop in many parts of the state. In the northeast corner are found many petrifactions in which the petrifying agent is iron oxide; in some areas, the state's fossil trees contain lovely, water-clear quartz crystals of small size, as well as drusy quartz linings of cracks and fractures. Most of the petrifactions occur in the Lafayette Formation, with lesser quantities found in the Wilcox and other Tertiary sediments. A considerable petrified forest area containing logs six feet in diameter occurs near Flora, about 18 miles northwest of the state capital at Jackson.

CISHOMINGO CO.: Paden area, Tuscaloosa Formation—*amber*.

COPIAH CO.: Wesson, 4 mi. E in gravel pit—*agates* (banded), *chalcedony, petrified wood*.

HARRISON CO.: Gulfport, 18 mi. NW at Bell Creek—*agates*.

TASSAHATCHI CO.: Charleston area—*amber*.

WAYNE CO.: Waynesboro, 7 mi. NW—*fossils, petrified palm*.

## MISSOURI

Two great river systems dominate Missouri—the Mississippi, with its flood plains flung across the southeastern portion, and the Missouri as a geographical dividing line. North of the Missouri, retreating Pleistocene glaciers built the fertile northern plains much like those of Iowa, while south of this pioneer transportation artery, rolling foothills rise to the Ozark Mountain Plateau. Cretaceous marshes and swamp forests left many coal deposits throughout the state, while epicontinental seas laid down extensive sand and limestone sediments.

BOLLINGER CO.:—*agate, petrified wood*.

BENTON CO.: Ozark Mountains, low hills along W edge—*agate, chert*—also in the southeast (bootheel) district.

CAPE GIRARDEAU CO.:—*agates, petrified wood*.

CLARK CO.: St. Francisville, base of bluffs along the Fox River—*chert, quartz crystal geodes*—also near Wayland.

CRAWFORD CO.:—*azurite*. Steelville, E, mines along Highway 8—*amethyst, hematite, quartz crystals*.

DADE CO.:—*agate, chert, petrified wood*.

FRANKLIN CO.: Stanton, Ruepple Mine—*amethyst, quartz crystals*.

IRON CO.: Iron Mountain area pits—*hematite, quartz*.

JACKSON CO.: Same as for Iron Co.

LEWIS CO.: La Grange, N, Mississippi River gravels—*agate*. Stoddard Highway 25 S of Dexter—*agate, chert*.

MADISON CO.: Ozark Mountains, W of Cape Girardeau—*jasper*. South of Highway 70, mine dumps at Einstein Silver Mine—*arsenopyrite, fluorite, quartz crystals, pyrite, sphalerite*.

MONITEAU CO.: Area gravel pits—*barite crystals*.

MORGAN CO.: Area gravel pits—*barite crystals*.

NEWTON CO.: Neosho, 8 mi. E at Granby—*calcite, cerussite, chert, dolomite crystals, galena, marcasite, pyrite, quartz crystals, sphalerite*.

STODDARD CO.: Malden area gravel pits—*fortification agate* (blue, gray, pink, white).

TRI-STATE DISTRICT: Wentworth area mine dumps—*lead* and *zinc* minerals, *pyrites, sphalerite*.

WASHINGTON CO.: Potosi area gravel pits and all old mine dumps—*barite crystals.*

## MONTANA

The name of this great state literally means "mountains," and the lofty Bitterroot Range, marking the western boundary, carries the Continental Divide along its ragged crest. Dominated by the complex Rocky Mountain system in the western and southwestern portions, Montana is noted for its fabulous mineral deposits of gold, silver, lead, copper, and sapphires. They were concentrated during the 2,000,000-year-long Laramide Revolution which uplifted the vast mountain chains to end the Mesozoic Era and usher in the Cenozoic. The imprint of Tertiary events lies everywhere in continental deposits of debris constantly eroded down from the rising mountains. Indeed, the Great Plains of the central and eastern sections are predominantly mid-Tertiary sands, clays, muds, gravels, and silts overlain by a thin veneer of Quaternary gravels. Each year, earthquakes smashing across the mountain areas remind us that the mountain-building forces are still at work. The rock collector is particularly fortunate in having easy access to the Yellowstone River gravel bars for 250 miles, from Billings to the North Dakota border, including benchlands and tributaries on both sides, for the gem stone wealth that occurs abundantly in the form of *agate, "Montana moss" agate,* and *jasper*.

BEAVERHEAD CO.: Dillon, NW, at Frying Pan Basin,

and at Camp Creek—*corundum, opalized* and *silicified wood.*
Grasshopper Creek gravels—*diamond.* Lost Creek—*amazonite.*
  BIG HORN CO.: Dryhead area, TX ranch on E flanks of
the Pryor Mountains S of Billings—*agate* (fortification in
bright colors), *chalcedony, jasper, concretions* (sandstone, resembling petrified turtles), *silicified coral.*
  CASCADE CO.: Great Falls, 11 mi. W in Vaughn area—
*silicified wood* (black), *teredo wood* (filled with *chalcedony*).
Neyhart, Hartley Mine—gemmy *sphalerite.*
  DAWSON CO.: Glendive area—*agate, jasper, opal* (all
mossy).
  DEER LODGE CO.: Blackfoot, Nelson Hill area—*diamond.*
Cable Mine—*chrysocolla.* Champion, 5 mi. E in gravels—*gold,
sapphire.* Dry Cottonwood Creek, upper 4-mi. stretch of gravels
starting 12 mi. NW of Butte—*gold, sapphire.*
  GALLATIN CO.: Bozeman area—*corundum.* Horseshoe
Hills—*dendritic shale, trilobites.* Manhattan, 5 mi. NW—*onyx.*
Mount Blackmore, summit—*agate, chalcedony, hyalite, gem
opal, petrified wood.*
  GRANITE CO.: Phillipsburg area mine dumps—*chryso-
colla, rhodochrosite.* Rock Creek, 16 mi. SW of Phillipsburg,
particularly Anaconda and Sapphire gulches and along tributary draws—*quartz crystals, sapphire.*
  JEFFERSON CO.: Boulder Basin District, and in Mill
Canyon—*tourmaline.* Pohndorf Amethyst Mine, 2 mi. NE of
Toll Mountain Picnic Grounds and 2 mi. N of Highway 10 S—
*amethyst, feldspar crystals, mica, quartz crystals (smoky), schorl.*
  JUDITH BASIN CO.: Utica, 15 mi. SW in Yogo Gulch—
*gold, ruby, sapphire* ("cornflower blue") occurring in igneous
dike intruded into limestone outcropping on hills above the
gulch.
  LEWIS & CLARK CO.: Helena area; (1) American Bar—
*cassiterite* (stream tin), *chalcedony, garnet, gold, kyanite, limonite after pyrite, sapphire, topaz.* (2) Eldorado Bar 12 mi. NE
and (3) French Bar 6 mi. SE of Eldorado Bar, (4) Magpie
Gulch, lower end at Emerald Bar, (5) Missouri River gravel
bars W and NE of Helena—same minerals as on American
Bar. Prickly Pear Creek at Emerald, Metropolitan, and Spokane bars—*gold, sapphire.* Very numerous additional bars,
benches, and gravels; inquire locally.

MADISON CO.: Alder, Ruby River, upstream—*almandine garnet*—also in gravels near Ruby Dam and in regional stream beds. Butte, 20 mi. E—*amethyst*. Cliff Lake—*serpentine*. Cow Camp, Elk Mountain and Finnegan Ridge—*chert, jasper*. Dillon, from 37 mi. E along the Sweet Water Road to the Ruby River—*garnet, wonderstone* (banded *rhyolite.*) Greenhorn Gulch—*quartz crystals, diamond*. Jefferson River, gravels, foothills near Silver Star—*agate, chalcedony, petrified wood*. Pole Creek—*garnets, gold, quartz crystals, ruby corundum, sapphire*. Silver Star District—*agate, jasper, petrified wood*. South Boulder Creek—*quartz crystals*. Twin Bridges, W at Crystal Butte—*rock crystal*. Virginia City—*garnets*.

MISSOULA CO.: Lolo Creek District—*quartz crystals* (clear, smoky).

PARK CO.: Carbella—*agate, quartz, petrified wood*. Clyde Park—*iceland spar*. Gardiner—*agatized wood, travertine*—also around Livingstone and Miner. Springdale—*iceland spar*. Yellowstone River gravels and tributaries—*natrolite*.

PRAIRIE CO.: Terry—*petrified wood*.

RAVALLI CO.: Eightmile Creek, near White Cloud Mine—*"parasite" beryl*. Sula, 2 mi. N—*beryl*.

SILVER BOW CO.: Brown's Gulch—alluvial *sapphires*. Butte; (1) Alice, Allie Brown, Lexington, and Rainbow mine dumps—*peacock copper, rhodochrosite, rhodonite*, (2) Emma Mine—massive *rhodochrosite*, (3) Gravelly Range S of Butte—*"onyx"* (silicified *rhyolite*). East Ridge foothills—*chrysocolla*.

YELLOWSTONE CO.: Custer area—*agate, jasper*.

# NEBRASKA

This rectangular Great Plains state rises westward from 840 to 5300 feet elevation so imperceptibly as to appear completely level. The fertile region west of the Missouri River is underlain to a great depth by loess, i.e., windblown soil. Eroded sandhills fan out across the west and northwest, while the far western portion rises to the foothills of the Rockies, disclosing spectacular bedrock formations. Extensive digging in the Niobrara Formation along the Niobrara River in Cherry, Dawes, Sheridan, and Sioux counties have yielded many fossil remains of such mid-Pleistocene mammals as beaver, bison, camel, dog, elephant, rodents, etc. The fossil collector will be especially fortunate near the communities of Agate, Bridgeport, Hay Springs, Scottsbluff, Sidney, and Valentine.

CHERRY CO.: Valentine regional gullies, stream beds, and washes—*opalized wood, petrified and fossilized bones.*

DAWES CO.: Crawford, 20 mi. N in Little Bad Lands— fossil specimens of *alligators, oredons, rhinos, sabre-tooth tigers.* Pine Ridge—*quartz concretions.*

DEUEL CO.: Chappell, surrounding hillsides—*agate, chalcedony, jasper, petrified wood.*

DOUGLAS CO.: Platte River gravels and in regional gravel pits—*agate* (banded, moss), *chalcedony, chert, flint, moss opal, opalized wood, petrified wood.*

GAGE CO.: Gravel quarries—*calcite* and *quartz crystals.*

JEFFERSON CO.: Fairbury and Stelle regional gravel pits and stream gravels—*agate, jasper, petrified wood.*

MORRILL CO.: Angora, 2 mi. E. of Angora Hill from Highway 19—*moss opal,* as nodules in limestone. Bayard area gravel pits, stream beds, and sand hills—*chalcedony, chert, flint.*

NEMAHAS CO.: Johnson, Platte River gravels—*agate* (common, moss), *jasper, petrified wood (cycads).*

SIOUX CO.: Orella area—*agates* (variously colored or mossy), *chalcedony, iris agate, petrified wood.*

## NEVADA

This semitriangular state lies within the Great Basin region of interior drainage, cut off from the moisture of the Pacific Ocean by the lofty Sierra Nevada Range on the west, a part of which composes the northwestern boundary between Nevada and California. The state is characterized by scores of short, high, extremely rugged mountain ranges separated by arid valleys, alkali sinks, and broad plains and "bajadas" clothed in sagebrush or creosote bush. Many hundreds of mines, great and small, dot the entire state, attesting to its enormous mineral wealth in *antimony, arsenic, copper, gold, lead, manganese, mercury, silver, tungsten,* and *zinc.* One may prospect the mine dumps for many colorful and interesting minerals.

CHURCHILL CO.: Fallon, 14 mi. out—*wonderstone* (banded *rhyolite*). Lahontan Dam, W end and along NE shore of Lahontan Reservior—*agate, chalcedony, jasper, petrified wood.* Rawhide, 6 mi. N and 2 mi. W on a secondary road—*opalized wood.* Sunnyside District—*azurite, malachite.*

CLARK CO.: Black Canyon of the Colorado River—*almandite garnet.* Bullion District—*azurite, chrysocolla, malachite.* Crescent, 3 mi. ESE and just S of Crescent Peak, about half way between Nipton, Calif., and Searchlight, Nev.—*turquoise.* Henderson, 1¾ mi. S, then 4½ mi. W to low hills—*chalcedony, onyx.* Las Vegas Wash—*amethyst.* White Basin—*fibrous ulexite.*

DOUGLAS CO.: Pine Nut Mountains, S part—*thulite (pink zoisite), topaz.*

ELKO CO.: Carlin—*rose quartz.* Contact, NE part of Elko Co. near Idaho state line, mine dumps—*azurite, malachite.* Midas, Rand Mine, 10 mi. out—*common opal.* Mountain City—*azurite, malachite.* Tuscarora silver mines—*citrine, quartz (rose) crystals, wonderstone* (banded *rhyolite*).

ESMERALDA CO.: Blair Jct., 9 to 11 mi. NNE at variscite mines—*variscite.* Candelaria, 1 mi. S in east foothills of Candelaria Mountains and 1 mi. W of Mount Diablo Silver Mine—*variscite.* Coaldale; (1) 10 mi. SSW on W side of Fish Lake—*Apache tears (obsidian),* (2) 3 to 6 mi. NE in Monte Cristo Mountains, variscite mines—*variscite,* (3) Monte Cristo Mountain area—*agate, chert, jasper, turquoise,* (4) 13 mi. SW and 1 mi. E of Highway 3A at the "Sump Hole"—*opalized wood.* Columbus, 1½ mi. NW—*variscite.* Fish Lake Valley, Emigrant Peak area—*petrified wood.* Goldfield; (1) city mine dumps—*gold, quartz crystals, pyrite,* (2) 3 mi. W—*massive opalite,* (3) S, at old Cuprite—*azurite, malachite,* (4) SW on Montezuma Mountain on SE, S, and W sides—*chalcedony, chert, jasper, quartz, obsidian, opalized wood,* (5) E, in Ralston Desert of Nye Co.—*chert.* Gold Mountain—*citrine, quartz crystals.* Palmetto Canyon—*citrine, quartz crystals.* Rock Hill Siding, 2 mi. W—*variscite.* Silver Peak Mines—*rose quartz.*

EUREKA CO.: Carlin, 10 mi. NW at Copper King Mine in Maggie Creek District—*faustite, montmorillonite clays, turquoise.* Eureka and Ruby Hill Districts—*azurite, malachite.*

HUMBOLDT CO.: Black Rock Desert, 50 mi. N of Gerlach in old Leadville District—*opalized* and *petrified wood.* Rainbow Ridge Mine—*rhodonite.* Virgin Valley, from Denio or

Quinn Crossing in Nevada or from Cedarville in California, 20 mi. SW of Denio at end of a road that turns S from Highway 8A a few miles off the Summit Lake Indian Reservation road; also on E side of the valley at Green Fire Mine as seams and irregular masses—*precious ("Virgin Valley") opal, chalcedony, lignite* (silicified, black), *pine* and *spruce cones* (petrified).

LANDER CO.: Austin area—*opal*. Battle Mountain; (1) 8 mi. SSW at Copper Basin, especially from the Blue Gem Turquoise Mine—*turquoise*, (2) Hot Springs Mining District 35 mi. S—*turquoise*, (3) Ivanhoe area, 45 mi. NE of Battle Mountain—*opalite*, (4) Lynn District 30 mi. NE—*turquoise*, (5) Pedro Claim—*turquoise*. Cortz, Fox Turquoise Mine—*turquoise*. New Pass area—*fossils*.

LINCOLN CO.: Acoma Mining District—*chalcedony*. Atlanta Mining District, N of Pioche along Highway 93—*chert, gold, pyrite*. Bristol Mining District—*azurite, chrysocolla, malachite*. Base of Sugar Loaf Peak—*turquoise*.

LYON CO.: Fernly, 5½ mi. S on W flanks of hills—*agate, chert, jasper*. Yerington District; (1) 1½ mi. NNW and (2) 8 mi. WNW of Yerington—*turquoise*, (3) Ludwig, ¾ mi. E— *thulite*, (4) Singatse Mountains mine dumps W of Yerington— —*chalcanthite* ("bluestone"), (5) Wilson Canyon 15.6 mi. S of Yerington—*agate, chalcedony, chert, jasper, petrified wood, turquoise*.

MINERAL CO.: Aurora—*jasper, quartz crystals*. Candelaria District, Reik Mine—*turquoise*. Luning Mining District— plum-colored *axinite*. Montgomery Pass, on Highway 6 at Queen Mountain—*obsidian*. Rand, 18 mi. S of Rawhide—*turquoise*. Sodaville, 8 mi. SW in E end of Excelsior Mountains— *banded rhyolite, turquoise, variscite*. Thorne, 5 mi. SE in Ryan Canyon—*thulite*. Walker Lake area, N of Hawthorne—*agate, chalcedony, fossils, petrified wood, turquoise*.

NYE CO.: Beatty; (1) area mine dumps—*common opal with cinnabar*, (2) Bullfrog mine dumps, 8 mi. W of Rhyolite—*amethyst, azurite, gold ore, malachite*, (3) 28 mi. N and ½ mi. E of Highway 95—*arrowheads, arrow cores, obsidian*, (4) Yucca Mountains—*geodes, nodules*. Belmont, 18 mi. E of Vanderbilt, Calif.—*turquoise*. Butler, 50 mi. E on Cactus Mountain—*turquoise*. Tonopah; (1) N—*jade, petrified wood, wonderstone* (banded *rhyolite*, (2) 10 to 12 mi. E—*algae and bogwood (petri-*

*fied), jade,* (3) Swab Mountain SE and 35 mi. E of Goldfield on S side of Cactus Range—*jasper, petrified wood,* (4) SW and W in various mining districts, *e.g.,* Columbus, Klondike, Lone Mountain, Silver Peak Marsh and Mining District, most of which are in Esmeralda Co. but mainly out of Tonopah—*agate, chalcedony, jasper, malachite, quartz and quartzite, opalite, turquoise, variscite, wood (fossil).*

PERSHING CO.: Buffalo Hill—*ammonites, cephalopods.* Mill City, 12 to 14 mi. out on E side of Star Peak—*geodes, nodules.* Oreana, 6 mi. N in Gypsy Queen Canyon—*dumortierite quartz.* Rochester Mining District, W side of Lincoln Hill—*dumortierite quartz.* Rye Patch, pegmatites intruded into limestone—*emerald.*

WASHOE CO.: High Rock Canyon, around headwaters of Little High Rock Creek—*obsidian nodules*—also at canyon crossing of Lost Creek Canyon Road. Leadville, ghost town, 8 mi. N near Highway 34—*agate, silicified wood.* Sparks—*agate, garnet, idocrase, obsidian.* Vya, 30 mi. S and on W side of Highway 34—*common opal.*

WHITE PINE CO.: Ely, Robinson Canyon to W on Highway 50, to Kimberley turnoff and 1 mi. NW, on hills to S—*garnets.* Late City, Nightingale District—*garnets.* Little Antelope Summit on Highway 50 about 40 mi. W of Ely—*wonderstone.*

## NEW HAMPSHIRE

Long known as the Granite State because of its bedrock granite exposures, New Hampshire was entirely covered to a great depth by the Pleistocene ice sheets. In receding, the ice scraped the mountains, peneplaned the upland areas, and rerouted the water courses into precipitous streams and innumerable lakes. Containing Mount Washington, highest peak in New England at 6288 feet, the residual White Mountains of the Appalachian chain stretch across the northern part of the state in a series of rugged ranges broken by sharp "notches." South of the mountain and lake area, the nearly level upland region is noted for its isolated peaks of resistant rock, called "monadnocks." From the Presidential Range on the east the land descends westward toward the Connecticut Valley. In the topsoils of rocky ridges throughout the counties of Berlin, Dummer, Kilkenny, Lancaster, Milan, Millsfield, Northcumberland, Odell, and Strafford amethysts are found.

BELKNAP CO.: Gilmanton—*jasper.*

CARROLL CO.: Conway Twp., Redstone Station, Redstone Red Quarry—*amethyst, apatite, quarts (smoky), rock crystal, topaz.* Lovejoy Gravel Pits, 2½ mi. NW of Conway—*microcline, smoky quartz, topaz.* North Chatam, 3½ mi. W on South Baldface Mountain—*biotite, microcline, muscovite, phenakite, smoky quartz.*

CHESHIRE CO.: Chesterfield and Westmoreland Twps., Spofford Lake, mines NW on W side of Highway 63—*fluorite.* Gilsum; (1) 2¼ mi. NNW at Island Mice Mine N of Keene—*beryl,* (2) 3½ mi. NNW at Britton Mine—*beryl,* (3) 5½ mi. N at Wenham Mine—*rose quartz.* Hinsdale, Walpole, and Winchester—*tourmaline.* Roxbury Twp., Keene; (1) 5 mi. ENE at Bassett Hill—*beryl,* (2) 4½ mi. E on S side of Horse Hill—*aquamarine.* Surrey—*amethyst.*

COOS CO.: Milan and Stark Twps., and surrounding region, especially (1) Diamond Ledge, on Percy Peak, (2) Green's Ledge, near Milan, and (3) Hutchins Mountain, near Stark—*albite, amethyst, beryl, chlorite, feldspar, fluorite, knebelite, limonite, molybdenite, muscovite, pyrite, quartz (smoky) crystals, sericite, topaz.* Stark Twp., Percy, 1¾ mi. NNW at Victors Head—same as listed above.

GRAFTON CO.: Franconia—*andradite garnet. Groton* Twp., North Groton; (1) ¾ mi. WNW at Charles Davis Mine —*aquamarine, beryl, brazilianite, lazulite,* (2) 2 mi. SW at Palermo Mine—*brazilianite, massive lazulite*—also at Palermo Quarry. Hanover—*jasper, rutilated quartz.* Sugar Hill; (1) 1½ mi. S on S side of Ore Hill—*amethyst, rock crystal,* (2) summit of Ore Hill—*staurolite* (fairy crosses)—also at Lisbon, and on the shores of Mink Pond. Warren—*essonite garnet, vesuvianite.*

HILLSBORO CO.: Francestown area—*jasper.*

MERRIMACK CO.: Wilmot Twp., Grafton, 3¼ mi. SE at Severance Hill—*beryl.*

ROCKINGHAM CO.: Raymond, Chandler Feldspar Mine —*spodumene.*

SULLIVAN CO.: Claremont and Grantham area in outcrops of micaceous slates—*staurolite* (fairy crosses). Newport, Smith Mica Mine at Chandler's Mill—*augelite, lazulite.* Springfield Twp., Grafton, 2¾ mi. SSW near summit of Pillsbury Ridge at Columbia and Reynolds mines—*aquamarine, beryl.* Various spots around Acworth and Beryl Mountain—*beryl, garnet, quartz crystals.*

## NEW JERSEY

The northern third of this gem stone state (approximately 120 mineral and gem stone species are known) lies within the Appalachian Highlands, with many northwest-southeast ridges separating lovely valleys of glacial lakes and pleasant streams. The Kittatinny Mountains, highest area in the state, cross the northwest corner from the New York border to the spectacular Delaware Water Gap. South of the Highlands, the piedmont plains of Triassic origin parallel U.S. Highway 1 from Newark to Trenton, broken by occasional traprock ridges that extend to the Palisades of the Hudson. In many counties exposures of Cretaceous marl sands yield *amber.* From Franklin southward to Ogdenburg wherever limestone outcrops reveal a contact zone with the enclosing rock, the rock collector will find *corundum* of facet quality.

BERGEN CO.: In a broad area passing through the counties of Essex, Hunterdon, Mercer, Morris, Passaic, and Somerset, basalt outcrops yield—*agate, amethyst druses, amethyst geodes, carnelian, chalcedony, datolite, natrolite, opal.*

CAMDEN CO.: Camden area—*amber.*

ESSEX CO.: Belleville and Bloomfield—*malachite.*

HUDSON CO.: Hoboken—*agate, amethyst.*

HUNTERDON CO.: Bryan—*spinel.*

MIDDLESEX CO.: Bergen Hill—*prehnite.*

MONMOUTH CO.: Long Branch area—*quartz crystals.*

MORRIS CO.: Dover; (1) area vein fillings in magnetite—*opal (isopyre),* (2) Mine Hill, Alan Wood iron mine near summit—*aventurescent feldspar, sunstone.* Sterling—*carnelian.* Turkey Mountain, W of Lake Valhalla in old quarries—*diopside, marble, serpentine.*

PASSAIC CO.: Packanack Lake, Alps Road—*pectolite.* Patterson, Prospect Park Quarry—*agate, amethyst, calcite, cachalong opal, quartz crystals, prehnite*—also from quarries at Great Notch, such as Frascinco Bros. Quarry, along with *thomsonite.* Ringwood, Ringwood Iron Mine—*calcite, chalcopyrite, cro-*

TYPICAL LAPIDARY—A rock collector's workshop consist of shelves to hold rock specimens, a workbench, a black light, and cutting and polishing machinery. In a surprisingly short time most rock collectors accumulate several tons of rocks and what to do with them becomes something of a family problem. (*Jay Ellis Ransom*)

GLACIAL DEPOSITS—A deposit of glacial boulders near the entrance to Blackwood Campground, Acadia National Park, Maine. (*Rocks and Minerals*)

FOSSIL HUNTERS—Rock collectors find that the sedimentary beds of America offer a wealth of prehistoric life remnants. (*California Division of Mines*)

TRILOBITE—This trilobite fossil once inhabited a Cambrian sea half a billion years ago. Trilobite is an "index fossil" inasmuch as it was probably the most highly organized life of Cambrian times. (*California Division of Mines*)

FOSSIL BEDS—The John Day Fossil Beds of central Oregon are a primary fossil collecting area; varieties of Tertiary mammalian remains are found eroding from the clay formations. (*Oregon State Highway Commission*)

SURF-WASHED AGATES—Up and down the Pacific coast of America the beaches at low tide yield a surprising variety of semi-precious stones and minerals, such as agate, jasper, jade, nephrite, moonstones, and gold. (*Oregon State Highway Commission*)

MINE DUMPS—The huge dumps of the Inspiration Open Pit Mine near Globe, Arizona are representative of all the mine dumps of the abandoned workings of the Western states. On these dumps the rock collector will often find colorful cabinet specimens, crystals, and rare earths. Collecting is rarely, if ever, prohibited. (*Jay Ellis Ransom*)

GLACIAL ERRATIC—A huge glacial erratic of coarse granite adorns this tranquil pasture in East Sutton, N. H. One-third of this giant is concealed beneath the soil. (*Rocks and Minerals*)

JURASSIC SEDIMENTS—Beds of bright red 160 million-year-old sediments of the Big Horn Canyon in northern Wyoming overlie Triassic sandstones 185 million years old at the base of the Big Horn Mountains. Fossil corals, belemnites, ammonites, and dinosaur bones have made these uplifted sediments rich hunting grounds for scientists. (*Jay Ellis Ranson*)

3000 FOOT MONADNOCK—Glaciated area near the summit of Mt. Kearsarge in central New Hampshire. (*Rocks and Minerals*)

ROAD CUTS—Road cuts and tunnels anywhere in America are natural rock collecting localities. Blasting often breaks loose crystal aggregates or opens hidden mineral veins containing highly prized gem specimens. (*Oregon State Highway Commission*)

BADLANDS FORMATIONS—This central Oregon geologic formation is typical gem stone collecting ground found in many states west of the Mississippi. The rock collector will find all types of agate, jasper, and chalcedony as well as petrified woods of every description eroding from such sedimentary deposits. Cretaceous fossils are often found in the draws and gullies. (*Oregon State Highway Commission*)

MAGNETITE IRON MINE—Amateur rockhounds at the famous French Creek Iron Mine at St. Peters, Chester County, Pennsylvania. (*Rocks and Minerals*)

BASALT QUARRY—The New Street Trap Rock Quarry, Paterson, N. J. Quarries and mine dumps are especially valuable collecting sites. (*Rocks and Minerals*)

Outcrop—A rock collector and amateur geologist, J. G. Ransom, examines a lava outcrop for malachite and agate nodules, found in the Mojave Desert. The surrounding region once produced considerable copper and gold; many varieties of gem stone minerals occur throughout the Mojave Desert region. (*Jay Ellis Ransom*)

Mud Flow—This silica-rich mud flow in the midst of volcanic rocks, occasionally encountered in the Western states, may also contain small diamonds. This Colorado Desert flow in the Turtle Mountains district is surrounded with colorful agate in veins up to four feet thick. (*Jay Ellis Ransom*)

cidolite, corundum, epidote, garnet, hornblende, limonite, orthoclase, pyrite, serpentine, zircon. West Patterson, New Street Quarry—prehnite, thomsonite. SALEM CO.: Harrisonville—amber. SOMERSET CO.: Bound Brook—agate. Pyson Station— quartz geodes. Somerville, 3 mi. N at Bridgewater Mine on First Watchung Mountain—turquoise. SUSSEX CO.: Andover; (1) area—spinal, (2) Old Iron Mine —garnet, hematite, limonite, magnetite. Franklin Furnace— amethyst. Franklin and Ogdenburg, New Jersey Zinc Co. mines —bustamite, calcite, cleiophane (colorless sphalerite), cyprine, idocrase, franklinite, friedelite, hodgekinsonite, rhodonite (zinc), wellemite, zincite. Franklin, Newton, Sparta area limestone quarries—corundum (blue, pink), ruby. Mine Hill— axinite. Sparta area—ruby. Sparta Junction, limestone quarry— actinolite, barite, biotite, fluorite, pyrite, quartz crystals, rhodonite, rutile, sphene, spinel, tourmaline. Sterling Hill, across Wallkill River Valley from Ogdenburg—zincite.

## NEW MEXICO

Roughly bisected by the Rio Grande River, semiarid New Mexico lies at a mean elevation of 5700 feet, hot in summer and bitterly cold in winter. It is topographically noted for its spacious grazing grasslands, wide deserts, broken mesas, volcanic necks, and heavily forested mountains marked by high, bare peaks. Cresting in the Sangre de Cristo Range, the mountains flank the Rio Grande through the central region, standing in broken groups that run north and south. Because millions of acres of this mineral-rich state are under federal control, the gem stone and mineral collector will find few obstructions to his prospecting. Indeed, few areas have been much explored for the gemstone minerals.

BERNALILLO CO.: Isleta Pueblo, E—opal (milk white), opalized and petrified woods. Rio Puerco Valley—agate, chalcedony, jasper, opalized and petrified wood. Tijeras Canyon District—fluorite.

CHAVES CO.: Lake Arthur, 16 mi. E—aragonite crystals.

CATRON CO.: Apache Creek—agate. Mogollon District— agate, chalcedony, fluorite, jasper. Plains of San Augustin, in volcanic tuffs—agate (moss), jasper. Taylor Creek District, extending into Sierra Co.—*agate, chalcedony, fluorite, jasper, topaz* (colorless).

COLFAX CO.: Raton coal field, Sugarite Mine—*amber.*

DONA ANA CO.: Area, many places—*fluorite.* Caballos Mountains, on county border—*agate, chalcedony, jasp-agate, jasper, quartz crystals.* Kilbourne Hole—*augite, peridot.* Las Cruces; (1) both sides of roads leading S, and (2) 5 mi. W on road to Mesilla—*obsidian.* Organ District, Quicksilver Mine—*chrysocolla, onyx, rock crystal* (with *chlorite* inclusions).

EDDY CO.: Carlsbad Caverns area limestones—*onyx.*

GRANT CO.: Black Range; (1) Great Republic Mine, and (2) west slopes—*albite, amethyst, biotite, sanidine, sphene.* Burro Mountains; (1) Cap Rock Mountain and Mimbres Mountains, W side—*agate, chalcedony, chert, chrysocolla, crypto-crystalline quartz, fluorite, jasper, rock crystal,* (2) Central District—same plus *onyx,* (3) Silver City, 10 mi. SW and 1½ mi. N of Tyrone, at the Azure Mine (particularly the Elizabeth Pocket), and in regional Indian excavations—*halloysite, quartz crystals, turquoise*—also ½ mi. SE at Parker Mine, and at other area mine dumps. Fierro-Hanover, Juniper, and Meerschaum Districts—*colored chert.* Fort Bayard—*fire opal.* Hachita District, in Little Hachita Mountains, any mine dump—*moonstones.* Red Rock, 6 mi. NE in Ricolite Gulch—*ricolite* (banded *serpentine*).

GUADALUPE CO.: Santa Rosa area coal seams—*jet.*

HIDALGO CO.: Hachita, around Playas Dry Lake and in the Hatchet Mountains—*agate (fortification, moss, plume), moss opal.* Lordsburg District, Peloncillo and Pyramid Mountains—*agate, chalcedony, chalcedony roses, jasp-agate, jasper.*

LINCOLN CO.: Ancho area—*jasper.* Hidalgo area mines and prospects—*fluorite.* White Oaks District—*banded onyx.*

LUNA CO.: Columbus; (1) 4 mi. W—*onyx,* (2) 12 mi. NW at Tres Hermanas Mountains—*dumortierite, quartz crystals.* Deming area and around Cooks Peak—*agate, chalcedony, fluorite, jasper.* Gap between Florida and Little Florida Mountains—*agate (sagenitic), blue chalcedony.* Fremont—*azurite, malachite.*

McKINLEY CO.: Furry Mountain's east slope—*garnet.* Gallup, SE in Zuni Mountains—*agate, jasper, petrified wood.* San Mateo, NE at Willow Springs—*agate, jasper, petrified wood.*

Thoreau, 12 mi. SE in coal seams S of Devil's Pass and in area outcrops—*amber* (*wheelerite*, or fossil resin)—also in most regional mines.

MORO CO.: Coyote—*azurite, malachite.*

OTERO CO.: Bent, 1½ mi. S in Tularosa District—"*Mexican" onyx.* Jarilla District, 50 mi. NNE of El Paso, Texas—*chalcopyrite, chrysocolla, gypsum, jarosite, kaolin, limonite, pyrite, turquoise.*

RIO ARRIBA CO.: Abiquiu area basalts—*labradorite.* Bromide and Petaca Districts—*amazonite, fluorite.* La Madera—*beryl, dumortierite.* Petaca District; (1) from Cerro Pedernal to W side of San Pedro Mountain, especially ½ mi. SE of La Medera—"*Pedernal" chert, dumortierite, specular hematite,* (2) 3½ mi. SW of South Petaca above Alamos Canyon at Sunnyside Mine W of Glode Road—*aquamarine, beryl.* Las Tablas, 1½ mi. SW and ¾ mi. SE of Persimmon Peak at Canary Bird Mine—*tourmaline.*

SANDOVAL CO.: Battleship Rock, Jemez Sulphur District—*obsidian, opalized wood* (in volcanic tuffs). Cochita District, Upper Percha Creek—*common opal.* Jemez; (1) area lavas—*moonstone,* (2) Jemez District and along the Rio Puerco Valley—*agate, chalcedony, jasper, quartzite, silicified wood.* Nacimiento Mountains, draws and washes—*agate, azurite, chalcedony, chrysocolla, malachite.* Placitas District—*cave onyx.* Rio Puerco coal field—*wheelerite* (fossil resin).

SAN JUAN CO.: area coal seams and mines—*jet.* Chaco Canyon, N along Bloomfield-Cuba highway—*chalcedony.* Durango-Gallup coal field—*wheelerite* (fossil resin). Between San Juan River and Chaco River, Ojo Alamo Formation—*chert, garnet, jasper, quartzite* (colorful), *petrified wood.*

SAN MIGUEL CO.: NW of Las Vegas—*petrified wood.*

SANTE FE CO.: Cerrillos, 6 mi. NNE and 20 mi. SSW of Santa Fe, on Turquoise Hill 3 mi. from Mount Chalchihuitl in Cerrillos Hills, and at Mount Chalchihuitl—*agate, chalcedony, petrified wood, turquoise.*

SIERRA CO.: Caballos Mountains; (1) area mines—*azurite, fluorite, malachite,* (2) W side and N of Truth Or Consequences—*agate, jasper.* Cutter, opposite Aleman Ranch—*jasper.* Derry and Lake Valley Districts—colorful *chert.* Engle, both sides of road from Elephant Butte and around Engle—

*agate, chert.* Jornada Valley; (1) 13 mi. E of Truth Or Consequences, at Hot Springs—*agate, chalcedony, "elixirite" (silicified wonderstone, i.e.,* banded *rhyolite), jasper, petrified wood,* (2) W side at Mockingbird Gap in San Andreas Mountains—*dendritic jasper.* Kingston District, Comstock Mine—*massive rhodonite.* Mud Springs Mountain, NE flanks—*agate, opalized* and *silicified wood, petrified palm.* Taylor Creek District—see Catron Co.

SOCORRO CO.: Fra Cristobal Range, N end and E side of Elephant Butte Reservoir—*opalized limbs, logs, and stem sections*—also S of the E end of Bernado Bridge across the Rio Grande River. NOTE: This field extends southward into Sierra Co. along the mountain range, and eastward into the Jornada Valley to the east of Truth Or Consequences. Grandview Canyon and Hansonburg—*fluorite.* Joseph area, in Joita Hills, at Mockingbird Gap, and around the Socorro Peaks—*agate, chalcedony, jasper, dendritic jasper, quartz crystals, quartzite* (colorful), *petrified wood.* Magdalena District, especially the Kelly Mine 3 mi. NE of Magdalena—*fossil crinoids and mollusk shells, smithsonite.* Socorro, 4 mi. NW and at Strawberry Peak, E side—*satin spar.*

TAOS CO.: Glenwoody and Picuris Districts—*staurolite* (fairy crosses)—also between Pilar and Velarde on Highway 64, with *garnets.* Red River District—*fluorite.*

TORRANCE CO.: Manzano Mountain schistose outcrops—*staurolite.*

VALENCIA CO.: Belen area, to Las Lunas and at Rio Puerco, as well as around Laguna—*agate.* Coal seam outcrops and coal mine dumps—*jet.* Zuni Mountains—*agate, azurite, jasper, malachite, petrified wood.*

# NEW YORK

With the eastern portion of New York state dominated by the great valley of the Hudson and Lake Champlain, the hilly northern section rises to the rugged Adirondack Mountains. Western New York is a rolling, hilly region extending to Lakes Erie and Ontario, cupping many smaller lakes in the folds of the glaciated hills, particularly Lake Oneida and the Finger Lakes. Most of southern New York is part of the Alleghany Plateau culminating in the Catskill Mountains. Pleistocene glaciers covered the region, and it is estimated that 1000 feet of ice lay over what is now New York City and 2500 feet over the Catskills. The outer (Ronkonkoma) and inner (Harbor Hill) moraines of Long Island are notable examples of glacial termination.

ERIE CO.: Buffalo, 2½ mi. E at Fogelsanger Quarry—*calcite, favosites* (petrified honeycomb coral), *petrified coral.*

ESSEX CO.: Cascades Lake—*labradorite.* Crown Point—*sunstone.* Olmstedville, 1 mi. W along Minerva Highway— *idocrase, microcline* (gem quality), *scapolite.* Newcomb Post Office, 1 mi. E around Lake Harris—*albite, amphiboles* (various), *apatite, graphite, mica* (*muscovite*), *pyrite, pyroxene, quartz crystals* (*smoky*), *scapolite, tourmaline, tremolite.* Opalescent River bars—*labradorite*—also in Keeseville quarries.

HERKIMER CO.: Middleville area sandstone outcrops— *rock crystal* ("Herkimer diamonds")—found principally (1) on N side of road from Middleville to Newport along a north-westerly belt, (2) eastward from Middleville 1 mi. toward N side of Fairfield highway, and (3) from Middleville to 3 mi. southward, most prolifically on top of a hill betwen Middleville and Herkimer.

JEFFERSON CO.: Muskalonge Lake, NE shore—*fluorite.* Pillar Point, opposite Sackett's Harbor—*barite crystals.*

LEWIS CO.: Natural Bridge, 3 mi. NE at a quarry—*serpentine, talc.*

New York City, Richmond Borough, SW tip of Staten Island in the Androvette Clay Pits, near Kreischerville on the shore of Arthur Kill—*serpentine.*

ORANGE CO.: Blooming Grove, along Hudson River— *bloodstone, jasper.*

OSTEGO CO.: Toddsville—*sapphire.*

PUTNAM CO.: Brewster, 6 mi. NW at Tilly Foster Iron Mine—*apatite, chondrodite, garnet* (*grossularite, uvarovite*), *sphene.*

SARATOGA CO.: Batchellerville, 12½ mi. N at Overlook —*rose quartz.* Saratoga Springs, W side of a point that is ½ mi. W of intersection of Highway 9 and the township road— *chrysoberyl.*

SCHOHARIE CO.: area outcrops—*silicified coral.*

ST. LAWRENCE CO.: De Kalb, Gouverneur, Pierrepoint

*—tourmaline.* De Kalb Twp.; (1) Loomis Talc Mine on Highway 58 NW of Fowler—*tremolite,* (2) Reese Farm, near Richville—*pyroxene, tourmaline (dravite), tremolite,* (3) at points 3 mi. NE and 5 mi. N of Richville—*achroite, diopside, white dravite.* Hailesboro, area limestone quarries—*apatite.* Macomb District—*fluorite.* Oswegatchie River outcrops around Gouverneur—*serpentine.*

SYRACUSE (City): Various peridotite outcrops—*peridotite.*

WARREN CO.: Horicon, S shore of Brant Lake road cut—*apatite, calcite, diopside, graphite, muscovite, pyrite, rutile, tourmaline.* North Creek; (1) 4 mi. WSW, mines around Gore Mountain, (2) W at Ruby Mountain, (3) S on Oven Mountain —*almandine garnet*—also on Humphrey Mountain 6½ mi. SW of the S end of Thirteenth Lake.

WESTCHESTER CO.: Bedford Twp., Bedford, ¾ mi. SE at Kinkel Quarry—*beryl (golden), citrine, quartz crystals (rose with asterism, smoky)*—also at Hobby Quarry 1½ mi. SE of Kinkel Quarry along Mianus River in North Castle, and at Baylis Quarry ½ mi. W of Kinkel Quarry. Chappaqua—*sunstone.* Port Chester, on Long Island Sound—*serpentine* (green, red, white). Peekskill—*thomsonite.*

## NORTH CAROLINA

With more than 300 varieties of gem stones and minerals, North Carolina is indeed a state of contrasts. From the tidewater swamps along the Atlantic, the land rises to 500 feet along the western edge of the upper coastal plain. Then begins the rolling hill country with its many swift streams descending the piedmont. On its west the land juts up into the Blue Ridge, then dips sharply to the broad Carolina highlands plateau, backed up against the Great Smoky Mountains. Here we find Mount Mitchell which, at 6684 feet, is the highest peak in the eastern United States. *Petrified wood* is found in the alluvial gravels of many counties, particularly Anson, Cumberland, Moore, Montgomery, and Wayne.

ALEXANDER CO.: Hiddenite District; (1) many area mine dumps—*aquamarine, beryl, quartz crystals, rutile crystals,* (2) All Healing Springs, pegmatite dikes—*beryl,* (3) 1½ mi. E of Hiddenite, on ridge between Davis Creek and Little Yadkin River—*aquamarine, beryl, quartz and rutile crystals.* Sharpe's

Twp.; (1) ½ mi. W and ¼ mi. E of Hiddenite—*aquamarine, calcite, chalcopyrite, dolomite crystals, emerald, hiddenite, monazite, muscovite mica, quartz* and *rutile crystals, schorl,* (2) 1 mi. N of Hiddenite on Warren Farm, near Salem Church and 300 yards from Taylorsville-Statesville Highway, 15 mi. NW of Statesville—*albite, amphibole, ankerite, apatite, aquamarine, arsenopyrite, beryl, calcite, chlorite, emerald, feldspar (orthoclase), hiddenite, muscovite, pyrite, quartz* and *rutile crystals, schorl, siderite, spodumene*—also Osborne-Lackey place 1/5 mi. to NW, with *aragonite.* Stony Point area—*chlorite, goethite, rock crystal (rutilated* and with *byssolite* inclusions). White Plains area; (1) Liberty Church, near Millholland's Mill, (2) Taylorsville—*rutile crystals.*

ALLEGHENY CO.: Independence, 7 mi. SE and 1½ mi. S of state line between Virginia and North Carolina, below Bald Knob—*garnet (spessartite), pyrolusite, rhodonite.*

ASHE CO.: Beaver Creek, 1½ mi. SW at South Hardin Mica Mine—*golden beryl.* Chestnut Hill Twp.—*rock crystal.* Elk Cross Roads, 2 mi. NW at Walnut Knob Mine ¾ mi. S. of Black Mountain—*aquamarine.* Piney Creek, N Fork—*rock crystal.*

AVERY CO.: Cranberry—*unakite.* Plumtree, 0.8 mi. NE, at Plumtree Mine—*oligoclase crystals.*

BUNCOMBE CO.: Tremont Mountain—*chrysoprase.*

BURKE CO.: Brindletown Creek gravels—*diamond, quartz crystals (rutilated, smoky).* Morgantown, 8 mi. WSW in South Mountains ½ mi. SW of Walker Knob—*aquamarine, golden beryl.*

CABARRUS CO.: Concord area—*agate, rutilated quartz.*

CHEROKEE CO.: Beaverdam Creek—*agate, jasper, petrified wood, smoky quartz.* Snow Bird Mountains, Parker Mine, and also at Marble, Moss Creek, and Unaka—*staurolite.*

CLAY CO.: Brass Town, 1 mi. E on Tusquitee Creek near Hayesville—*staurolite.* Buck Creek; (1) Cullakanee Mine, 6 mi. N of Georgia border and 20 mi. SW of Franklin—*corundum, opal, peridot,* (2) Maney Cut, and other area mines—*corundum* (pink), *smaragdite* (green *amphibolite).* Cat Eye Cut, 600 feet SW of Chestnut Knob—*"cat-eye" corundum* (asterated). Elf, on Shooting Creek—*corundum* (red, in nodules found in green *amphibolite), opal, quartz crystals, smaragdite* (green *amphibolite*). Hayesville, E, on Penland Bald—*garnets*. Red Corundum Knob—*actinolite, corundum* (pink), *kyanite, olivine, ruby, serpentine*.

CLEVELAND CO.: Cesar, 2 mi. W—*agate, rutilated quartz crystals*. Hollybush, W side of Broad River, in pegmatite—*yellow beryl*. Kings Mountain—*diamond*. Shelby, 4¾ mi. S. 30° W, near E bank of First Broad River and ½ mi. NE of dam—*aquamarine, beryl, biotite, emerald, muscovite, smoky quartz crystals, tourmaline*.

DAVIDSON CO.: Linwood, 5 mi. NW and 1 mi. S of Taro —*amethyst*.

FRANKLIN CO.: Portis Mine—*diamond*.

GASTON CO.: Clubbs and Crowders Mountains—*kyanite, lazulite, muscovite*.

HALIFAX CO.: all area Quaternary gravels—*petrified wood*.

HAYWOOD CO.: Waynesville—*tourmaline*.

GRANVILLE CO.: Reeds Creek—*agate, jasp-agate, quartz crystals*.

IREDELL CO.: Statesville area; (1) ½ mi. W of Cook Farm, (2) 1½ mi. S of Cook Farm, (3) 4½ mi. WNW of Mooresville, (4) 3 mi. S of Statesville, and (5) 12½ mi. S of Statesville—*agate, amethyst, quartz crystals*. Statesville Quarry—*oligoclase sunstone*.

JACKSON CO.: area pegmatites—*golden beryl*. Grimshawe Mine, 1¾ mi. E of summit of Whiteside Mountain and ½ mi. NE of Whiteside Cove—*golden beryl*. Johns Creek junction with Caney Fork, a ridge 1¼ mi. SSE—*golden beryl*. Montvale area stream gravels—*ruby, sapphire*. Sapphire area; (1) stream gravels, border of Transylvania Co., (2) Sapphire and Whitewater mines, (3) 2 mi. SSW of Sapphire at Beryl Mines, ½ mi. N of summit of Sassafras Mountain—*corundum, golden beryl*. Webster area *dunite* outcrops—*bronzite* (altered *enstatite*), *websterite (bronzite-diopside)*. Willets, Sugar Loaf Mountain —*garnets*.

LINCOLN CO.: Cottage Home—*diamond*. Denver, 1¼ mi. SW and 2 mi. NE of Iron Station, on a farm—*amethyst*.

MACON CO.: Asheville, Morgan Hill—*chrysoprase*. Franklin; (1) Cowee Creek Ruby Tract 8 mi. N, and in many area mine dumps—*beryl, bronzite, chromite, corundum, fibrolite, gahnite (zinc spinel), garnet (rhodolite),* gold, *hornblende, ilmenite, iolite* (colorless), *kyanite, monazite, pleonaste* (black *spinel*), *pyrite, quartz crystals, ruby, rutile crystals, staurolite* (transparent), *tremolite, zircon,* (2) Corundum Hill, 4½ mi. ESE of Franklin on S slope of Higdon Mountain ½ mi. N of Highway 64, to west of Crows Branch creek junction with the Cullasaja River—*corundum* (in *dunite*) *opal, ruby, sapphire,* (3) 6½ mi. E of Franklin at Mincey Mine, near Ellijay on North Prong of Ellijay Creek—*bronzy corundum (pearl), ruby.* Mason Mountain, ½ mi. S of crest—*biotite, garnet (rhodolite), gedrite (anthophyllite), hypersthene, kyanite, quartz crystals.* Tessentee Creek mouth; (1) 2 mi. NE at Connally Mine, and (2) 4 mi. E, in gravels—*amethyst, quartz crystals.*

MADISON CO.: Bear Creek—*staurolite.* Marshall, Little Pine Creek—*garnets (rhodolite).* Reed's Creek—*jasper.*

MASON CO.: Hanging Dog and Persimmon creeks—*staurolites.*

McDOWELL CO.: Dysortville, Muddy Creek—*diamond.*

MECKLENBURG CO.: Caldwell area—*agate, jasper, petrified wood.* Todd's Branch gravels—*diamond.*

MITCHELL CO.: Bakersville; (1) 1 mi. N at base of Meadows Mountain—*moonstone, transparent oligoclase,* (2) 3 mi. E—*albite, epidote,* (3) 4½ mi. ENE and 1 mi. NE of Hawk Post Office, Hawk Mica Mine at junction of Soapstone Branch and left fork of Cane Creek—*moonstone, oligoclase* (transparent), *thulite* (pink *zoisite*). McKinney Mine—*amazonite, sunstone.* Roan Mountain—*unakite.* Spruce Pine; (1) 1½ mi. SW and ½ mi. ESE of Chalk Mountain, at McChone Mines—*amazonite, aquamarine, beryl, spodumene,* (2) 5 mi. NW at Putnam Mine, and on dumps of adjoining Deer Flat and Pine Mountain mines—*thulite.* (3) Wiseman Tract 1.8 mi. NNE and ¼ mi. SW of English Knob—*aquamarine, golden beryl.*

MOORE CO.: Shut-In Creek—*jasper.*

ORANGE CO.: Hillsboro—*moss agate.*

ROWAN CO.: Gold Hill—*sunstone.* Mount Ulla area—*amethysts, quartz crystals.*

RUTHERFORD CO.: J. D. Twitty placer mine—*diamond.*

STOKES CO.: Coffee Gap in Lauratown Mountains—massive *lazulite* in *quartz.*

WAKE CO.: Raleigh, 5 mi. NE—*amethyst, quartz crystals.*
WARREN CO.: Warrenton, 11 mi. S and at a spot 2 mi. S of
Inez—*amethyst, quartz crystals.*
WILKES CO.: Headwaters of Honey Creek, gravels—*amethyst, rock crystal, smoky quartz.*
YANCY CO.: Blue Rock Road, Spider Mine—*thulite.*
Bowditch, 1.9 mi. E at Gibbs Mine on W bank of South
Toe River—greenish transparent *oligoclase.* Burnsville, 2.3 mi.
SSE at Ray Mica Mine 1.7 mi. NE of Vixen—*amazonite, aquamarine, beryl, emerald.* North Toe River, out of Spruce Pine—
*dithene* (kyanite crystals). Yellow Mountain, 4 mi. SE of Bakersville—*dithene.*

## NORTH DAKOTA

This fertile state is the geographical center of North America. The eastern half, part of which was once the bottom of
the great Pleistocene Lake Agassis, constitutes the lowlands.
West of the Red River Valley escarpments rise 300 feet to the
glacial drift prairies of scattered lakes, occasional moraines, and
rolling hills. Farther west, along the Little Missouri lie the
strongly eroded, scenic Badlands where the prospector will find
much *petrified wood* and many varieties of *cryptocrystalline
quartz.*
BILLINGS CO.: Medora, Badlands area—*agate, chalcedony,
silicified wood.*
GRANT CO.: Wade area, 55 mi. SW of Bismark, Hell Creek
Formation on Cannonball River—*silicified pine cones.*
HETTINGER CO.: Mott, 11 mi. N, surface of hills and
washes—*agate, chalcedony, jasper, petrified wood.*
McKENZIE CO.: Missouri River and Yellowstone River
gravels—*"Montana" moss agate.*
MORTON CO.: Mandan area hills and washes—*agate, chalcedony, chert, teredo wood (silicified).*
STARK CO.: Dickinson area—*agate, chalcedony.*
WILLIAMS CO.: same as McKenzie Co.

## OHIO

Except for a small area of fairly rugged hills in the southeastern corner, Ohio is mostly level, with some mildly rolling
country, from the sand dunes along Lake Erie to the gorge-cut

plateau along the Ohio River. There are few localities containing worthwhile gem stones or minerals, although excavations into the underlying black, Upper Devonian (New Albany) shales occasionally yield examples of silicified wood, mostly *Callixylon oweni* and *Callixylon newberryi*. The western counties have rock quarries in which the collector may find *celestite, dolomite crystals, fluorite, galena, gypsum crystals, marcasite, pyrite, selenite, and sphalerite*. In the southeast portion clay beds yield nodules of *hematite, limonite, and siderite*. Probably the best collecting locality in Ohio is Clay Center Quarry between State Routes 51 and 579 about 12 miles east of Toledo.

CLERMONT CO.: Milford—*diamond*.

LICKING CO.: Franklin and Hopewell Twps., an area 8 mi. long by ¼ mi. wide extending from 3 mi. SE of Newark to 12 mi. NW of Zanesville—*agate, amethyst, carnelian, chalcedony, chert* (various colors), *flint, jasp-agate, jasper, quartz crystals* (*smoky*), *rock crystal*.

SCIOTO CO.: area quarries yield *catlinite*.

## OKLAHOMA

The high, short-grass region of western Oklahoma is part of the arid Great Plains, broken by the Black Mesa in the Panhandle and the Witchita Mountains in the southwest. The southwestern region, especially Beckham and Tillman counties, yields considerable *alabaster, agatized* and *petrified wood* from stream gravels. Along the Cimarron and North Canadian rivers, gravel bars produce *agates, jasp-agate,* and *jasper,* as well as the *fossil bones* and *teeth* of Pleistocene mammals. Central and eastern Oklahoma is mostly prairie, rising northeastward to the Ozark Mountains and southeastward to the Ouachita Mountains.

BECKHAM CO.: Area gypsum quarries, including those in the counties of Blaine, Greer, Harper, Jackson, and Major—*alabaster, petrified wood*.

CADDO CO.: Apache, 4 mi. SW—*calcite rhombs* (fluorescent).

CANADIAN CO.: El Reno—*agate*.

DEWEY CO.: Seiling and Taloga—*agate, dendrites, jadeite, jasp-agate, jasper, petrified wood*.

GREER CO.: Mangum; (1) area quarries—*alabaster,* (2)

N of town—*agatized* and *silicified wood*. Wichita Mountains, mines—*amphibole, zircon.*

HARPER CO.: Buffalo area—*agate, chalcedony, chert, jasper.*

JACKSON CO.: Altus—*smoky quartz crystals.*

LINCOLN CO.: Northern portions—red *"medicine rock."*

MAJOR CO.: Fairview—*agates, jadeite, jasper.*

McCURTAIN CO.: Glover Creek—*quartz crystals.* Wichita Mountains—*rutilated quartz crystals, zircon.*

OTTAWA CO.: Oklahoma District, Pritcher, near Miami—*sphalerite.*

PAYNE CO.: Kendrick—red *"medicine rock."*

PUSHMATAH CO.: Antlers—green *quartz crystals.*

WOODS CO.: almost anywhere in stream beds, fields, washes, etc.—*agate (banded, mossy), chalcedony, chert, jasper*—especially S of Alva.

## OREGON

The lengthy Cascade Mountain Range, cresting in many snow-covered volcanic cones, easily divides Oregon into two major parts. Western Oregon, a strip of rainy country about 100 miles wide, is marked by the Coast Range and many capes and headlands jutting into the Pacific Ocean. Eastern Oregon constitutes two-thirds of the state, mostly as a high, basalt-covered plateau region. The sweeping southeastern portion, which includes the glaciated, isolated Steens Mountains, is parched wasteland, while the Columbia Plateau basalts lay over much of the northeastern portion, broken by the primitive Wallowa Mountains and the north-south Blue Mountain range. During Oligocene and Miocene times, the Cascade volcanos spread volcanic ash rich in silica over much of the state. Hence, Oregon, particularly the central region, is one of the most prolific gemstone collecting regions in the world. Central Oregon, alone, embraces several thousand square miles of territory in which almost every type of quartz family mineral can be found, along with such oddities of the mineral kingdom as *fossils, geodes, nodules,* and *thundereggs.* So many are the collecting localities that only a few of the most important can be listed here. Much the same thing can be said about Western Oregon, where nearly every creek, river, or stream descending to the Pacific Ocean includes attractive gem stone minerals and petrified wood in its gravel bars.

BAKER CO.: Baker; (1) area included by Baker, Durkee, and Richland—many varieties of *quartz family gemstones*, (2) E, in volcanic rocks and in Powder River gravels along Richland Valley—*chalcedony geodes* lined with *drusy quartz*. Durkee; (1) 2 mi. N at gypsum quarry—*gypsum, satin spar*, (2) Pleasant Valley—*opalized wood* (black and white banded), (3) Shirttail Creek—*agate, chalcedony, jasper, "Oregon jade" (plasma agate*, green), *petrified wood*. Greenhorn District gravels—*agate, gold, silicified wood (Tempskya)*. Huntington, near Milepost 393 on Highway 30—*geodes, quartz crystals*.

BENTON CO.: Willamette River gravels, especially 8 mi. S of Corvallis—*agate, bloodstone, jasper*.

CLACKAMAS CO.: Clackamas River gravels—*agate, jasper, petrified wood*.

CLATSOP CO.: Nehalem River gravels—*agate, carnelian, jasper*.

COLUMBIA CO.: Nehalem River gravels, between Clear Creek and Vernonia—*agate, carnelian, chalcedony, jasper*. Gable beaches—*thomsonite*. Vernonia RR cuts—*zeolites*.

CROOK CO.: area of W half of county, especially between Highway 20 and 26—*agate, chalcedony, chert, jasper, petrified wood, quartzite* (colorful). Carey Ranch—*"Carey plume" agate (flame plume), chalcedony, jasper*. John Davis River—*opal*. McAllister Butte near Ochoco River—*moss agate*. Prineville area; (1) S, in Bear Creek gravels, and (2) 19 mi. S on Highway 27 and 2 mi. S of junction of Bear Creek and Crooked River, on E side of Taylor Butte—*agate (moss), chalcedony, drusy quartz* in *agate*, (3) 11 mi. SE, in Eagle Rock District, Crooked River—*dendritic agate*, (4) Powell Butte—*plume agate*, (5) 5 mi. E on Highway 26, Ochoco Lake shores above the dam—*"Ochoco" jasper*, (6) E, at Ochoco Nodule Beds on Wild Cat Mountain—*agate (plume), chalcedony, opal, thundereggs (agate* centers).

CURRY CO.: Brookings—*jade*. Ocean beaches N and S of the mouths of Chetco and Rogue Rivers—*agate, californite (idocrase), jasper*. Rogue River gravels; (1) mouth of river, near Wedderburn—*grossularite garnet*, (2) upstream from Gold Beach, near Agness—*agate, carnelian, chalcedony, grossularite garnet, gold, jasper, quartz crystals.* Sugarloaf Peak from Pistol River via Forest Service roads, talus slopes and area stream gravels—*nephrite, serpentine.*

DESCHUTES CO.: Bend, 30 mi. S, between Paulina Lake and East Lake—*obsidian.* Terrebone—*geodes, nodules.*

DOUGLAS CO.: Ashland, E on Greensprings Mountain—*agate nodules, carnelian, chalcedony, jasper.* Big Butte area—*agate.* Cedar Springs Mountain—*malachite.* Medford, 12 mi. N at Table Rock Mountain—*agate, petrified wood.* North Umpqua and South Umpqua River gravels especially 22 mi. E of Roseburg—*agate, carnelian, chalcedony, jasper, petrified and silicified wood, teredo* (worm-bored) *petrified wood.* Riddle (Nickel Mountain)—*chrysoprase, nickel* ore specimens. Roseburg, 12 mi. E along Davis Creek—*orbicular jasper.* Rogue River gravels from 4 mi. E of Central Point to 15 mi. E of Eagle Point; also in Butte Creek gravels—*moss agate.* Umpqua River gravels—*"Oregon jade" (massive grossularite garnet).*

HARNEY CO.: Burns area; (1) W, and S of Buchanan, and (2) E side of Steen Mountains W of Alvord Ranch on road between Folly Farm and Denio—*agate, geodes, jasper, quartz, thundereggs,* (3) 18 mi. N on Highway 395 then 7 mi. W, Silvies Canyon in Myrtle Park—*wood opal,* (4) 40 mi. E at Warm Springs Reservoir—*chalcedony, jasper, petrified wood.*

JACKSON CO.: Cave Creek—*rhodonite.* Old mines—*gold.*

JEFFERSON CO.: Antelope 15 mi. SE—*fossil ferns (Osmundites oregonensis).* Ashwood area; (1) including Hay Creek, Madras, and Willowdale—*agate, chalcedony, geodes, jasper, thundereggs,* (2) 22 mi. E at Horse Heaven Mine—*morrisonite (chert).* Butte Falls—*bloodstone*—also at Eagle Point. John Day River tributaries—*fossil Osmundites oregonensis.* Madras 12 mi. NE and 4 mi. SE of Willowdale, Fulton Agate Beds formerly known as the Priday Ranch—*agate* (lace, plume, polka dot)*; chalcedony, jasper, precious opal, thundereggs (agate* and *chalcedony nodules).* McLeod area basalt outcrops—*natrolite.*

JOSEPHINE CO.: Cave Creek (area around Oregon Caves) —*agate, chalcedony, gold nuggets, jasper, petrified wood, rhodonite.* Holland 1½ mi. S along Althouse Creek—*agate, garnet, gold, jasper, quartz crystals, serpentine.* Waldo and Galice Districts—*azurite, chrysocolla, malachite.*

KLAMATH CO.: Crater Lake National Park (immediately

S)—*"Crater Lake flower" jasper.* Klamath River gravels—*agate, chalcedony, jasper.*

LAKE CO.: Hampton 12 mi. SE, off Highway 20, at Glass Buttes—*obsidian* (banded, black, brecciated, green, irridescent (rainbow), red, snowflake). Hart Mountain, NE of Plush; (1) W flanks—*agate, chalcedony, geodes, jasper, opal, thundereggs,* (2) summit, cavities in Tertiary basalts—*chalcedony, opal* (common, precious). Lakeview; (1) area—*geodes, nodules, sanidine, sanidine-sunstone,* (2) 8 mi. S in Crane Canyon—*agate, jasper, thundereggs.* Quartz Pass, near Quartz Mountain —various *cryptocrystalline quartz* minerals and gemstones.

LANE CO.: Goshen, 3 mi. E at Mount Pisgah—*agate, calcite, heulandite, jasper, mesolite, quartz crystals.*

LINCOLN CO.: Newport area beaches to N—*agate, chalcedony, jasper, petrified wood* (worm-bored), *quartz crystals.* Yachats; (1) area beaches—*agate (sagenite), chalcedony, jasper (orbicular), moonstones, silicified coral enhydros* (water-filled *chalcedony geodes)*—especially on a beach 2 mi. N of China Creek mouth to Commings Creek beach 3 mi. S of Yachats, (2) Big Creek gravels—*garnets.*

MALHEUR CO.: Brogan and Ironsides area—*agate, chalcedony, chert, jasper, petrified wood.* Jordan Valley gravels— *chert.* Malheur Caves, 32 mi. E—*geodes, nodules.* Nyssa; (1) immediate area—*agate, geodes, jasper, nodules, petrified wood,* (2) 35 mi. S, extending over Idaho border—*agate, geodes, jasper, petrified wood.* Owyhee Dam, 10 mi. NW, near Nigger Rock—*agate, chalcedony, jasper, quartzite, petrified wood.* Rockville; (1) upstream along Sucker Creek from Homedale to Rockville—*opalized wood,* (2) N, along Sucker Creek—*agate, chalcedony, fossil wood, jasper,* colorful *quartzite.*

MORROW CO.: Parkers Mill S, at Opal Butte—*hyalite, opal.*

POLK CO.: Dallas—*jasper.*

SHERMAN CO.: Biggs, 5 mi. S along Highway 97, and 5 mi. S of Rufus—*agate, jasper (wascoite-type).*

UNION CO.: Starkey (Orofino Mine)—*agate.*

WALLOWA CO.: Joseph, on Lower Inmaha River—*prase.*

WASCO CO.: Antelope; (1) area—*agate (iris, moss), chalcedony, chalcedony geodes, jade, jasp-agate, jasper,* (2) 1¼ mi. E in quarry—red *jasper,* (3) 10½ mi. E—*jasper,* (4) 6.8 mi. S, on road to Ashwood—green *moss agate.* Mosier; (1) area stream gravels—*petrified wood, silicified pine cones,* (2) Upper Chenowith Creek, over hills from Mosier—white *opalized wood.* Warm Springs Indian Reservation; (1) area—*brecciated jasper,* (2) S side of Mutton Mountain—*agate,* black *agate* in *geodes, chalcedony geodes,* (3) mountains N of Wapinitia—*agate, jasper.* The Dalles, S 13½ mi. up Mill Creek road—*opalized* and *silicified wood.*

WHEELER CO.: Clarno Fossil Beds—*agate, fossils, jasper.* Dayville; (1) 7 mi. NW, and (2) 13 mi. E—*fossil bone, wood.* All along John Day River—*fossil bone, wood.*

## PENNSYLVANIA

Long known as the Keystone State, Pennsylvania's geologic history is extraordinary. Except for the coastal plains southeast of Philadelphia and around Lake Erie, the state today is mostly rolling hills and mountain ridges slashed by narrow valleys. High mountain ridges, remnants of an ancient peneplain, rise from the Delaware River into the piedmont, while the central portion holds the sprawling parallel Blue and Allegheny Mountain systems. Drainage rivers, older than the mountains themselves, cut spectacularly scenic "water gaps" through the mountains.

The basic formation of the state is the coarse, deltaic *Pottsville conglomerate* which, as sediments, was eroded from the steep western slopes of Appalachia. This ancient continental land mass, now entirely eroded away and with its roots sunk beneath the Atlantic off the shores of New England, was the original "source land" for the erosinal debris which filled the western trough, or "geosyncline," during Ordovician and Silurian times when most of the United States area was under a shallow, epeiric sea. Also at this time, the widely extended beds of Pennsylvanian marine limestones were laid down.

Meanwhile, during the whole of the Carboniferous Age, vast, lush growths of *Sigillaria, Lepidodendron,* and *Calamites* trees were being repeatedly covered by sediments to form the enormous anthracite and bituminous coal beds which underlie much of Pennsylvania today. It is little wonder that the state lends its name to this greatest coal-producing period of the world, 30,000,000 years long, during which the Appalachian sedimentary deposits reached thicknesses of four to five thousand feet.

ADAMS CO.: Buchanan Valley, W side and on W side of Piney Mountain—*"piedmontite"*. Caledonia State Park area— *agate, jasper.* Hamilton and Washington Twps. mines, especially Bingham Mine 2½ mi. WSW of Maria Furnace and 1 mi. NNE of Gladhill—*azurite, copper, cuprite, epidote, malachite, quartz, rhyolite (orbicular).*

BEDFORD CO.: Morrison Cove Valley, between New Enterprise and Waterside, and around Salemville—*amethyst, rock crystal.*

BERKS CO.: Reading; (1) Fritz Island—*azurite, malachite,* (2) along Delaware and Schuylkill Rivers—*jasper.*

BUCKS CO.: Feasterville—*sunstone.* Rocksville area; (1) E of Churchville Station, (2) S and SE of Holland Station, (3) NE of Leonard's Station, (4) ¼ mi. SE of Roelof's Station, (5) 1½ mi. N of Woodburne Station, (6) all other outcrops of regional Triassic formations—*agate, chalcedony, chert, silicified wood.* Southhampton Twp., Neshaminy Falls, 2 mi. N and ¾ mi. W of Nashaminy Creek at Vanartsdalen Quarry—*"chesterlite" (orthoclase moonstone).*

CARBON CO.: Jim Thorpe—*jasper.*

CHESTER CO.: Birmingham Twp.; (1) Pocopson Station, ¼ mi. E—*rutilated amethyst,* (2) West Chester, 2½ mi. S on W side of Osborn Hill—*corundum, quartz crystals* (clear, smoky). Chester, Northrop area—*beryl (gem), garnet.* East Bradford Twp., Sconneltown S and SW, between Brandywine Creek and Plum Run—*rock crystal.* East Marlboro Twp., Willowdale 1 mi. SW on W branch of Red Clay Creek—*rock crystal.* French Creek—*calcite* with *quartz crystals, malachite.* Hauto area—*quartz crystals.* Kennett Twp., Kennett Square; (1) ½ mi. SE at Pierce's Paper Mill on E branch of Red Clay Creek, (2) 2 mi. SE on Cloud's Farm on a brook that enters the E branch, (3) Fairville area quarries—*labradorite, oligoclase sunstone.* London Grove Twp., Avondale; (1) ¼ mi. E— *quartz crystals* (clear, smoky), *rutile crystals,* (2) Leiper Quarry —*garnet (almandite, essonite),* (3) ¼ mi. NW, and (4) 1 mi. SW of Chatham—*apatite.* Newlin Twp., Unionville, ½ mi. NE at Corundum Hill—*beryl (gem), corundum, diaspore, quartz crystals* (yellow). Nottingham Twp.—*sunstone.* Sadsbury

Twp.; (1) Parkesburg, and (2) Pomeroy—*rutile crystals.* Townships of Pocopson and Westown, in many outcrops— *quartz crystals* (clear, smoky).

CUMBERLAND CO.: Carlisle; (1) 1½ mi. NW—*agate, jasper, quartz (amethystine), quartz crystals* (clear, smoky), (2) 1 mi. E of Carlisle Interchange on the Pennsylvania Turnpike, S side of Highway 11—*banded agate.*

DELAWARE CO.: Aston Twp., Chester Heights, 1 mi. S on Greens Creek—*almandine garnet;* Morgan Station; (1) ¼ mi. S—*corundum,* (2) Dutton's Mill Road, in a pegmatite dike— *amethyst,* (3) Village Green—*corundum, quartz crystals* (yellow). Birmingham Twp., Chadd's Ford, 1½ mi. S on Brandywine River—*amethyst.* Chester Twp.; (1) Bridgewater Station of Pennsylvania RR, opposite at John Mullen's Quarries on E side of Chester Creek—*mica, quartz crystals, sphene,* (2) Chester Station, ¼ mi. E in Shaw & Earey Quarry N of the B&O railroad—*amethyst, smoky quartz crystals,* (3) Upland, E, around Henvi's Quarry N of Chester Creek—*amethyst in geodes*—also near Waterville Road. Lower Chichester Twp., Trainer Station, 1½ mi. N on a knoll near Linwood Mill Dam—clear and smoky *quartz crystals.* Marple Twp.—*amethyst, quartz crystals, rutilated quartz crystals.* Middletown Twp., Media; (1) Black Horse, ¼ mi. S along road to Elwyn—*corundum,* (2) Black Horse, ¾ mi. NE or 1 mi. W of Media—*albite moonstone, amazonite, oligoclase sunstone, orthoclase sunstone,* (3) Black Horse, SW to Chrome Run—*albite moonstone, oligoclase sunstone* in widespread pegmatite dikes, (4) Blue Hill, 2½ mi. NW—*amazonite, orthoclase sunstone,* transparent *oligoclase,* (5) 1 mi. W of Media, at Mineral Hill—*albite, amazonite, moonstone, orthoclase sunstone,* (6) Lenni Station, E in RR cut —*albite moonstone, amazonite, oligoclase sunstone,* (7) Lenni Station, 1 mi. N on Dismal Run—transparent *oligoclase,* (8) Crosierville, ½ mi. W on S side of Chester Creek opposite Lenni—*amethyst.* Newton Twp. 1 mi. W of Newton Square— *oligoclase moonstone* in pegmatite outcrops and in road cuts. Pennsbury Twp., Chadd's Ford 1 mi. SW—transparent *oligoclase.* Ridley Twp.; (1) Crum Lynne RR Station, ½ mi. S at Ward's Quarry on E side of Crum Creek—*amazonite,* (2) Leiperville, ½ mi. W at Deshong's Quarry on E side of Ridley Creek—*aquamarine. golden beryl.* Springfield Twp., Avondale

Leiper's Quarry on E side of Crum Creek—*aquamarine, golden beryl.* Thornbury Twp., Glen Mills—*albite moonstone, amethyst, quartz crystals (rutilated).* Upper Chichester Twp.; (1) Boothwyn, 2 mi. N and E of the Chelsea-Boothwyn Road—*amethyst crystals, rutilated amethyst*—also ½ mi. N on Armstrong Farm E of Chelsea Road, (2) ⅜ mi. SW of Boothwyn Station W of east branch of Naaman's Creek and on N side of B&O railroad—*sphene.* Upper Darby Twp., ½ mi. W of Upper Darby Post Office—*quartz crystals* (large, clear, smoky). Upper Providence Twp.; (1) Darby, 3½ mi. below at Shaw & Ezrey Quarry near Chester and White Horse—*aquamarine, beryl,* (2) Media area, 2½ mi. NW and ¾ mi. NE of Sycamore Mills, at Blue Hill Crossroads—*quartz crystals* (blue, green), (3) Media area, 1½ mi. NE and 1 mi. E of Rose Tree Dam on Crum Creek—*amethyst* (deep purple), (4) Sycamore Mills, E along Ridley Creek in pegmatite dikes—*amazonite, orthoclase, sunstone,* transparent *oligoclase.*

FRANKLIN CO.: Caledonia State Park—*agate, jasper.*

LANCASTER CO.: Bart Twp., Mount Pleasant 1 mi. NW —*amethyst.* Cedar Hill Quarry—*aragonite, calcite, chromite, magnesite, williamsite.* Fulton Twp., Rock Springs Run, 1¼ mi. NNE of Rock Springs, Md., and ⅓ mi. W of Jenkins Corner—*moss agate.* Lancaster (Blue Ball Quarry)—*calcite, dolomite, fluorite, hematite, pyrite, quartz* and *rutile crystals.* Paradise Twp.; (1) Bainbridge, 1 mi. N in fields—*petrified wood,* (2) Churchtown, 2 mi. NW—*petrified wood*—also 3 mi. NE, (3) Kinzer—*rutilated quartz crystals.* Texas—*serpentine.* Woods Chromite Mine—*garnet (uvarovite), serpentine.*

LEHIGH CO.: Allentown, 7 mi. S, near Pennsylvania Turnpike—*chert* (colored). Bethlehem, 5 mi. S at Friedensville zinc mines—*aragonite, jasper, prase, pyrite, quartz crystals, smithsonite, sphalerite.* Shimersville, ¾ mi. N—*corundum* (large, asterated)—also 2 mi. SE of Macungie.

MONROE CO.: Stroudsburg—*quartz crystals.*

MONTGOMERY CO.: Alsace Twp.; (1) Spies Church, 1½ mi. NNW, and (2) Jacksonwald, 1½ mi. S at Kinsey Hill—*chalcedony, jasp-agate, jasper.* Durham Twp., Durham area Cambrian quartzites—*chalcedony, jasp-agate, jasper.* Morganville Station; (1) ¼ mi. E, and (2) Jarrettown and Maple Glen gravel pits—*petrified wood.* Oley Twp.; (1) Friedensburg, (2)

Bowers Station, 1 mi. S on Flint Hill, and (3) Olney Furnace, 1¾ mi. NE at Green Hill—*amethyst, chalcedony, petrified wood.* Richmond Twp.; (1) Fleetwood—*chalcedony, chert,* (2) Fritztown—*agate, amethyst, chalcedony, jasper.*

NORTHAMPTON CO.: Forks Twp., Chestnut Hill N of Easton in old quarries—*bronzite, precious serpentine, williamsite.* Lower Saucon Twp., Redington, S and 5 mi. E of Bethlehem on South Mountain—*catseye, chalcedony, chert* (many colors), *prase, quartz crystals.* Newlin Twp., Corundum Hill, 2 mi. NE of Unionville—*noble serpentine.*

WESTMORELAND CO.: Greensburg, 7 mi. E—*quartz crystals.*

YORK CO.: York Haven, 2 mi. S and SW—*petrified wood.*

## RHODE ISLAND

Named from the principal island in Narragansett Bay, Rhode Island's surface is rolling and hilly, cut by short, swift streams that pour over many waterfalls. Sandwiched between Connecticut and Massachusetts, the state's geology partakes of both.

PROVIDENCE CO.: Cumberland Hill and Diamond Hill quarries—*agate, chalcedony, jasper, quartz crystals*—also in Calumet Hill with *rutilated quartz.* Mount Hope Bay area beach gravels—*agate, amethyst, carnelian, jasper*—also near Pawtuxet, S of Providence. Lincoln Twp., North Providence, 5 mi. N in Dexter, Lime Quarry—*bowenite (jade-like serpentine)* —also in Conklin and Harris quarries nearby.

## SOUTH CAROLINA

This subtropical state divides broadly into three regions: the coastal plain, separated from the piedmont plateau of the upcountry by the fall line and, in the extreme northwestern corner, the Blue Ridge Mountains. Although clay, gravel, and limestone deposits are well developed industrially, there are few mineral and gem stone localities of any consequence. In the northern counties there are, however, placer deposits which yield *gold* and occasional *diamonds.*

ANDERSON CO.: Anderson, 3¼ mi. NNE—*aquamarine.*

CHEROKEE CO.: Earles Station, Blacksburg, 10 mi. S of Shelby, North Carolina—*emerald.*

CHESTERFIELD CO.: Jefferson, 3 mi. W at Brewer Mine on Brewer Knob—*topaz*.

GREENWOOD CO.: Shoals Junction; (1) 1½ mi. SE, and (2) 1 mi. SW or 3 mi. SE of Donalds—*amethyst, quartz crystals*.

## SOUTH DAKOTA

From east to west South Dakota rises some 6000 feet to Mount Harney in the Black Hills, at 7242 feet the highest point in America east of the Rockies. The Missouri River cuts a broad swath through the central region. Eastward lies good grazing land, but to the west the country is arid, desolate, and rough. The Badlands National Monument preserves an extremely eroded area of fantastic shapes and startling scenery, carved out of sandstone strata which are most colorful between White River and the south fork of the Cheyenne.

Cambrian rocks are exposed as bands around the "dome uplift" of the granite Black Hills. Here, too, the famed Dakota Sandstone, which underlies most of the Great Plains, is bent sharply upward into spectacular hogbacks. Laid down in Early Cretaceous times as the continental seas were advancing from the south, the porous Dakota Sandstone represents "top-set" beds, wave-reworked and spread as a vast deltaic accumulation of water-absorbing sands covering thousands of square miles with remarkable homogeniety. Into this formation are drilled the state's artesian wells, providing an inexhaustible supply of cold, Rocky Mountain melted-snow water.

Gravel pits in the eastern counties yield *agate, chalcedony, jasper,* and *quartzite*. While collecting mineral specimens is not permitted in any national monument or park, the area immediately outside the Badlands National Mounment yields plenty of *petrified "sponge," silicified coral, silicified wood,* and *marine fossils*. Pegmatite outcrops in the basal Black Hills area granites, especially near Custer and Glendale, produce *apatite crystals, blue apatite (massive), geodes (quartz),* and *jade*. The Black Hills lignite beds yield *amber* and *gastroliths* (dinosaur gizzard stones), and from the "Spearfish" red beds comes *alabaster*. Early day gold mining at Lead and Deadwood produced many frontier legends, and the rock collector will find this region particularly interesting.

CAMPBELL and CORSON COS.: Mobridge area, N along

the Missouri River on hillsides, ridges, and stream banks—*petrified wood, wood opal*—also near Little Eagle and along the Grand River 20 mi. N of Mobridge.

CUSTER CO.: Fairburn, 15 mi. E, and along the Cheyenne River from Creston (Pennington Co.) to Orella, Nebraska, and S of the State Game Farm on Highway 16—*"Fairburn" agate nodules.* Hells Canyon from Highway 16—*agate nodules, geodes.* Red Canyon and the regional Bad Lands area—*agate (banded), fossil bone, coral, cycads, palm wood, jade, jasper.* Scott Rose Quartz Quarry, 6 mi. E of Custer on French Creek —*aquamarine, milky* and *rose quartz, spodumene.*

FALL RIVER CO.: Cycad National Monument, area just outside, particularly from Parker Peak 1½ mi. E of Highway 18 and 2 mi. S of Minnekahta—*silicified cycad stumps*—also between Parker Peak and Hot Springs, 12 mi. E of Minnekahta.

HARDING CO.: Little Missouri River, gravel bars and tributaries—*chalcedony nodules (dendritic), moss agate.*

LAWRENCE CO.: (1) Spearfish Canyon, and (2) Whitewood Creek—*amethyst, chalcedony geodes, petrified cycad* and *palm wood.*

MEADE CO.: Deadwood area (Black Hills)—*agate,* colorful *chert.* Maurine, 5 mi. ESE on top of Fox Ridge—*moss agate.* Wasta, N, bed of Elk Creek—*barite geodes.*

MINNEHAHA CO.: Sioux Falls area gravels—*agate, catlinite, jasper.*

PENNINGTON CO.: Black Hills area, Bear Butte Creek, Box Elder Creek, Warrens Gulch—*amethyst.* Custer area pegmatite dikes and Helen Beryl Mine—*beryl, garnet, spodumene.* Imlay—*geodes.* Keystone area (Bob Ingersoll Mine)—*beryl (golden), garnets, quartz crystals, spodumene, tourmaline.* Quinn—*moss agate.* Scenic (badlands region)—*agate, aquamarine, beryl, chalcedony, carnelian, garnet, jasper* (plain and orbicular).

TODD CO.: Mission, W, in Little White River gravels of the South Fork—black *silicified wood.*

## TENNESSEE

This long, east-west state shows three sharply defined geographic divisions: in the east are the Great Smoky Mountains and the Cumberland Plateau, with heavily forested foothills and narrow valleys; the central region is rich, gently rolling grass land; and Western Tennessee comprises alluvial river bottomlands. The Great Smoky Mountains constitute a vast geologic "thrust mass" which developed along the Appalachian fault belt so that very ancient Proterozoic crystalline rocks, which make up the bulk of the mountains, overlie much younger rocks of sedimentary origin. Western counties yield *agate, jasper,* and *travertine,* while the central stream gravels offer *calcite* and *quartz* pebbles. The eastern mountain counties produce industrial quantities of *coal, limestone, clay, marble,* and *zinc,* as well as the usual gravel and building stone.

BRADLEY CO.: Cleveland area—*sphalerite.*

CARTER CO.: Watauga—*barite, fluorite, galena, sphalerite.*

CLAIBORNE CO.: Straight Creek District—*sphalerite.*

GREEN CO.: Greenville—*sphalerite.*

HAMBLEN CO.: Russellville—*quartz geodes.*

HARDIN CO.: Coffee Bluff (on the Tennessee River)—*amber.*

KNOX CO.: Mascot—*sphalerite.*

MONROE CO.: Area deposits—*malachite.* Sweetwater area—*sphalerite.*

POLK CO.: Ducktown area mines—*chalcopyrite, pyrite, pyrrhotite.*

ROANE CO.: South bank of Clinch River—*diamond.*

UNION CO.: Luttrell (Flat Creek)—*diamond.*

WASHINGTON CO.: Bumpass Cove, Embreeville District—*cerussite.*

## TEXAS

This spade-shaped state reveals a varied topography. In the east, between Sabine and the Trinity River, is a region of cypress swamps and pine-covered hills, while all along the Gulf Coast stretch low, wet plains. Rolling blackland prairies make central and northern Texas one of the most fertile regions in the world. A north-south geologic division occurs along the Balcones Escarpment, a long, curving fault line through the central area marked by rough, tree-covered hills and many waterfalls. West of the escarpment lies the Edwards Plateau and the north central plains. The latter belong to the Great Plains, but are sharply divided by the Cap Rock from the high, wind-swept and canyon-cut Ilano Estacado, or "Staked Plains," famed for their winter blizzards and searing summers.

The Panhandle and all of West Texas is arid, the land rising by sweeping plains and rough uplands to the western mountains. The region west of the Pecos is noted for the celebrated Davis Mountains recreational areas and the wilderness of the Big Bend of the Rio Grande River. Here, too, the Guadalupe Mountains crest out in El Capitan, the highest point in the state. This flat-topped escarpment is protected from excessive erosion by a cap rock of massive Permian limestone, a great reef formed of corals and calcareous algae more than 200,000,000 years ago.

Generally speaking, the gem stone fields of Texas can be grouped into several broad area in each of which specific collecting localities are far too numerous to list. (1) Gravel beds of the Delta area (Rio Grande River) from north of Laredo to about 20 miles south of Falcon Dam yield enormous quantities of *agate* of every description, *amethystine, sard, carnelian, flower jasper, chalcedony, quartz geodes, rock crystals, etc.* (2) The Big Bend area, including Needle Peak and Bouquet from 17 miles south of Marfa is very productive of all types of *agates, jaspers, fireopal, spinel,* etc., but is especially noted for its *"pom-pom"* or *"bouquet"* agates. (3) A 100-mile-wide region from the lower Rio Grande to the Louisiana border, known as the Catahoula Group, includes the counties of Bryan, Freer, George West, Giddings, Gonzales, Kennedy, and Nagadoches. Throughout this area one can collect *agate* (especially near Pecos), *petrified ferns* and *palm wood,* tropical *silicified woods,* and *opalized Golden Pine wood.*

ARMSTRONG CO.: Amarillo, SE, in Palo Duro Canyon—*agatized wood.*

BASTROP CO.: Smithville (wide area)—*agate, petrified wood.*

BREWSTER CO.: Alpine, 16 mi. S on Highway 118, in a lava flow—*plume agate nodules, moss agate, chalcedony, jasper, quartz*—also W of Glass Mountains. Eagle Pass and on Terlingua Creek—*amber.* Woodward Ranch—*agate ("Texax" plume), labradorite, precious milk opal.*

COMAL CO.: New Braunfels area—*petrified wood.*

CULBERSON CO.: Van Horn, 5 mi. W—*turquoise*—and

on NE side of Carrizozo Mountains 1 mi. N of Texas & Pacific RR, along with *limonite.*

DUVAL CO.: Freer, areas to SW—*agate, silicified* and *teredo wood.*

FOARD CO.: Section 64, Block 44—*diamond.*

GONZALES CO.: Gonzales area and along Peach Creek—*agate, petrified wood.*

GRIMES CO.: Lamb Springs, 2 mi. SW to 2 mi. NE of Kieth—*tektites (bediasite)*—also in gravels of Alum, Dinner, Jarvis, and Lake creeks and around head of Gibbons Creek.

HUDSPETH CO.: Sierra Blanca, 8 mi. NW in Sierra Blanca Mountains—*turquoise.* Van Horn area—*agate, carnelian, chalcedony, jasper*—especially along S edge of Quitman Mountains, with *amethyst.*

JEFF DAVIS CO.: Fort Davis area—*chalcedony, jasper.*

LAMPASAS CO.: Lampasas, 6 mi. N on Little Lucy Creek—*celestite.*

LAVACA CO.: Moulton area gravel beds—*agate, petrified wood.*

LIVE OAK CO.: Three Rivers (Catahoula Formation)—*agate, chalcedony, jasper, petrified palm.*

LLANO CO.: Area pegmatites and at Grit—*topaz, zircon.* Babyhead, 1¾ mi. SSE in series of *llanite* dikes to summit of Miller Mountain—*llanite, opal-quartz.* Between Llano and Wilbern's Glen on S side of Babyhead Mountain E to Wilbern's Gap—*llanite, opal-quartz.*

MASON CO.: Area granite outcrops of the Llano Uplift—*amazonite, feldspar, smoky quartz, topaz* (blue, colorless), black *tourmaline (schorl)*—also (1) E side of Highway 87 near Mason, (2) Katemcy, 12 mi. N of Mason, and (3) Streeter, on Highway 377, 8 mi. W of Mason.

MONTGOMERY CO.: *diamond.*

PARKER CO.: Stover Peak—*prase.*

PRESIDIO CO.: (1) Chinati Mountains to Marfa, and (2) between the Chinati Mountains and Davis—*agate* (common, "bouquet"), *chalcedony.* San Carlos coal beds—*jet.*

REEVES CO.: Balmorhea—*onyx.*

SAN PATRICO CO.: Mathis area—*moss agate.*

SAN SABA CO.: Barton, NE, on Hinton Creek—*chalcedony, chert.*

STARR CO.: Rio Grande River gravels for 150 miles, especially from Eagle Pass southward to Laredo—*agate* (many types), *agatized coral, chalcedony* (plain, mossy), *jasper, petrified wood.*

TRAVIS CO.: Austin, 5 mi. W, Mount Bonnell area—*cele stite.*

## UTAH

With an average altitude of one mile above sea level, Utah's eastern half consists of massive mountain ranges and deep-cut, irregular plateaus. The snowy Uinta Mountains, capped by 13,498-foot Kings Peak, stretch along the southern Wyoming border, the only east-west mountain system in America. It descends southward to uninhabitable pine-clad plateaus that break sheer in enormous exposures of red and white sandstone cliffs. These Jurassic formations were formed primarily by the consolidation of ancient sand dunes, clearly revealed in the wind-rippled and cross-bedded layers of Zion National Park.

Erosion by the Colorado River and its tributaries has cut fantastic, sheer-walled canyons of extraordinary depth to provide scenery of remarkable color and grandeur. Wind and rain have combined to carve out such photogenic regions as Arches and Rainbow Bridge national monuments. These agencies of erosion also served to concentrate an enormous wealth of uranium in the Chinle and Morrison sandstones, particularly in the mile-high Four Corners region where Utah, Arizona, Colorado, and New Mexico meet on the Navajo Indian Reservation.

The Wasatch Mountain Range, running south from the Idaho border, marks the abrupt transition between the mountainous eastern half and the low, arid, desert playas or dry-lake bottoms of western Utah. The level, gravelly deserts now so blisteringly hot in summer were once entirely submerged beneath the awesome Pleistocene Lake Bonneville. Elevated, wave-cut beach lines that mark the regional mountain sides show that the surface of the original Ice Age inland sea was some 1500 feet above present-day Great Salt Lake, its much reduced principal remnant.

BEAVER CO.: Beaver, S, in Blue Valley—*black agate.* Copper Gulch and Frisco—*garnets.* Milford, E, in Mineral Mountains—*azurite, malachite, opal, quartz crystals (smoky), sheelite crystals.*

BOX ELDER CO.: Copper Mountain Mine—*chrysocolla.* Fairfield area—*chalcedony, chert, limonite, pyrite-in-variscite, white quartz.* Lucin, 5 mi. NW, on N side of Utahlite Hill— *variscite.* Willard (Promontory Point)—*obsidian.*

DAVIS CO.: Area mines—*azurite, malachite.*

EMERY CO.: Castle Valley and Summerville districts— *azurite, malachite.* Green River, 30 mi. SW along Highway 24 in San Rafael Swell—*agate, carnotite, chalcedony, chert, dinosaur bones, gastroliths, jasper, silicified wood*—also 4½ mi. S of Woodside in Morrison Formation exposures.

IRON CO.: Newcastle area—*chalcedony geodes.*

GARFIELD CO.: Circle Cliffs area—*agate, jasper, petrified wood.* Escalante—*dinosaur bone, gastroliths.* Hatch, 1½ mi. S on Mammoth Creek, in area quarries—*onyx.*

GRAND CO.: Colorado River valley, slopes, bars, washes— *agate, chalcedony, chert, jasper, opal, opalized wood, quartz*— also at Agate Switch. Moab, 5 mi. N in Cutler Formation— *agate, chalcedony, chert, dinosaur bone (silicified), petrified wood, silicified shale.* Thompson area, 7 mi. SW of Cisco, and throughout area S of Thompson in Dakota and Morrison Formations—*agate, agatized clams, carnotite, carnotite wood, gastroliths, jasper, jasperized dinosaur bones* and *knuckles* (deep red), *lizzard tail casts, petrified wood*—especially in area of Cactus Rat and Yellow Cat uranium mines, southward to Arches National Monument.

JUAB CO.: Jerico area—*plume agate.* Levan, 13 mi. S in hillside seams—*agate (fortification), chalcedony.* Thomas Mountains, Topaz Cove at S base of the mountains and just N of Thomas Pass on Highway 149—*beryl, bixbyite, calcite, fluorite, garnet, hematite, pseudobrookite, quartz crystals, topaz* —also in NE part of range 3 to 4 mi. S of Dugway Road. Tintic —*azurite, chrysocolla, malachite, pyrite.*

KANE CO.: Mt. Carmel-Orderville area washes—*septarian nodules.*

MILLARD CO.: Clear Lake, ½ mi. NE of RR station, in lava upthrust in center of an alkali flat—*labradorite.* Milford, 30 mi. N, near Black Rock—*snowflake obsidian* (black, red, both).

SALT LAKE CO.: Big and Little Cottonwood Canyons— *azurite, malachite.* Bingham (Old Jordan Mine)—*opal.* Murray—*onyx.*

SAN JUAN CO.: La Sal District—*azurite, malachite.* Mexican Water; (1) 10 mi. N at Moses Rock, and (2) 2 mi. N of Moses Rock field, along W edge of Comb Ridge—*pyrope garnets.*

SEVIER CO.: Ball Mine—*azurite, malachite.*

TOOELE CO.: Clifton District—*azurite, malachite, pyrope garnets.* Drum Mountains (N side)—*agate, amethyst, jasper, quartz crystals.* Dugway Range; (1) Dugway Pass—*amethysts, quartz crystals,* (2) Simpson Springs—*geodes, morganite, nodules.* Ibapah Mountain—*aquamarine.* Stockton, 9 mi. W or 10 mi. S 65° W of Tooele, at Amatrice Mine—*quartzite, variscite.*

UINTA CO.: Dyer Mine—*azurite, malachite.*

UTAH CO.: Fairfield, 5½ mi. W, at Utahlite Mine—*calcite, crandallite, dehrnite, deltaite, dennisonite, lewistonite, variscite* and such additional rare phosphate minerals as *englishite, gordonite* (colorless), *millisite, montgomeryite, overite, sterrettite.* Lehi (Pelican Point area)—*onyx.*

WASHINGTON CO.: Castle Cliff Station, NW, in Beaver Dam Wash—*agate, jasper, "picture stone"* (banded *rhyolite*). Cedar Breaks National Monument (outside borders)—*agate (moss), chalcedony, jasper, petrified wood.* Central area— *chalcedony geodes.* Hurricane (across river)—*scenic sandstone.* Lucern Claim—*garnets.* St. George (Dixie Apex Mine)—*azurite, malachite.*

WAYNE CO.: Hanksville; (1) broad surrounding area— *agate, jasper, petrified wood,* (2) 10 mi. S, Coaly Basin in Coaly Wash 5 mi. W of Fairview Ranch—*jet.* Torrey—*jasper, petrified and jasperized dinosaur bone.*

WEBER CO.: Area mines—*azurite, malachite.* Strongs Canyon—*garnets.*

# VERMONT

Vermont is noted for its several mountain systems collectively known as the Green Mountains, from the principal range of that name. This range actually divides the state into two halves, and caps out in Mount Mansfield at 4393 feet. East of the Green Mountains are the Granite Hills, noted for their building stone and monument granite. In the southwest the Taconic Mountains contain many important marble deposits.

in the west extending along the Vermont shore of Lake Champlain are the Red Sandrock Hills. Very few mineral or gem stone localities are known. However, the Rochester, Warren, and Windham valleys have deposits which yield highly prized *verde antique serpentine.*

CHITTENDEN CO.: Burlington, 9 mi. N off Highway 2, on the Parrott Farm—*agate, chert, jasp-agate, jasper.*

RUTLAND CO.: Rutland Station, 3¾ mi. SE on N side of Round Hill, which is on the W flank of the Green Mountains —green *aventurine.*

## VIRGINIA

The eastern, or Tidewater region, of this nearly triangular state is relatively flat and swampy, cut by four great tidal rivers which empty into Chesapeake Bay. Back of the coastal flats the rolling, fertile piedmont broadening southward toward North Carolina rises along its western edge abruptly into the heavily forested Blue Ridge, capped by Mount Rogers at 5720 feet. Between the Blue Ridge and the Appalachian plateau farther west lies the famous and historic Valley of Virginia, a province of ridges and valleys interconnected by many water gaps. Chief of these is the scenic Shenandoah Valley. Thousands of visitors annually visit the shores, mountains, mineral springs, and historic sites, and the rock collector will find many localities worth investigating for gem stones.

ALBEMARLE CO.: Faber Mine—*azurite, smithsonite.*

AMELIA CO.: Amelia; (1) Morefield Mine off Highway 628, 4 mi. ENE of Amelia—*amazonite, beryl, phenakite, topaz* (blue), (2) 1¼ mi. N 35° E, at Richeson Mica Mine—*amazonite, muscovite mica,* (3) Rutherford Mine, 1¼ mi. N—*albite, amazonite, amethyst, circrolite, cleavelandite, feldspar, garnet (spessartite), mica, microcline, microlite, moonstone, quartz crystals, topaz* (blue).

AMHERST CO.: Amherst, 7 mi. NNW and ⅓ mi. N of Sandidges Post Office—*amethyst, quartz crystals.* Fancy Hill —*amethyst.* Sweet Briar, 2 mi. E—*chrysocolla.*

APPOMATTOX CO.: Mouth of Wreck Island Creek, 2 mi. upstream—*chrysocolla.*

ARLINGTON CO.: Kirkwood Road, Spout Run banks— *jasper.*

AUGUSTA CO.: Spottswood—*quartz crystals.*

BEDFORD CO.: Moneta-Bells District—*vesuvianite.*

BLAND CO.: Point Pleasant, N side of Walkers Mountain—*quartz crystals.*

CAMPBELL CO.: Synch Station copper prospects—*turquoise.*

CHARLOTTE CO.: Brookneal; (1) ⅓ mi. NNE, and (2) 10 mi. NE—*amethyst*—also Charlotte Court House; (1) 2¼ mi. WNW, and (2) 4 mi. S.

CHESTERFIELD CO.: Itterdale, Mosely Junction, and Skinquarter—*petrified and opalized wood.*

CULPEPPER CO.: Drakesville—*azurite.*

FAIRFAX CO.: Centreville; (1) Bull Run Soapstone Quarry —*moss agate*, (2) W, at Centreville Quarry on S side of Highway 29-211—*apophyllite, byssolite, prehnite, thaumasite.*

FLOYD CO.: Piedmont and Blue Ridge areas—*staurolites.* Willis, 2.2 mi. ESE—*clear quartz crystals.*

GILES CO.: Newport, 3½ mi. WSW, at Spruce Run—*quartz crystals* (distorted).

GOOCHLAND CO.: Oliver, O. W. Harris Mica Mine Farm 7.7 mi. W of Highway 1 along State Highway 738, in creek gravels—*garnet, kyanite, moonstone, rutile crystals.*

HALIFAX CO.: Virgilia District, Gillis Mine—*chrysocolla.*

HANOVER CO.: Ashland area—*staurolite* (fairy crosses).

HENRICO CO.: Manchester area stream gravels—*diamond.*

HENRY CO.: Axton and Ridgeway areas—*garnets.*

LONDON CO.: Leesburg, Arlington Quarry—*quartz crystals.*

LOUISA CO.: Trevilians, 4 mi. SW—*amethyst, quartz crystals.*

MADISON CO.: Mineral, Armenius Mine—*azurite, garnet.* Stanley, ½ mi. E at Fisher's Gap—*azurite.* Syria (Rose Run)—*jasper.*

MECKLENBURG CO.: Virgilia District, Pontiac Mine—*azurite, bornite, calcite, malachite.*

MONTGOMERY CO.: Luster's Gate dolomites—*quartz crystals.* Shawnsville, SW, Bonys Run—*smithsonite.*

NELSON CO.: Arrington, 8½ mi. WNW and 2½ mi. NE of Lowesville—*amethyst, rock crystal,* Irish Creek, S of Vesuvius and SW of Montebello—*cassiterite, moonstone* (blue).

ORANGE CO.: Vaucluse Gold Mine—*diamond.*
PAGE CO.: Ida, 0.9 mi. NW at Hoak Hill—*epidote, hematite, jasper* (red, orbicular).
PATRICK CO.: Stuard area, 4 mi. SW to 19 mi. NE—*staurolite* (fairy crosses)—also from 9 mi. NE of Stuart to beyond the Franklin Co. line. (See also, Fairystone State Park).
POWHATAN CO.: Flat Rock, 3.6 mi. NE at Herbbe No. 2 Mine on State Highway 613—*amazonite, quartz crystals.*
PULASKI CO.: Delton area mines—*smithsonite.*
PRINCE EDWARD CO.: Rice, 3 mi. N, via Highway 619, on both sides of Sayler's Creek—*amethyst, feldspar, graphic granite, quartz crystals* (clear, milky, smoky).
PRINCE WILLIAM CO.: Minnieville, W—*amethyst, quartz crystals.* Quantico area—*petrified and opalized wood.*
ROCKBRIDGE CO.: Irish Creek—*beryl, quartz crystals.*
ROCKINGHAM CO.: Elkton; (1) 1 mi. W—*quartz crystals,* (2) SE, at High Knob—*azurite.*
RUSSELL CO.: Castlewood, 10 mi. N—*smithsonite.*
SMITH CO.: Sugar Grove—*rhodonite.*
TAZEWELL CO.: Pounding Mill—*diamond.*
WARREN CO.: Riverton—*calcite, quartz crystals.*
WYTHE CO.: Austinville—*smithsonite.*

## WASHINGTON

The topography of this Northwest Coast state is remarkably varied, bold, and geologically interesting. Snowy, glacier-flanked volcanic cones, with Mount Ranier highest at 14,408 feet, line the Cascade Mountains. Running north and south, this great range divides the state into a western part (green, wet, sea-girt) and an eastern part (arid, basaltic, canyon-cut). Puget Sound with its more than 300 forested islands and many gem-stone beaches bisects the western portion, creating the Olympic Peninsula. Here, rising to heights above 7000 feet, the Olympic National Park constitutes the most rugged and inaccessible wilderness area in America. To its south Grays and Willapa Harbors reach far inland from the sea, surrounded by heavily timbered hills. Throughout the western portion the rock collector will find road cuts, stream beds, and farmers' fields productive of highly prized *agatized clams, oysters,* and other Miocene *fossils,* as well as localities too numerous to be listed in detail for hunting *agate, carnelian,* and *jasper.*

Eastern Washington, known mostly as the Inland Empire, forms the major portion of the Columbia Plateau. This vast, arid, almost level region of Miocene basalts embraces some 225,000 square miles, lapping over into British Columbia, Idaho, and Oregon. At a time when the Cascade mountains were pushing upward, extremely fluid, basic lavas poured out of enormous fissures to fill all pre-existing valleys, lakes, and swamps and covered residual granite domes to depths of 500 to 3700 feet. The basalt flows came in many series, often separated by long intervals when soils formed and great forests grew, only to be covered by newer lavas or by volcanic ash, rich in silica. The result is, today, that there are more collecting localities than can be detailed for some of the loveliest gem-quality *opalized* and *silicified* woods in the world.

Both portions of the state are drained by the Columbia, one of the truly great rivers of the world and which, during Tertiary times drained an immense level region of lakes and swamps rich in vegetation. Throughout Oligocene and Miocene times as the volcanoes poured out their ash and lava, the river maintained its westward course, carving the great Columbia River Gorge transversely through the rising Cascade Mountains, now many thousands of feet deep. With its principal tributary the Wyoming-spawned Snake River cutting its own mighty canyon through the lava plateau, the Columbia River separates Washington from Oregon. Its sandy beaches yield great quantities of gem stone materials and prehistoric Indian artifacts. Tens of thousands of exquisite obsidian arrowheads have already been gathered into museum collections.

CHELAN CO.: Lyman Lake, W, at Crown Point Mine— *quartz crystals.* Negro Creek, N side, at Davenport property— *geodes, nodules.* Wenatchee, Number One Canyon—*onyx.*

CLALLAM CO.: Agate Beach, on Strait of Juan de Fuca— *agate, chert, jasper.* Dungeness and Soleduck river gravels— *agate, jasper (orbicular).* Lake Crescent, 1 mi. NW of W end— *jasper.* La Push, ocean beaches—*agate, jasper.*

CLARK CO.: Bell Mountain Mine—*plasma agate, rock crystal.* Washougal—*moss agate,* especially 2½ mi. NE with *amethysts.*

COWLITZ CO.: Cloverdale, 4 mi. E—*agate (fortification),*

*carnelian, chalcedony, geodes (amethyst-lined).* Kalama and Kelso, hills to E—same as above, with *jasper.* Kelso, S, base of cliffs along Highway 99—*agate* with water bubbles.

DOUGLAS CO.: Bridgeport area—*jadeite.* Waterville—*common opal.*

FRANKLIN CO.: Ringgold, area river bench gravels—*agate.*

GRANT CO.: Grand and Moses Coulee area, also at Trinidad—*opalized logs* in lava outcrops. Quincy area, in diatomaceous earth deposits—*common-opal* nodules. Vantage, Columbia river gravels—*agate, opalized* and *silicified wood.*

GRAYS HARBOR CO.: Moclips, N, along ocean beaches and in regional stream gravels—*agate, jasper.* Oakville, 10 mi. N, in road cuts and stream banks—*agatized* and *chalcedonized clams* and *oysters.*

JEFFERSON CO.: Agate Beach—same as in Clallam Co. Kalaloch area gravels—*agate, jasper.* Mount Anderson and Rustler Creek, Olympic Mountains—*rock crystal.* Queets area beaches—*agate, chert, jasper.*

KINGS CO.: (1) Bear Basin, (2) Devil's Canyon, and (3) W side of Denny Mountain, above Denny Creek—*rock crystal.*

KITTITAS CO.: Area; (1) most of county outside Gingko Petrified Forest State Park, (2) nearly all of eastern part, and (3) along Columbia River W and S from Vantage—*opalized* and *petrified wood.* Cle Elum and Ellensburg area; (1) NE, in basalt flows—*blue-chalcedony nodules,* (2) NW—*agate.* Liberty; (1) 2 mi. NE, in 2-square-mile area of stream beds and talus slopes—*agate, chalcedony nodules,* (2) 2½ mi. out at summit of Crystal Mountain—*chalcedony nodules, geodes,* (3) 5 mi. NW at Red Top Mountain, 1 mi. W of Highway 97, and along Middle Fork of Teanaway River—*agate, chalcedony nodules,* and (4) 4½ mi. NW of Red Top Mountain, at Ryepatch—*agate.* Saddle Mountains area, especially near Vantage and Crab Creek Canyon—*opalized wood.*

KLICKITAT CO.: Horse Heaven Hills, Eocene Latah Formation exposures of whitish volcanic ash occur along some 120 miles, extending from near Glenwood north into southern Yakima Co. and east into Benton Co.—*opalized* and *silicified wood.* This top quality gem wood occurs abundantly in the following order, as: *redwood* (Sequoia), *oak* (many varieties), *swamp cypress (Taxodium), elm, maple, willow, cedar, poplar, chestnut, alder, birch, persimmon,* and *laurel.* Mabton-Prosser area—*opalized wood*—also immediately N and NW of Roosevelt. Yakima Ridge, 1 mi. NW of Goldcreek and S of Cairn Hope Peak—*opalized wood.* The area includes the Rattlesnake Hills in Yakima Co. Warwick, 2 mi. W and 20 mi. NE of Goldendale—*agate, carnelian, jasper, wood.*

   LEWIS CO.: Chehalis; (1) 5 mi. S, above Forest in Newaukum River gravels, (2) 15 mi. S, near Toledo—*geodes, nodules,* (3) S, around Mary's Corner—*agate, carnelian, chalcedony, geodes, jasper, petrified wood*—also in stream gravels around Centralia and North Fork of the Chehalis River. Doty area—*peridot.* Lucas Creek, tributary of Newaukum River, in road and RR cuts and ditches along State Highway 12 between Adna and Pe Ell—*agate, carnelian, chalcedony, geodes, jasper, petrified wood.* Morton, area mercury mines—*chalcedony,* clear and spotted with *cinnabar.* Salmon and White Rivers, all tributaries also, in gravels, as well as loose in farmers' fields throughout the region—*agate, carnelian, geodes.*

   LINCOLN CO.: Little Spokane River bars—*garnets, quartz crystals.* Mondovi; (1) ½ mi. N, (2) 1 mi. NW—*precious opal, quartz crystals*—(3) 3 to 4 mi. NW—*fire opal.* Pullman, 5 to 6 mi. N, close to Idaho border—*fire opal.*

   OKANOGAN CO.: Nespelem, N, Nespelem River gravels —*agate, chalcedony.* Riverside, 7 mi. NE, above mouth of a Tunk Creek tributary to Okanogan River—*quartz crystals, thulite* (pink *zoisite*). Tunk Creek gravels—*corundum* (blue, pink), *thulite.*

   PACIFIC CO.: Adna, between Adna and Raymond, in every stream bed along Highway 12 for some 40 miles—*agate, carnelian, chalcedony, jasper.* Greens Creek, between Menlo and Raymond—*agatized shells, chalcedony replacements of ammonites, gastropods (snails)*—also Willapa River gravels, near Lebam.

   PEND OREILLE CO.: Metaline Falls, Josephine Mine—*smithsonite.* Newport—*amethyst.* Sacheen Lake—*garnets.*

   SKAMANIA CO.: Table Mountain, area W and NW and N of a line drawn between Mounts Adams and St. Helens—*agate, carnelian, chalcedony, jasper, quartz crystals.*

   SNOHOMISH CO.: Monte Cristo District—*azurite, malachite.* Sultan Basin, NE rim—*garnets.*

STEVENS CO.: Loon Lake, copper mines—*azurite, malachite.*
WALLA WALLA CO.: Whitman Creek—*opal.*
WHITMAN CO.: Bald Butte, S of—*smoky quartz crystals.*
YAKIMA CO.: (1) Rattlesnake Hills, S of Yakima Ridge, (2) Saddle Mountains, (3) Sunnyside Road S of junction with Cold Springs to Yakima road—*opalized* and *silicified wood.*

## WEST VIRGINIA

With coal mining the major industry in more than half its 55 counties, about one-sixth of West Virginia lies in the valley and ridge province to the east of the Allegheny escarpment. Most of the rest of the state is covered by the Allegheny plateau so that with a mean elevation of 1500 feet, it is the highest state east of the Mississippi. Almost no gemstone or mineral collecting localities within its extremely irregular borders are known. However, limestone quarries reveal fractures in which the rock collector may find crystals of *barite, calcite, celestite,* and *gypsum.* In exposures of the older sandstones, fractures show small, well-developed *quartz crystals.*
MERCER CO.: Willowton area quarries—*onyx.*
MONROE CO.: Peterstown—*diamond.*

## WISCONSIN

Bordered by lakes and rivers, Wisconsin is a state fashioned by the advance and retreat of the four great glacial periods of the Pleistocene. Indeed, it lends its name to the last great advance of the ice, which reached its maximum extent about 20,000 years ago and is still retreating from the Northern Hemisphere. With some overlap into the bordering states, nearly 10,000 square miles of the southwestern portion—the Driftless Area—escaped the ice. It was protected by the Keweenaw and Gogebic Ranges, an Ordovician dome-uplift of Pre-Cambrian rocks across the northern counties. These "highlands" deflected the ice advance. Consequently, the Driftless Area presents many interesting examples of the earth's mantle surface that must have been common over all the northern states region before the ice scraped and scoured it to bedrock. In retreating, the ice left thousands of lakes scattered over the state, some of great scenic beauty. At the same time, unstratified drift deposits of unusual interest, known as drumlins, were left concentrically over eastern Wisconsin. In many of these drumlins, *diamonds* of unknown origin have been found.

ASHLAND CO.: Area stream gravels, especially the Chippewa River—*agate, jasper.*

BAYFIELD CO.: *agates, jasper.*

BARRON CO.: Devil's Lake area quarries—*catlinite, quartzite*—also Rice Lake area quarries.

CLARK CO.: Owen area gravels—*jasper.*

DANE CO.: Oregon, 2½ mi. SW in Kettle Moraine—*diamond.*

IOWA CO.: Area mine dumps; (1) Cobb, 5 mi. N at Eberle Mine on Highway 80, (2) ½ mi. W to NW¼NW¼ Sec. 2, T. 6N, R. 1E, and (3) 4 to 5 mi. SW at Centerville, on Hiland Co. Trunk 1—*aurichalite, azurite, chalcocite, chalcopyrite, cuprite, malachite, smithsonite, sphalerite.* Linden area mines, near Highway 39—*barite, calcite, galena, marcasite, nickel minerals, pyrite, smithsonite, sphalerite*—also at Dodgeville mines in E part of town.

IRON CO.: *agates, jasper.*

MARATHON CO.: Wausau—*albite (peristerite),* in area pegmatites.

OZAUKEE CO.: Saukville, 26 mi. N of Milwaukee—*diamond.*

PIERCE CO.: Rock Elm Twp., Plum Creek gravels—*diamond, gold.*

RACINE CO.: Burlington area—*diamond.*

WASHINGTON CO.: Kohlsville—*diamond.*

WAUKESHA CO.: Eagle, Kettle Moraine—*diamond.*

WOOD CO.: Central area gravels—*agate, aventurine, quartzite*—also on regional mine dumps.

## WYOMING

This exactly rectangular state is literally the "end of the Great Plains." From the South Dakota border the Black Hills descend westward into eroded badlands and sagebrush plains that stretch to the Powder River ("a mile wide and an inch deep"). Beyond, the Great Plains end in the wooded foothills of the towering Big Horn Mountains. The generally high tablelands of southeastern Wyoming are interrupted by the snowy Laramie and Medicine Bow ranges, while western and northwestern Wyoming is all rugged, impenetrable mountains that support the erratic Continental Divide. Here, the volcanic-conglomerate Absoraka Range of Miocene origin, the Gros Ventre and Wind River ranges, along with the most ancient Pre-Cambrian Tetons along the Idaho border guard the approaches to Yellowstone National Park.

In the central part of the state, south of the interesting hot springs region of Thermopolis, the famed Wind River Canyon cuts a 20-mile-long gorge through the eroded Owl Creek Mountains to reveal the whole geologic history of North America from the most ancient Pre-Cambrian schists, layer by layer right up to the last Quaternary gravels in streams still flowing, thus encompassing an estimated four billion years of geologic time. South of the Wind River Range lies the Great South Pass, made famous by the Old Oregon Trail. Here, the rock collector finds himself in the heart of a fabulous gold mining, gem stone, and *petrified wood* country. To the south and east lies the vast Red Desert—heart of the *Wyoming jade* fields— while westward are whole mountains of fossil fish and widespread *opalized* and *silicified* forests with stone stumps and tree trunks two to six feet through, containing cavities, or "vugs," of lovely *amethyst crystals*. All areas of this frontier state have interesting minerals and gem stones to offer the prospector, including fossil *dinosaur bones, gastroliths,* and Mesozoic *shellfish* of every description.

ALBANY CO.: Como Bluff, N of Highway 30, near Carbon Co. border—*petrified dinosaur bones.* Holmes, Grand Encampment District—*azurite, malachite.* Marshall—*agate, opalized* and *silicified wood.* Medicine Bow, 36 mi. NE on W slopes of Laramie Mountains—*agate, chalcedony, jasper.* Metamorphic rocks outcropping in Laramie Mountains—*iolite (cordierite).*

BIG HORN CO.: Badlands area—*dinosaur bones, gastroliths*—especially W of Greybull. Lovell; (1) badlands eastward toward Big Horn Mountains—*ammonites, cephalopods, dinosaur bones,* (2) hills lying S—*calcite, gypsum,* (3) SE, along flanks of Sheep Mountain—*fossil shellfish,* (4) 40 mi. N, the TX Ranch straddling Montana Border at E end of Pryor Mountains—*concretions, "Dry Head" fortification agate, jasper, petrified coral, prehistoric Indian artifacts.* Medicine Mountain—

*petrified coral, quartz.* Spence—*calcite* in bluffs along RR.

CARBON CO.: Medicine Bow, 35 mi. N—*opalized wood.*
Saratoga, along both sides of Highway 130 to Wolcott Junction
—*opalized wood* (fluoresces green). Sweetwater River gravels—
*agate.* Rawlins-Medicine Bow-Leo area—*jade.*

CONVERSE CO.: Glenrock, E, in Boxelder Creek Canyon
S of its junction with the North Platte River—*chalcedony
geodes, quartz crystals.*

CROOK CO.: Warren's Peak area—*azurite, malachite.*

FREMONT CO.: Beaver Divide, N side, and Green Mountains—*agate* (banded, moss), *aventurine, garnet, sapphire.* Fort
Washakie, 10 mi. NW in wide area along Highway 287—*agate
(moss), chalcedony, jasper.* Granite Mountains, NW of—*chalcedony.* Kortez Dam area, below Seminoe Dam on North Platte
River—black *nephrite.* Lander area; (1) including Cottonwood,
Haypress, and Warm Springs the collecting area centered at
Lander runs approximately 140 mi. E to W, and 60 mi. N to S,
including parts of Carbon, Natrona, Sublette, and Sweetwater
counties. It also takes in Farson, W of South Pass, the Red
Desert, S and SE of South Pass, and Seminoe Dam and Alcova—
*agate, jasper, nephrite* ("Wyoming" jade,) (2) 48 mi. SW, near
Granite Peak in SE end of Wind River Range—*"Wyoming"
jade.* Long Creek, N, to its junction with the Sweetwater River
—*agate, nephrite.* Marion—*rhodonite, ruby.* Riverton, Wind
River valley and tributaries—*agate, jasper.* Shoshone, 15 mi.
NE, or 20 mi. SE of Thermopolis in Hot Springs Co., and E of
Wind River Canyon—*aquamarine, beryl, feldspar, muscovite
mica.* Southeast of Wind River, all SE part of county N of
Sweetwater River—*agate, jasper.* South Pass and Atlantic City
area—*agate, chalcedony, gold, jade, jasper, muscovite mica,
petrified wood (agatized, opalized), quartz crystals, searlesite,
shortite crystals, tourmaline (massive).* Split Rock, area surrounding corner made by Carbon, Fremont, and Natrona counties—*nephrite, jade, "Sweetwater" agates.* Townships 30, 31 N;
Ranges 89, 90, 91 W, north of Sweetwater River—*"Sweetwater"
agates.* Warm Springs region, foothills and draws of Wind River
Range—*agate, chalcedony, jasper, nephrite, quartz crystals,
silicified wood.*

GOSHEN CO.: Jay Elm District—*agate, malachite, onyx.*

HOT SPRINGS CO.: Area quarries—*alabaster.* Big Horn

River bluffs—*travertine.* Hot springs geysers—*geyserite.*
JOHNSON CO.: Big Horn Mountains—*azurite, malachite.*
Buffalo, 12 mi. E, along both sides of Highway 16—*agate, chalcedony, gastroliths, jasp-agate, jasper, quartz crystals, petrified wood.* Crazy Woman Creek, Crazy Woman Petrified Forest—*opalized* and *silicified wood.*
LARAMIE CO.: Chugwater—*bloodstone (heliotrope).*
LINCOLN CO.: Badland area, Green River, especially along Ham's Fork, and all adjacent areas—*agate, chalcedony, chert, jasp-agate, jasper, quartz crystals, petrified and silicified wood, turritella agate* (brown *agate* filled with silicified shells of *Goniobasis)*—also in outcrops of Green River Formation in this and other counties. Kemmerer, 12 mi. W—*fossil fish.*
NATRONA CO.: Casper; (1) area quarries—*agate, alabaster, amazonite,* (2) 40 mi. W, Poison Spider Creek and broad surrounding region—*agate, chalcedony, jasp-agate, jasper.* Sage Hen Creek—*agate.* Split Rock, 8 mi. E—*"Sweetwater" agate.*
PARK CO.: Kirwin—*azurite, malachite.* Meeteetse, Greybull River gravels—*agate, jasper.* Sunlight country, remote—*agate, chalcedony, gold, jasper, petrified and opalized wood.*
PLATTE CO.: Guernsey, 2 mi. NW, Hartville deposits—*agate, (seam, seam moss), chalcedony.*
SWEETWATER CO.: Farson area; (1) Big Sandy River and tributaries, (2) Eden Valley, (3) Oregon Butte, E of, (4) Pacific Springs, SE of, (5) eastward to Red Desert, and (6) Wind River Range draws, flanks, foothills, and slopes—*agate, chalcedony, jasp-agate, jasper, silicified wood* (black, highly prized). Granger, buttes along Highway 30 to Blacks Fork—*turritella agate.* Green River, 20 mi. E, broad belt along both sides of Highway 30 to Fort Bridger in Uinta Co.—*agate, chalcedony, chert, jasper, petrified wood.* Green River Formation—see Lincoln Co. Superior, 15 mi. N, slopes of Steamboat Mountain in the Leucite Hills—*agate, chalcedony, jasper.* Wamsutter, 15 mi. SW, Delaney Rim—*turritella agate.*
TETON CO.: Absoraka Range, through middle of Jackson Hole—*opalized wood.* Thorofare wilderness area stream gravels—*agate, jasper, opalized and silicified wood.*
UINTA CO.: Fort Bridger area gravels—*agate* (common), *turritella, jasper, silicified algae.* Highway 30, base of buttes along way between Blacks Fork Creek and Granger—*silicified*

*algae, turritella agate.* Green River Formation—see Lincoln Co.

WASHAKIE CO.: Worland, broad area bench gravels and sides and bottoms of regional draws, washes—*agate, chalcedony, jasper* (red, yellow), *quartzite.*

YELLOWSTONE NATIONAL PARK: While no collecting is permitted here, or in any national park or monument, an enormous quantity of gemstone minerals which can be listed for the Park itself also can be found in the regional streams, talus slopes, and erosional debris outside the Park boundaries. These include: *agate, amethyst, chalcedony, chert, jasp-agate, jasper, geodes, fossils, nodules, obsidian, opal, opalite, petrified wood (opalized, silicified), rock crystal, thundereggs, travertine* (including *geyserite*).

# CHAPTER VIII

# Mineral Essentials

/\/\/\/\/\/\/\/\/\/\/\/\/\/\/\/\

In order to assist the prospector to identify minerals and gem stones, such as are located by site in Chapter VII, the following alphabetical list of minerals is presented together with their essential characteristics, since for most of them identification is quite practicable by their physical properties.

ACHROITE: Colorless *tourmaline, q.v.*

ACTINOLITE (TREMOLITE): Calcium magnesium (iron) silicate, $Ca_2(Mg,Fe)_5Si_8O_{22}(OH)_2$—*actinolite;* $Ca_2Mg_5Si_8O_{22}$-$(OH)_2$—*tremolite;* monoclinic-prismatic; luster glassy; color white, light green, dark green, violet; H, 5-6; S.G.*, 3-3.3: fracture subconchoidal to uneven; cleavage perfect prismatic: transparent to translucent.

ADAMANTINE SPAR: Bronzy brown chatoyant *corundum, q.v.*

ADAMITE: Basic zinc arsenate, $Zn_2(OH)AsO_4$; orthorhombic-rhombic bipyramidal; luster glassy; color yellowish, greenish, rose to violet; H, 3.5; S.G., 4.3-4.4; fracture uneven; cleavage domal; brittle; transparent to translucent; often fluorescent yellow-green.

* H-hardness; S.G.-specific gravity.

**AGATE:** Colorfully banded *chalcedony, q.v.*

**ALBITE:** Common rock-forming mineral of *plagioclase* series, *q.v.*, sodium aluminum silicate, $NaAlSi_3O_8$; triclinic-pinacoidal; luster glassy: color white; H, 6; S.G., 2.63; fracture conchoidal; cleavage good at 94°, poor prismatic; internal flashes.

**ALBITE MOONSTONE:** Variety of *albite, q.v.,* with bluish reflections.

**ALLANITE:** Rare-earth silicate, $(Ca,Ce,La,Na)_2(Al,Fe,Be,Mn,-Mg)_3$—$(SiO_4)_3(OH)$; monoclinic-prismatic; luster resinous; color black to dark brown; H, 5.5-6; S.G., 2.7-4.2; fracture subconchoidal to uneven; cleavage poor; translucent on edges; radioactive.

**ALMANDINE GARNET:** Iron aluminum silicate, $Fe_3Al_2Si_3-O_{12}$; cubic-hexoctahedral; luster glassy; color deep violet-red; H, 6-7.5; S.G., 4.3; fracture conchoidal to uneven; cleavage none; transparent to translucent.

**ALUNITE:** Aluminum potassium sulphate, hydrous, $KAl_3-(SO_4)_2(OH)_6$; hexogonal-ditrigonal pyramidal; luster vitreous to pearly; color white, grayish, flesh-red; H, 3.5-4; S.G., 2.6-2.9; fracture flat conchoidal to uneven; cleavage fair basal, poor rhombohedral; brittle; translucent to transparent; may fluoresce orange.

**AMBER:** Petrified resin; luster oily; color yellowish to reddish- or yellowish-brown; H, 2-2.5; S.G., 1.05-1.10; fracture conchoidal; cleavage none; transparent.

**AMAZONITE:** Variety of *microcline feldspar, q.v.;* color bright green.

**AMETHYST:** Variety of transparent *quartz* crystal, *q.v.;* color violet to purple.

**AMBLYGONITE:** Lithium aluminum fluophosphate, $LiAl-(PO_4)(F,OH)$; triclinic-pinacoidal; luster glassy; colorless to white, light greening-gray; H, 5.5-6; S.G., 3-3.1; fracture uneven; cleavage perfect basal; brittle; transparent to translucent; fluorescent (often) weakly orange.

**AMPHIBOLITE:** Metamorphic rock composed of *amphibole* or *hornblende, q.v.* (Massive *hornblende* is *amphibole.*)

**ANALCITE (ANALCIME):** Hydrous sodium aluminum silicate, $NaAlSi_2O_6 \cdot H_2O$; cubic-hexoctahedral; luster glassy; colorless, white, greenish, reddish; H, 5-5.5; S.G., 2.3; fracture subconchoidal; cleavage slightly cubic; transparent to translucent.

ANATASE: Titanium oxide, $TiO_2$; tetragonal-ditettragonal bypyramidal; luster adamantine to submetallic; color blue. brown, light yellow; H, 5.5-6; S.G., 3.8-3.9; fracture subconchoidal; cleavage perfect basal and pyramidal; streak white; brittle; translucent to transparent.

ANDALUSITE: Aluminum silicate, $Al_2SiO_5$; orthorhombic-rhombic bipyramidal; luster glassy; color brown, gray, pink, white; H, 7.5; S.G., 3.1-3.2; fracture conchoidal; cleavage fair prismatic; transparent to translucent.

ANDESINE: Variety of *plagioclase, q.v.*; H, 6; S.G., 2.68; derived from fine-grained *andesite* lavas.

ANDESITE: Basic volcanic lava composed mainly of *plagioclase feldspar.*

ANDRADITE GARNET: Calcium iron silicate, $Ca_3Fe_2Si_3$-$O_{12}$; cubic-hexoctahedral; luster glassy; color pale browns to black; H, 6-7.5; S.G., 3.8; fracture conchoidal to uneven; no cleavage; transparent to translucent.

ANHYDRITE: Calcium sulphate, $CaSO_4$; orthorhombic-rhombic bipyramidal; luster glassy to pearly; colorless, gray, lilac, white; H, 3-3.5; S.G., 3; fracture uneven to splintery; cleavage good pinacoidal; transparent to translucent.

APACHE TEARS: Variety of obsidian, *q.v.*, as small nodules.

APATITE: Calcium fluo- (or chloro-) phosphate, $Ca_5(Cl,F)$-$(PO_4)_3$; luster glassy; colorless, blue, brown, green, violet, white, yellow; H, 5; S.G., 3.1-3.2; fracture conchoidal; cleavage slightly basal; brittle; translucent to transparent; may fluoresce yellow-orange.

APOPHYLLITE: Hydrous calcium, potassium fluosilicate, $KCa_4FSi_4O_{10} \cdot 8H_2O$; tetragonal-ditetragonal bipyramidal; luster glassy; colorless, greenish, pale pink, white; H, 4.5-5; S.G., 2.3-2.4; fracture uneven, cleavage perfect basal; translucent to transparent.

AQUAMARINE: Blue and blue-green varieties of *beryl, q.v.*

ARAGONITE: Calcium carbonate, $CaCO_3$; orthorhombic-rhombic bipyramidal; luster vitreous; colorless, light yellow, white; H, 3.5-4; S.G., 2.9-3; fracture subconchoidal; cleavage poor; brittle; translucent to transparent; fluorescent; phosphorescent.

ARGENTITE: Silver sulphide, $Ag_2S$; cubic-hexoctahedral; luster metallic; color dark lead-gray; H, 2-2.5; S.G., 7.3; fracture subconchoidal; cleavage poor cubic; sectile (cuts with a knife).

ARIZONA RUBY: *Pyrope garnet, q.v.*

ARSENOPYRITE: Iron sulpharsenide, FeAsS; monoclinic-prismatic; luster metallic; color silver-white; H, 5.5-6; S.G., 5.9-6.2; fracture uneven; cleavage prismatic; brittle.

AUGELITE: Basic aluminum phosphate, $Al_2(PO_4)(OH)_3$; monoclinic-prismatic; luster glassy; colorless, rose, yellowish, white; H, 4.5-5; S.G., 2.7; fracture conchoidal; cleavage good (two); brittle; translucent to transparent.

AUGITE: A mixed silicate mineral of calcium, magnesium, iron, and aluminum (dark green to black variety of *pyroxene*) charcteristic of basic lavas; $Ca(Mg,Fe,Al)(Si,Al)_2O_6$; monoclinic-prismatic; luster glassy; color black to dark green; H, 5-6; S.G., 3.2-3.4; fracture uneven; cleavage perfect prismatic.

AUTUNITE: Hydrous calcium uranium phosphate, $Ca(UO_2)_2(PO_4)_2 \cdot 11H_2O$; tetragonal-ditetragonal bipyramidal; luster glassy to pearly; color greenish yellow to lemon; H, 2-2.5; S.G., 3.1; cleavage perfect basal and prismatic; brittle; translucent; brilliant green fluorescence.

AVENTURINE: Name given to various minerals, such as the *feldspars* because of contained waferlike inclusions that reflect the light like tiny mirrors, an effect known as "aventurescence."

AXINITE: Hydrous borosilicate of calcium, manganese, and iron aluminum, $H(Ca,Mn,Fe)_3Al_2B(SiO_4)_4$; triclinic-pinacoidal; luster glassy; color gray, violet-brown, yellow-orange; H, 6.5-7; S.G., 3.3-3.4; fracture conchoidal; cleavage one good; translucent to transparent.

AZURITE: Basic copper carbonate, $Cu_3(OH)_2(CO_3)_2$; monoclinic-prismatic; luster glassy; color light blue to black; H, 3.5-4; S.G., 3.8; fracture conchoidal; cleavage one good, two poor; brittle; transparent in thin slivers.

AZURMALACHITE: A double mineral combining *azurite, q.v.,* and *malachite, q.v.,* in alternating bands.

BABINGTONITE: Hydrous calcium iron silicate, $Ca_2Fe''Fe'''Si_5O_{14}(OH)$; triclinic-pinacoidal; luster glassy; color black; H, 5.5-6; S.G., 3.4; fracture conchoidal; cleavage two pinacoidal; translucent on thin edges.

BANDED RHYOLITE: Porous *rhyolite* in which mineral-laden infiltrations of water leave bands; also called *wonderstone;* colors cream, pale brown, red, yellow.

BARITE: Barium sulphate, $BaSO_4$; orthorhombic-rhombic bipyramidal; luster glassy; colorless to bluish, brown, reddish, yellow; H, 3-3.5; S.G., 4.3-4.6; fracture uneven; cleavage perfect basal and prismatic; brittle; translucent to transparent.

BAUXITE: A mixture of aluminum oxides, $Al(OH)_3 + Al,-H_2O$; amorphous; luster dull; color white to red-brown; H, 1-3; S.G., 2-2.5; fracture earthy.

BECKITE (BEEKITE): Silicified *coral.*

BENITOITE: Barium titanium silicate, $BaTaSi_3O_9$; hexagonal-ditrigonal bipyramidal; luster glassy; color blue to white; H, 6-6.5; S.G., 3.6; fracture conchoidal; cleavage poor pyramidal.

BERTRANDITE: Hydrous beryllium silicate, $Be_4Si_2O_7$-$(OH)_2$; orthorhombic-rhombic pyramidal; luster pearly to glassy; colorless, flesh-colored; H, 6; S.G., 2.6; fracture flaky; cleavage perfect basal, good prismatic; translucent to transparent.

BERYL: Beryllium aluminum silicate, $Be_3Al_2Si_6O_{18}$; hexagonal-dihexagonal bypyramidal; luster glassy; color blue *(aquamarine)*, yellow-brown *(golden beryl)*, green *(emerald)*, pink *(morganite)*, white; H, 8; S.G., 2.6-2.8; fracture conchoidal; cleavage poor basal; translucent to transparent (gemmy).

BIOTITE: Hydrous silicate of potassium, magnesium, iron, and aluminum, $K(Mg,Fe)_3AlSi_3O_{10}(OH)_2$; monoclinic-domatic; luster glassy; color dark brown to black; H, 2.5-3; S.G., 2.8-3.4; flexible-elastic; cleavage perfect basal; opaque to translucent.

BLOODSTONE: Dark green *agate, q.v.,* spotted with blood-red dots. A variety of *moss agate* with iron oxide inclusions.

BORAX: Hydrous sodium borate, $Na_2B_4O_7 \cdot 10H_2O$; monoclinic-prismatic; luster glassy; colorless, bluish, grayish, yellowish; H, 2-2.5; S.G., 1.7; fracture conchoidal; cleavage three, one good; brittle; translucent to transparent; efflorescent.

**BORNITE:** Copper iron sulphide, $Cu_5FeS_4$; cubic-hexoctahedral; luster bronzy metallic tarnishing to purple; H, 3; S.G., 4.9-5.4; fracture uneven; cleavage poor octahedral; brittle.

**BOURNONITE:** Lead copper sulphantimonide, $PbCuSbS_3$; orthorhombic-bipyramidal; luster metallic-adamantine; color grayish-black to black; H, 2.5-3; S.G., 5.8-5.9; fracture subconchoidal to uneven; cleavage one good, two less at right angles; brittle.

**BRAZILIANITE:** Basic sodium aluminum phosphate, $NaAl_3$-$(PO_4)_2$ $(OH)_4$; monoclinic; luster glassy; color chartreuse-yellow; H, 5.5; S.G., 2.98; fracture conchoidal; cleavage one perfect; crystals wedge-shaped.

**BROCHANTITE:** Basic copper sulphate, $CU_4(SO_4)(OH)_6$; monoclinic-prismatic; luster glassy; color bright to dark green; H, 3.5-4; S.G., 4; fracture conchoidal; cleavage perfect side pinacoidal; translucent to transparent; splintery or flaky.

**BRONZITE:** Variety of *enstatite, q.v.* Shows strong submetallic brownish luster. A silicate of magnesium and iron.

**BROOKITE:** Titanium oxide, $TiO_2$; orthorhombic-rhombic bipyramidal; luster adamantine to submetallic; color black, reddish-brown; H, 5.5-6; S.G., 3.9-4.1; fracture subconchoidal to uneven; cleavage poor prismatic and basal; streak white to gray or yellowish; brittle; translucent to opaque.

**BRUCITE:** Magnesium hydroxide, $Mg(OH)_2$; hexagonal-scalenohedral; luster waxy or pearly; color greenish, blue, yellow, pearly white; H, 2.5; S.G., 2.4; cleavage micaceous; flexible, nonelastic plates; sectile; transparent; blue fluorescence.

**BYTOWNITE:** A variety of *plagioclase feldspar,* a sodium calcium silicate; triclinic; H, 6; S.G., 2.73; crystals often twinned; color white to transparent.

**CALIFORNITE:** Massive green variety of *idocrase (vesuvianite), q.v.,* in which *grossularite garnet* is intimately mixed with the hydrous calcium iron magnesium silicate.

**CALCITE:** Calcium carbonate, $CaCO_3$; hexagonal-hexagonal scalene-hedral; luster glassy; colorless; pale tints, white; H, 3; S.G., 2.7; fracture conchoidal; cleavage rhombohedral; brittle; translucent to transparent; phosphorescent.

CARNELIAN: Red to reddish-yellow variety of *chalcedony,*
   *q.v.*

CARNOTITE: Hydrous potassium uranium vanadate, $K_2$-
   $(UO_2)_2(VO_4)_2 \cdot 3H_2O$; orthorhombic (?); luster earthy; color
   bright yellow; soft; S.G., 4.1; crumbly, powdery; sectile;
   opaque; uranium fluorescent.

CASSITERITE: Tin oxide, $SnO_2$; tetragonal-ditetragonal bipyramidal; luster adamantine to greasy; color black, red-
   brown, yellowish; H, 6-7; S.G., 6.8-7.1; streak white; fracture
   subconchoidal to uneven; cleavage poor prismatic; brittle;
   translucent to transparent.

CATLINITE (PIPESTONE): Very fine-grained metamorphosed clay; luster glossy; color red; smooth texture; compact; sectile (easily carved); Minnesota *catlinite* is *sericite*
   partly replaced by *pyrophyllite* and stained with *hematite.*

CAT'S EYE: A silky chatoyancy found in such gem stones as
   *corundum, tourmaline, hypersthene, nephrite, quartz, apa-
   tite,* etc.; due to presence of inclusions, tubes, or starlike
   radiations; not to be confused with true asterism, as in *star
   sapphire.*

CELESTITE: Strontium sulphate, $SrSO_4$; orthorhombic-
   rhombic bipyramidal; luster glassy; colorless to bluish, red-
   brown, white; H, 3-3.5; S.G., 3.9-4; fracture uneven; cleavage
   perfect basal and prismatic; brittle; translucent to transparent.

CERARGYRITE: Silver chloride, AgCl; cubic-hexoctahedral;
   luster adamantine; colorless to greenish-gray or gray; H, 1-1.5;
   S.G., 5.5; fracture conchoidal; no cleavage; sectile. So also is
   BROMYRITE (silver bromide, AgBr).

CERUSSITE: Lead carbonate, $PbCO_3$; orthorhombic-rhombic-
   bipyramidal; luster adamantine; colorless, yellowish, gray,
   white; H, 3-3.5; S.G., 6.5-6.6; fracture conchoidal; cleavage
   good prismatic; brittle; translucent to transparent; fluorescent.

CHABAZITE: Hydrous silicate of calcium, sodium, aluminum
   with potassium, $(Ca,Na,K)_7Al_{12}(Al,Si)_2Si_{26}O_{80} \cdot 40H_2O$; hexagonal-hexagonal scalenohedral; luster glassy; colorless, pink,
   white; H, 4-5; S.G., 2.1-1.2; fracture uneven; cleavage good
   rhombohedral; translucent to transparent.

CHALCANTHITE: Hydrous copper sulphate, $CuSO_4 \cdot 5H_2O$; triclinic-pinacoidal; luster vitreous; color sky-blue; H, 2.5; S.G., 2.3; fracture conchoidal; cleavage three poor; translucent to transparent.

CHALCEDONY: Microcrystalline variety of *quartz, q.v.,* usually colorless to white. Banded *chalcedony* is *agate;* H, 6.5-7; S.G., 2.6; luster glassy, fracture conchoidal; translucent.

CHALCEDONY ROSES: Flowerlike growths of *chalcedony*; luster glassy; color pink, violet, sometimes *carnelian* (red) centers.

CHALCOCITE: Cuprous sulphide, $Cu_2S$; orthorhombic-bipyramidal; luster metallic; color lead-gray; H, 2.5-3; S.G., 7.2-7.4; fracture conchoidal; cleavage poor prismatic; slightly sectile.

CHALCOPYRITE: Copper iron sulphide, $CuFeS_2$; tetragonal-scalenohedral; luster metallic; color golden; H, 3.5-4; S.G., 4.1-4.3; fracture uneven; cleavage one poor; brittle.

CHALCOSIDERITE: Hydrated basic copper iron phosphate as end-product of a *turquoise* series in which all aluminum is replaced by iron, $CuFe_6(PO_4)_4(OH)_8 \cdot 4H_2O$; rare green crystals.

CHERT: Microscopically grained *quartz* without banding; luster glassy; color dull; H, 7; S.G., 2.6; fracture conchoidal; opaque.

CHESTERLITE: Variety of *orthoclase moonstone, q.v.,* of gray to black color found in Chester Co., Pennsylvania.

CHIASTOLITE: Earthy variety of *andalusite, q.v.*

CHLORASTROLITE: Possible variety of *prehnite* or related to *zeolites.* Called *greenstone* around Lake Superior, or "green star." H, 5-6; S.G., 3.2.

CHLORITE: Group name for hydrous silicates of iron, magnesium, and aluminum, $(Mg,Fe,Al)_6(Si,Al)_4O_{10}(OH)_8$; monoclinic-prismatic; luster glassy to pearly; color black, brown, green, rose, yellow, white; H, 2-2.5; S.G., 2.6-3; flexible leaves; cleavage perfect micaceous; opaque to transparent.

CHLOROPHANE: A thermoluminescent (greenish glow) *fluorite, q.v.*

CHONDRODITE: Magnesium fluosilicate, $2Mg_2SiO_4 \cdot Mg(OH,F)_2$, and member of *humite* group, *q.v.;* orthorhombic, monoclinic; luster glassy; color reddish-brown to yellow; H,

6-6.5; S.G., 3.1-3.2; fracture subconchoidal; cleavage basal; translucent to transparent.

CHROMITE: Ferrous chromic oxide, $FeCr_2O_4$; cubic-hexoctahedral; luster submetallic; color black, streak brown; H, 5.5; S.G., 4.1-4.9; fracture uneven; cleavage none; brittle.

CHRYSOBERYL: Beryllium aluminum oxide, $BeAl_2O_4$; orthorhombic-rhombic bipyramidal; luster glassy; color blue-green, gray, greenish-yellow, yellow, brown (*alexandrite* variety is violet-red in artificial light); H, 8.5; S.G., 3.5-3.8; fracture conchoidal to uneven; cleavage three fair; brittle; transparent.

CHRYSOCOLLA: Hydrous copper silicate, $CuSiO_3 \cdot 2H_2O$; orthorhombic (?); luster glassy; color green, greenish-blue, sky-blue; H, 2-4; S.G., 2-2.4; fracture conchoidal; brittle to sectile.

CHRYSOLITE: Golden-yellow variety of *olivine, q.v.*

CHRYSOPAL: Common opal stained by nickel minerals.

CHRYSOPRASE: *Chalcedony* colored a warm green by infusion of nickel silicates.

CINNABAR: Mercuric sulphide, $HgS$; hexagonal-trigonal trapezohedral; luster adamantine; color bright to brick red; H, 2.5; S.G., 8.1; fracture subconchoidal; cleavage perfect prismatic; translucent to transparent.

CINNAMON-STONE: Self-explanatory term for *grossularite garnet, q.v.*

CITRINE: *Rock crystal (quartz)* stained yellow by traces of iron.

CLEAVELANDITE: Bladed variety of *albite, q.v.*

COLEMANITE: Hydrous calcium borate, $Ca_2B_6O_{11} \cdot 5H_2O$; monoclinic-prismatic; luster glassy; colorless to white; H, 4-4.5; S.G., 2.4; fracture subconchoidal to uneven; cleavage perfect side pinacoid; brittle, transparent.

COLUMBITE: Columbate of iron and manganese, $(Fe,Mn)(Cb,Ta)_2O_6$; orthorhombic-rhombic bipyramidal; luster submetallic to resinous; colorless to black and reddish-brown; H, 6; S.G., 5-8; streak brown to black; fracture uneven; cleavage front and side pinacoid; opaque to transparent. See also *tantalite.*

CONCRETIONS: Nodular sandstone balls cemented about a nucleus, which may consist of a *fossil, agate,* or other hard substance. Takes various forms; some resemble fossil turtles.

**COPIAPITE:** Basic ferric sulphate, $(Fe,Mg)Fe_4(SO_4)_6(OH)_2\cdot10H_2O$; triclinic-pinacoidal; luster pearly; color ocher to sulphurous; H, 2.5-3; S.G., 2.1; cleavage micaceous; translucent.

**COPPER:** Element, Cu; cubic-hexoctahedral; luster metallic; color copper; H, 2.5-3; S.G., 8.9; ductile and malleable.

**CORAL:** Organic calcareous, branching structure, often found in limestone regions fossilized or silicified.

**CORDIERITE (IOLITE):** Magnesium aluminum silicate with iron, $(Mg,Fe)_2Mg_2Al_4Si_5O_{18}$; orthorhombic-rhombic bipyramidal; luster glassy; color gray and blue; H, 7-7.5; S.G., 2.6-2.7; fracture subconchoidal; cleavage poor pinacoidal; translucent to transparent; *dichroite, q.v.*

**CORUNDUM:** Aluminum oxide, $Al_2O_3$; hexagonal-scalenohedral; luster adamantine; colorless, blue, brown, black, red, violet, yellow (red is *ruby*, blue is *sapphire*); H, 9; S.G., 3.9-4.1; fracture conchoidal to uneven; cleavage none; brittle but tough; translucent to transparent; fluorescent orange, yellow, or red; triboluminescent.

**COVELLITE:** Cupric sulphide, CuS; hexagonal-dihexagonal bipyramidal; luster metallic, color blue tarnishing purple to black; H, 1.5-2; S.G., 4.6; flexible plates; cleavage basal; sectile; translucent in thin plates blue-green.

**CRISTOBALITE:** Silicon dioxide, $SiO_2$; tetragonal-trapezohedral; luster glassy; color white; H, 5-7; S.G., 2.3; translucent; often confused with *quartz* or *tridymite.*

**CRYOLITE:** Sodium aluminum fluoride, $Na_3AlF_8$; monoclinic-prismatic; luster glassy or greasy; colorless or white; H, 2.5; S.G., 2.9-3; fracture uneven; no cleavage; brittle; translucent.

**CUPRITE:** Cuprous oxide, $Cu_2O$; cubic-gyroidal; luster adamantine; color red; H, 3.5-4; S.G., 5.8-6.1; fracture conchoidal; cleavage poor octahedral; brittle; translucent.

**CYCAD WOOD:** Silicified wood of the genus *Cycadeoidaceae*; members of family have ovoid or short-columnar trunks covered by long persistent leaf bases and multicellular hairs.

**CYPRINE:** Massive blue *idocrase, q.v.*

**DANBURITE:** Calcium borosilicate, $CaB_2Si_2O_8$; orthorhombic-rhombic bipyramidal; luster glassy; colorless, gray, white, brownish, light yellow; H, 7; S.G., 3; fracture uneven to conchoidal; cleavage poor basal; translucent to transparent.

DATOLITE: Basic calcium boron silicate, $Ca_2B_2(SiO_4)_2(OH)$; monoclinic-prismatic; luster glassy to porcelaneous; colorless, yellow-green, reddish, white; H, 5-5.5; S.G., 2.8-3; fracture conchoidal to uneven; no cleavage; translucent to transparent.

DESCLOIZITE: Basic lead, copper-zinc vanadate, $(Zn,Cu)Pb(VO_4)(OH)$; orthorhombic-rhombic bipyramidal; luster greasy; color brown, black, green, cherry red, yellow-brown; H, 3.5; S.G., 6.2; streak brownish-red to yellow-orange; fracture small conchoidal areas; no cleavage; brittle; translucent to transparent. See also *mottramite*.

DIAMOND: Element, C; cubic-hextetrahedral; luster adamantine; color white to gray-black tints; H, 10; S.G., 3.52; fracture conchoidal; cleavage perfect octahedral; brittle; combustible.

DICHROITE: Blue and yellow variety of *cordierite, q.v.*

DINOSAUR BONE: Calcareous skeletal remains of Mesozoic dinosaurs preserved by silica infusions; agatized, jasperized, silicified; often highly colored, especially red (*jasper*); luster glassy; H, 7; fracture conchoidal. See *quartz*.

DIOPSIDE: Calcium magnesium silicate, $CaMgSi_2O_6$; monoclinic-prismatic; luster glassy; color green, brown, white; H, 5-6; S.G., 3.3-3.5; fracture conchoidal; cleavage perfect prismatic; translucent to transparent. See *hedenbergite*.

DIOPSIDE-JADEITE: An intermediate between *jadeite* and *diopside, q.v.* A silicate of sodium, calcium, and aluminum.

DIOPTASE: Hydrous copper silicate, $H_2CuSiO_4$; hexagonal-rhombohedral; luster glassy; color emerald-green; H, 5; S.G., 3.3-3.4; fracture conchoidal to uneven; cleavage perfect rhombohedral; translucent to transparent.

DISTHENE: *Kyanite, q.v.*

DOLOMITE: Calcium magnesium carbonate, $CaMg(CO_3)_2$; hexagonal-rhombohedral; luster glassy to pearly; colorless, pinkish; white; H, 3.5-4; S.G., 2.8; fracture conchoidal; cleavage rhombohedral; brittle; translucent to transparent.

DREIKANTER: Three-cornered stones shaped by wind-blasting; luster smooth polished; color varied but usually dark; H, 5-7; S.G., depends on variety, i.e., *jadeite, quartz family,* etc. A curio.

DUMORTIERITE: Hydrous aluminum borosilicate, $Al_8BSi_3$-$O_{19}(OH)$; orthorhombic-rhombic bipyramidal; luster glassy to pearly; color blue, violet-pink, violet; H, 7; S.G., 3.3-3.4; fracture conchoidal; cleavage poor pinacoidal; translucent.

ELBAITE: Pink *tourmaline, q.v.*

ELIXIRITE: Local New Mexico name for a *banded rhyolite, q.v.* A colorful silica gem stone similar to *wonderstone*; an alteration product of sandstone; color brown, orange-yellow, purplish-brown, yellow-brown; H, 6.5; S.G., 2.8.

EMERALD: Green *beryl, q.v.*

EMERY: Dark gray to massive black *corundum, q.v.*

ENSTATITE: Magnesium iron silicate, $Mg_2Si_2O_6$, with *hypersthene, q.v.*; orthorhombic-rhombic bipyramidal; luster glassy to silky; color bronzy, greenish, grayish, yellowish; H, 5.5-6; S.G., 3.2-3.9; fracture uneven; cleavage perfect prismatic; translucent to transparent on edges.

EOSPHORITE: Hydrous basic manganese aluminum phosphate, $(Mn,Fe)Al(PO_4)(OH)_2 \cdot H_2O$; orthorhombic-rhombic bipyramidal; luster glassy; color brown; H, 5; S.G., 3.1; fracture uneven; cleavage perfect front pinacoid; brittle; translucent to transparent.

EPIDOTE: Hydrous calcium iron silicate, $Ca_2(Al,Fe)_3(SiO_4)_3$-$(OH)$; monoclinic-prismatic; luster glassy; color greens, brown; H, 6-7; S.G., 3.4-3.5; fracture uneven; cleavage perfect basal; translucent to transparent; also called *pistacite* because of characteristic "pistachio green" color; pleiochroistic.

ESSONITE (HESSONITE): Brownish or brownish-red *grossularite garnet* of facet grade, *q.v.*

FAIRY CROSSES: *Staurolites, q.v.*

FAUSTITE: A *turquoise, q.v.*, in which zinc replaces copper, with chemical formula $ZnAl_6(PO_4)_4(OH)_8 \cdot 5H_2O$.

FIBROLITE: *Sillimanite, q.v.*

FLINT: Fine-grained quartz-rich material similar to *chert, q.v.*

FLUORITE: Calcium fluoride, $CaF_2$; cubic-hexoctahedral; luster glassy; colorless, brown, black, white, all pastel intermediate tints; H, 4; S.G., 3-3.3; fracture conchoidal; cleavage perfect octahedral; brittle; transparent; fluorescent; thermoluminescent.

FORTIFICATION AGATE: *Agate, q.v.,* in which bands take sharp abrupt turns.

FOSSILS: Any remnant, impression, or trace of plant or animal life from a former geologic age; includes *petrefactions, casts, replacements* of cell for cell, and often referred to as agatization, jasperization, silicification, etc., according to manner of preservation, color, translucency or opaqueness.

FULGARITE: Silicic tube of sandstone formed by lightning in sand, sometimes forked; luster glassy; brittle.

GABBRO-DIORITE (Orbicular): Compact white feldspar with inclusions of circular spherules of dark green *hornblende* peculiar to Davie Co., North Carolina.

GAHNITE: Dark green *spinel, q.v.*

GALAXITE: Black *spinel* grains, *q.v.,* found near Galax, New Jersey.

GALENA: Lead sulphide, PbS; cubic-hexoctahedral; luster metallic; color lead-gray; H, 2.5-2.7; S.G., 7.4-7.6; fracture even; cleavage perfect cubic; brittle.

GARNET: A series of silicates of aluminum with magnesium, iron, and manganese; with a second series of calcium silicates with aluminum, chromium, and iron; luster glassy; color (see under series names of *almandine, andradite, grossularite, pyrope, spessartite,* and *uvarovite*; also for chemical formulas); H, 6-7.5; S.G., 3.5-4.3; fracture conchoidal to uneven; no cleavage; translucent to transparent.

GEODES: Hollow concretionary or nodular stones frequently lined with *calcite, quartz,* or *amethyst* crystals.

GEYSERITE: Hot-springs opal deposited around geysers, forming terraces, basins, and cones. Basic formula: $SiO_2 \cdot nH_2O$.

GINGKO WOOD: Agatized, opalized, or silicified wood of the order Gingkoales, of which the Maidenhair tree, *Gingko biloba,* is the sole surviving member of this Mesozoic tree.

GOETHITE: Hydrogen iron oxide, $HFeO_2$; orthorhombic-rhombic bipyramidal; luster adamantine-metallic to silky; color black to brownish black; H, 5-5.5; S.G., 3.3-4.3; streak yellow to brownish-yellow; fracture uneven; cleavage side pinacoid; brittle; thinly translucent.

GOLD: Element, Au; cubic-hexoctahedral; luster metallic; color bright to silvery yellow; H, 2.5-3; S.G., 19.3; malleable and ductile.

GOLDEN BERYL: Golden yellow variety of *beryl, q.v.* Sometimes called *heliodor.*

GOSHENITE: Colorless *beryl, q.v.,* found at Goshen, Massachusetts.

GRAPHITE: Element, C; hexagonal-dihexagonal bipyramidal; luster submetallic; color black; H, 1-2; S.G., 2.3; streak black; flexible plates; cleavage perfect basal; opaque; greasy feel.

GREENSTONE: See *chlorastrolite.*

GROSSULARITE GARNET: See *garnet;* $Ca_3Al_2Si_3O_{12}$; color various pale tints but not red; S.G., 3.5. Member of the second, or calcium series of garnets.

GUMMITE: Uranium oxides with water; luster greasy to waxy; color grayish-yellow to orange-red; H, 2.5-5; S.G., 3.9-6.4; no fracture or cleavage; brittle; translucent; radioactive.

GYPSUM: Calcium sulphate, hydrous, $CaSO_4 \cdot 2H_2O$; monoclinic-prismatic; luster glassy, pearly, silky; colorless, light tints, white; H, 2; S.G., 2.3; fracture fibrous or conchoidal; cleavage two, one perfect micaceous; sectile; fluorescent.

HALITE: Sodium chloride, NaCl; cubic-hexoctahedral; luster glassy; colorless, white; H, 2.5; S.G., 2.1-1.6; fracture conchoidal; cleavage perfect cubic; brittle; transparent; soluble in water.

HAWK'S EYE: *Quartz* crystals in which hairlike inclusions are arranged in parallel streaks, exhibiting a silky luster and strong chatoyancy; also called *tiger's eye* or *falcon's eye.*

HEBRONITE: See *amblygonite;* named after Hebron, Maine.

HELIODOR: *Golden beryl, q.v.*

HELIOTROPE BAUXITE: *Bauxite, q.v.,* spotted red and green, locally named in Saline Co., Arkansas.

HEDENBERGITE: Calcium iron silicate, $CaFeSi_2O_6$; member of *diopside, q.v.,* series.

HEMATITE: Ferric oxide, $Fe_2O_3$; hexagonal-scalenohedral; luster earthy or metallic; color black, red; H, 1-6.5; S.G., 4.9-5.3; streak red; fracture conchoidal to uneven; no cleavage; brittle.

HEMIMORPHITE: Hydrous zinc silicate, $Zn_4Si_2O_7(OH)_2 \cdot H_2O$; luster glassy; color white, often stained; H, 4.5-5; S.G., 3.4-3.5; fracture uneven, poor conchoidal; cleavage prismatic; translucent to transparent.

HERDERITE: Calcium beryllium fluophosphate, $CaBe(PO_4)$-(OH,F); monoclinic-prismatic; luster greasy to glassy; colorless, bluish-green, yellowish, white; H, 5-5.5; S.G., 2.9-3; fracture subconchoidal; cleavage partially prismatic; brittle; translucent to transparent; may fluoresce deep blue.

HESSONITE: See *essonite.*

HEULANDITE: Hydrous silicate of sodium, calcium, potassium and aluminum, $(Ca,Na,K)_6Al_{10}(Al,Si)Si_{29}O_{80} \cdot 25H_2O$; monoclinic-prismatic; luster glassy; color reddish, yellowish, white; H, 3.5-4; S.G., 2.2; streak white; fracture subconchoidal to uneven; cleavage perfect side pinacoid; translucent to transparent.

HEXAGONITE: Lilac variety of *tremolite, q.v.*

HIDDENITE: Green gemmy *spodumene, q.v.*

HORNBLENDE: A series of aluminous amphiboles lumped together, $CaNa(Mg,Fe)_4(Al,Fe,Ti)_3Si_6O_{22}(O,OH)_2$; monoclinic-prismatic; luster glassy; color green (*edenite*), bluish-green (*paragasite*), black; H, 5-6; S.G., 2-3.4; fracture subconchoidal to uneven; cleavage prismatic; edges translucent to transparent.

HORN SILVER: *Cerargyrite-bromyrite, q.v.*, so named because of its waxy or hornlike appearance.

HORSE CANYON AGATE: *Moss agate, q.v.*, of unique beauty found in Horse Canyon, off Cache Creek Canyon, Kern Co., California.

HOWLITE: Calcium silicoborate, $Ca_2SiB_5O_9(OH)_5$; monoclinic; luster dull to subvitreous; color white with black streaks; H, 3.5; S.G., 2.5-2.6; fracture even; no cleavage; translucent to opaque.

HUMITE: A group of magnesium fluosilicates that includes *chondrodite, clinohumite, humite,* and *norbergite, q.v.* *Humite* is $3Mg_2SiO_4 \cdot Mg(OH,F)_2$; orthorhombic and monoclinic; luster glassy; color reddish-brown to yellow; H, 6-6.5; S.G., 3.1-3.2; fracture subconchoidal; cleavage basal; translucent to transparent.

HYACINTH: Orange to reddish-brown *grossularite garnet, q.v.*

HYALITE: Clear, colorless *opal, q.v.* Also called *water opal.*

HYDROPHANE: Chalky white, opaque *opal* (*cachalong* type) which is water-absorbent, becoming clear after soaking when some may show typical opalescent color play.

HYDROZINCITE: Basic zinc carbonate, $Zn_5(OH)_6(CO_3)_2$; monoclinic; luster dull; color light grey, yellowish, white; H, 2-2.5; S.G., 3.6-3.8; fracture irregular; no cleavage; earthy; translucent; fluorescent blue.

HYPERSTHENE: Magnesium iron silicate, $(Mg,Fe)_2Si_2O_6$; orthorhombic-rhombic bipyramidal; see *enstatite*.

IDOCRASE (VESUVIANITE): Hydrous calcium, iron, magnesium silicate, $Ca_{10}Al_4(Mg,Fe)_2Si_9O_{34}(OH)$; tetragonal-ditetragonal bipyramidal; luster glassy; color blue (*cyprine*), brown, green, yellow; H, 6.5; S.G., 3.4-3.5; fracture conchoidal to uneven; cleavage poor prismatic; translucent to transparent.

ILMENITE: Iron titanium oxide, $FeTiO_3$; hexagonal-rhombohedral; luster metallic to submetallic; color brownish-black to black; H, 5-6; S.G., 4.1-4.8; streak brownish-red to ocher yellow, or black; fracture conchoidal to subconchoidal; no cleavage; brittle; weakly magnetic.

INDICOLITE: Blue *tourmaline, q.v.*

IOLITE: *Cordierite, q.v.*

IRON: Element, Fe, rare except in *meteorites;* cubic-hexoctahedral; luster metallic; color steel-gray; H, 4-5; S.G., 7.3-7.8; fracture hackly; cleavage cubic; magnetic.

IRON ROSES: Thin flat scaly growths of *hematite, q.v.*

ISOPYRE: Impure *common opal, q.v.*, found in Morris Co., New Jersey.

JADE: See *jadeite* and *nephrite*; a term collectively applied to both minerals which are chemically distinct. *Jadeite* is a *pyroxene* while *nephrite* belongs to the amphibole group close to *actinolite, q.v.*

JADEITE: Sodium aluminum silicate, $NaAlSi_2O_6$; monoclinic-prismatic; luster glassy to silky; color green (light, malachite, emerald), lilac, reddish-brown, yellow-brown, violet, white; H, 6.5-7; S.G., 3.3-3.5; fracture difficult as toughness is characteristic, hence splintery; cleavage prismatic; translucent to opaque.

JAMESONITE: Lead, antimony, iron sulphide, $Pb_4FeSb_6S_{14}$; monoclinic; prismatic; luster metallic; color dark gray; H, 2.5; S.G., 5.5-6; cleavage across elongation; brittle.

JAROSITE: Basic hydrous sulphate of iron and potassium, $KFe_3(SO_4)_2(OH)_6$; hexagonal-ditrigonal pyramidal; luster vitreous to subadamantine; color clove brown to ocher yellow; H, 2.5-3.5; S.G., 2.9-3.3; fracture uneven; cleavage perfect basal; sectile or brittle; translucent.

JASP-AGATE: Intermediate between *agate, q.v.,* and *jasper, q.v.;* luster glassy, fracture conchoidal, H, 7; translucent to opaque; an opaque moss or plume *agate.*

JASPER: Silicified material ranging from pure *chalcedony, q.v.,* to consolidations of miscellaneous material into hard (7), compact, colorful masses; an impure *chalcedony* of slight translucency and no banding, related to *chert* and *flint.*

JASPILLITE: *Specularite, q.v.,* which is a basic jaspery material laced with bands of dark steel-gray *hematite.*

JELINITE: Brownish to yellowish dark-colored *amber, q.v.,* found in Ellsworth Co., Kansas; luster resinous to waxy; fracture conchoidal; cloudy to translucent.

JET: Variety of *lignite, q.v.,* a woody coal; streak brown; H, 3-4; S.G., 1.3; color dull black; combustible; easily carved and takes a high polish.

JOSEPHINITE: A nickel-iron alloy found as nuggets in placers; see *iron.*

KAOLIN: Hydrous aluminum silicate, $Al_2Si_2O_5(OH)_4$; monoclinic-prismatic; luster dull; color white or stained black, brown, or red; H, 2-2.5; S.G., indeterminable, but usually taken as 2.6; earthy, cleavage micaceous; opaque.

KAOLINITE: Principal clay mineral, basically aluminum silicate; color brown, gray, red, yellow, white; an alteration product of *microcline* or *orthoclase;* strong clay odor when damp.

KIMBERLITE: Variety of *peridotite, q.v.,* in which *diamond* occurs.

KINRADITE: San Francisco, California, Bay regional chert in which colorful spherules are small; found in Marin Co.

KUNZITE: Gemmy lilac crystals of *spodumene, q.v.,* pinkish to pale purple.

KYANITE: Aluminum silicate, $Al_2SiO_5$; triclinic-pinacoidal; luster glassy; colorless to bluish or greenish in splotches; H, 5 lengthwise, 7 across prism; S.G., 3.6-3.7; fracture splintery across crystals; cleavage perfect pinacoidal; translucent to transparent.

LABRADORITE: Member of *plagioclase* series, *q.v.* coarsely crystalline; color blue (butterfly's wing); H, 6; S.G., 2.71.

LACE AGATE: *Agate, q.v.*, containing ribbonlike and flower-like patterns enclosed in translucent *chalcedony*; basically the same as *banded agate*.

LAKE SUPERIOR AGATE: *Keeweenaw agate* (Michigan and Minnesota), a name applied to characteristic chalcedonic material of exceptional beauty and design.

LAZULITE: A high magnesium phosphate, $(Mg,Fe)Al_2(PO_4)_2$-$(OH)_2$; monoclinic-prismatic; luster glassy; color blue; H, 5.5-6; S.G., 3.1-3.4; fracture uneven; cleavage poor prismatic; brittle; translucent to transparent. See *scorzalite*.

LAZURITE (LAPIS LAZULI): Sodium aluminum silicate, $Na_{4-5}Al_3Si_3O_{12}S$; cubic-hexoctahedral; luster glassy; color blue, greenish blue, violet-blue; H, 5-5.5; S.G., 2.4-2.5; fracture uneven; cleavage poor dodecahedral; translucent.

LEOPARDITE: A black-spotted *quartz porphry* found at Belmont Springs, Mecklenburg Co., North Carolina.

LEPIDOLITE: Hydrous fluosilicate of lithium, potassium, and aluminum, $K_2Li_3Al_4Si_7O_{21}(OH,F)_3$; monoclinic domatic; luster pearly to vitreous; color gray-green, lilac, light yellow; H, 2.5; S.G., 2.8-3.3; elastic plates; cleavage perfect basal or micaceous; translucent to transparent.

LEUCITE: Potassium aluminum silicate, $KALSi_2O_6$; tetragonal-trapezohedral; luster glassy; colorless to gray and white; H, 5.5-6; S.G., 2.4-2.5; fracture conchoidal; cleavage imperfect dodecahedral; translucent to transparent.

LIGNITE: A low-grade coal in which woody structure is distinct.

LIME-DRAVITE: White *tourmaline, q.v.*, $CaMg_3B_3Al_3(Al_3Si_6$-$O_{27})(O,OH)_4$.

LIMONITE: Various hydrous ferric oxides, $FeO(OH)\cdot nH_2O$; amorphous; luster dull to glassy; color brownish-black to yellow; H, 2-5.5; S.G., 2.7-4.3; streak brown to yellow; fracture conchoidal; earthy; no cleavage; brittle; *limonite cubes* as pseudomorphs after *pyrite*.

LINTONITE: Variety of *thomsonite, q.v.*; extremely compact; olive-green; translucent.

LITCHFIELDITE: A soda-rich *syenite* found at Litchfield, Kennebec Co., Maine.

LITHARGE: Lead oxide, PbO; orthorhombic-rhombic bipyramidal; forming red edge of *massicot* scales.

LITHIA TOURMALINE: Red, green, to blue *tourmaline, q.v.*, with basic formula $Na(Al, Fe, Li, Mg)_3B_3Al_3(Al_3Si_6O_{27})(O,OH,F)_4$.

LLANITE: An igneous rock in Llano Co., Texas; a reddish porphry containing reddish *microcline, albite, orthoclase, quartz,* and flakes of *biotite mica.*

LODESTONE: Variety of *magnetite, q.v.*

MAGNESITE: Magnesium carbonate, $MgCO_3$; hexagonal-hexagonal scalenohedral; luster dull to glassy; colorless, light tints, white; H, 3.5-5; S.G., 3-3.2; fracture conchoidal to smooth; cleavage rhombohedral; brittle; translucent to transparent.

MAGNETITE: Iron oxide (ferrous and ferric), $Fe_3O_4$; cubic-hexoctahedral; luster metallic; color black; H, 6; S.G., 5.2; streak black; fracture subconchoidal to uneven; cleavage none; brittle; magnetic; also sometimes called *lodestone, q.v.*

MALACHITE: Basic copper carbonate, $Cu_2Co_3(OH)_2$; monclinic; luster silky to vitreous; color dark green; H, 3.5-4; S.G., 3.9-4; fracture splintery; cleavage basal; brittle; translucent.

MALACOLITE: White fluorescent crystals of *diopside, q.v.*

MANGANAPATITE: Variety of *apatite, q.v.*, in which crystals resemble green *tourmaline,* but are softer; H, 5.

MARCASITE: Iron sulphide, $FeS_2$; orthorhombic-bipyramidal; luster metallic; color brass-yellow; H, 6-6.5; S.G., 4.9; fracture uneven; cleavage poor prismatic; brittle.

MAREKANITE: Mahogany *obsidian, q.v.*, in which both black and reddish-brown streaks and swirls occur.

MARGARITE: Hydrous calcium aluminum silicate, $CaAl_4Si_2O_{10}(OH)_2$; monoclinic-prismatic; luster pearly; color gray, pink, violet, white; H, 3.5 (cleavage face), 5 (prism face); S.G., 3-3.1; no fracture; cleavage perfect micaceous; translucent to transparent; brittle.

MARMOLITE: Micaceous *serpentine, q.v.*

MELANITE: Black *andradite garnet, q.v.*

MERCURY: Element obtainable by direct heating of *cinnabar,* Hg; hexagonal-rhombohedral (frozen at -40° F); luster metallic; color silver-white; liquid; S.G., 13.6.

MESOLITE: *Zeolite* family, *q.v.,* sodium calcium aluminum silicate, $(Na,Ca)_2Al_2Si_3O_{10} \cdot 3H_2O$; monoclinic; luster glassy; colorless, cream, green, yellow, white; H, 5; S.G., 2.2; cleavage prismatic; closely related to *natrolite, q.v.*

METEORITES: Stony or iron-nickel masses from outer space, usually iron with nickel or chromium, and magnetic. Etching of a polished surface by acid shows a crystal pattern, known as Widmanstaetten lines.

MICROCLINE: Potassium aluminum silicate, $KAlSi_3O_8$; triclinicpinacoidal; luster glassy; color flesh, green, red-brown, white; H, 6; S.G., 2.5-2.6; fracture conchoidal; cleavage two good at near 90°, poor prismatic; translucent.

MICROLITE: Complex tantalum oxide with calcium, sodium, oxygen, and hydroxyl, $(Na,Ca)_2Ta_2O_6(O,OH,F)$; cubic-hexoctahedral; luster resinous; color greenish-yellow, yellow, yellow-brown; H, 5-5.5; S.G., 4.2-6.4; fracture subconchoidal to uneven; cleavage none; brittle; translucent to transparent.

MILKY QUARTZ: Crystallized *quartz* of milky coloration, *q.v.*

MILLERITE: Nickel sulphide, NiS; hexagonal-dihexagonal bipyramidal; luster metallic; color brass-yellow; H, 3-3.5; S.G., 5.3-5.6; fracture uneven; cleavage two rhombohedral; brittle.

MOLYBDENITE: Molybdenum disulphide, $MoS_2$; hexagonal-dihexagonal bipyramidal; luster metallic; color lead-gray; H, 1-1.5; S.G., 4.7-4.8; a streak gray; flexible leaves; cleavage perfect micaceous basal; sectile.

MONAZITE: Cerium lanthanum phosphate, (Ce,La,Y,Th)$(PO_4)$; monoclinic-prismatic; luster subadamantine to resinous; color reddish-brown to yellow; H, 5-5.5; S.G., 4.9-5.3; streak yellow-brown; fracture conchoidal to uneven; cleavage one good; brittle; translucent to transparent.

MONTANA MOSS AGATE: Black mossy *agate, q.v.,* peculiar to Yellowstone River in Montana; contains dendritic growths of manganese oxide showing clouds, bands, and scenery of bright brownish-orange, reddish-brown, to black suspended in clear *chalcedony.*

MOONSTONE: Adularescent *feldspar, q.v.,* variety *orthoclase;* color silvery-blue.

MORDENITE: Member of *zeolite* family, *q.v.,* and closely related to *heulandite, q.v.;* color white to cream; found as nodules.

MORGANITE: Pink *beryl, q.v.*

MORRISONITE: Colorful banded *chert, q.v.,* found near Ashwood, Oregon.

MOSS AGATE: Generic term to describe all *chalcedony, q.v.,* containing mossy or dendritic growths. Where growths show delicate plumes billowing upward through clear *chalcedony,* it is known as *plume agate.*

MOSS OPAL: *Common opal, q.v.,* penetrated with dendritic growths similar to those that form in *agate* or *jasper.*

MOTTRAMITE: Basic lead, copper, zinc vanadate, $(Cu,Zn)Pb(VO_4)(OH)$; see *descloizite.*

NATROLITE: Hydrous sodium aluminum silicate, $Na_2al_2Si_3O_{10} \cdot 10H_2O$; orthorhombic-rhombic pyramidal; luster glassy; colorless to white; H, 5-5.5; S.G., 2.2; fracture uneven; cleavage good prismatic; translucent to transparent; fluorescent orange.

NEPHRITE: Intermediate "jade mineral" between *actinolite* and *tremolite, q.v.,* and member of amphibole group; a calcium magnesium silicate with some iron; luster glassy; color greenish to dark green to black; H, 5-6; S.G., 2.9-3; fracture splintery as material is fibrous and extremely tough; monoclinic.

NEPTUNITE: Sodium, potassium, iron manganese titanosilicate; $(Na,K)(Fe,Mn,Ti)Si_2O_6$; monoclinic-prismatic; luster glassy, color black, reddish; H, 5-6; S.G., 3.2; fracture splintery; cleavage perfect prismatic; translucent on edges.

NICCOLITE: Nickel arsenide, NiAs; hexagonal-dihexagonal bipyramidal; luster metallic; color copper; H, 5-5.5; S.G., 7.8; fracture uneven; no cleavage; brittle.

NITER: Potassium nitrate, $KNO_3$; orthorhombic-rhombic bipyramidal; luster glassy; color white; H, 2; S.G., 2.1; fracture none; cleavage good; sectile; known as "saltpeter."

NORBERGITE: Member of *humite* group, *q.v.*, $Mg_2SiO_4 \cdot Mg(OH,F)_2$.

NOVACULITE: Pure white porous *quartz* cemented with *chalecedony*, known as "Arkansas stone," often colorfully stained and dendritic; occurs brecciated in shades of black, brown, green, gray, orange, red, and yellow.

OBSIDIAN: Extrusive, glassy igneous volcanic rock, mostly silica and alumina with small quantities of iron oxide, potassium and sodium oxides, lime, and magnesia. Occurs in colors of black (mostly), red to brown streaked, snowflake or flowering, rainbow, black with gold or silvery inclusions, etc. No crystalline structure, hence considered a rock rather than a mineral; fracture conchoidal; H, 5; S.G., 2.3-2.4; brittle; nodular (Apache tears) or massive as in Yellowstone Park.

OLIGOCLASE: A *plagioclase* series member of sodium aluminum silicate, next to *albite, q.v.*, $NaAlSi_3O_8$; triclinic-pinacoidal; luster glassy; color bluish to clear, or reddish-gold *(sunstone)*; H, 6; S.G., 2.65; fracture conchoidal; cleavage two good at 94°, two poor prismatic; translucent to transparent.

OLIVINE: Name applied to a series of magnesium iron silicates, $(Mg,Fe)_2SiO_4$; luster glassy; color brown, green, light gray; H, 6.5-7; S.G., 3.3-3.4; fracture conchoidal; cleavage one fair, one poor; translucent to transparent. NOTE: Gem *peridot* is the *chrysolite* variety of olivine, while *dunite* is a pure olivine rock.

ONYX: Variety of *calcite, q.v.*, or a type of *chalcedony* showing strongly constrasting straight color bands, usually black and white. *Calcite onyx* is soft, like marble (3), whereas siliceous *(agate)* onyx ("true onyx") has a hardness of 6-7. *Cave onyx* is cold water deposited *travertine,* brown in color.

OÖLITE: Silicified *limestone* containing small spherical concretions; color red or black. The name refers to its appearance like fish roe, and "oölitic" may be applied to *jaspers, cherts,* and *flint.*

OPAL: Silicon dioxide, $SiO_2 \cdot nH_2O$; amorphous; luster glassy to resinous; colorless and all light tints, rainbow, fire, black; H, 5-6; S.G., 1.9-2.2; fracture conchoidal; translucent to transparent; fluorescent yellow-green. There are two types; *com-*

*mon opal* and clear opal or *hyaline,* while the finest type is termed *precious opal* and shows a brilliant display of colors. *Precious opal* is subdivided into *white opal, black opal,* and *fire opal;* completely colorless and transparent opal is known as *hyalite* or *water opal.* Chalky white, opaque opal is *cachalong; prase opal* or *chloropal* is greenish *common opal.*

OPALITE (MYRICKITE): Impure forms, usually massive, of *common opal;* often colored red by inclusions of *cinnabar.*

OPALIZED WOOD: Petrified wood in which opal, often colorfully stained, has replaced the cell structure.

ORBICULAR JASPER: *Jasper, q.v.,* containing spherules of earthy matter as nuclei for radial growth of *chalcedony-type quartz* crystallizations; also known as *"fish-egg" jasper, "flower" jasper,* or *"poppy" jasper.* Closely related is *orbicular chert.*

ORBICULAR RHYOLITE: A *copper rhyolite,* consisting of small oval amygdules of clear *quartz, epidote,* and *copper* ores in a colorful pattern; color patchy green, orange, and red.

ORPIMENT: Arsenic trisulphide, $As_2S_3$; monoclinic-prismatic; luster resinous to pearly; color yellow to orange-yellow; H, 1.5-2; S.G., 3.4-3.5; flexible leaves; cleavage perfect micaceous; sectile; translucent to transparent.

ORTHOCLASE: Potassium aluminum silicate, $KAlSi_3O_8$; monoclinic-prismatic; luster glassy; colorless, brown, flesh, yellow, white; H, 6; S.G., 2.6; fracture conchoidal; cleavage two good at 90°, fair prismatic; translucent to transparent.

PECTOLITE: Hydrous calcium sodium silicate, $Ca_2NaSi_3O_8$ (OH); triclinic-pinacoidal; luster silky; color gray to white; H, 5; S.G., 2.7-2.8; fracture splintery; fibrous; translucent.

PERIDOT: *Chrysolite* variety of *olivine,* often found as gemmy crystals, color bright yellow-green.

PERIDOTITE (PYROXENITE): Dark rock composed principally of *olivine, q.v.,* and *pyroxene, q.v.;* a matrix of *diamonds.*

PERLITE: Porous, puffy, lightweight *obsidian, q.v.,* an alteration material due to weathering and entrapment of air; often contains *Apache tear* nodules and larger masses of *obsidian.*

PERTHITE: A variety of *feldspars* in which several species, *e.g.*, *albite* and *microcline*, are interbraided and crisscrossed; see *amazonite*. Colors green, flesh-red, green and white.

PETALITE: Lithium aluminum silicate, $LiAl(Si_2O_5)_2$; monoclinic; luster glassy, color white; H, 6-6.5; S.G., 2.4-2.5; shatters; cleavage perfect; brittle; transparent to pearly masses; may be called *castorite*. Sometimes confused with *spodumene*, *q.v.*

PETOSKEY AGATE: A *coral limestone* found in Michigan, called thus although no *agate* is present.

PETOSKEY STONES: More appropriate term for *petoskey agates, q.v.*, since they are found near Petoskey, Emmet Co., Michigan.

PETRIFIED WOOD: General term referring to all fossilized wood; however, there should be a distinction between gemmy *agatized, opalized,* and *silicified* woods of hardness 7 and "petrifactions." The latter type is wood preserved by such infiltrating agencies as iron oxide, iron sulphide, calcium carbonate, magnesium carbonate, uranium oxides *(carnotite)*, vanadium and manganese oxides; altogether there are some 20 petrifying mineral substances which preserve woody structures from decay. *Carnotite wood* is especially rich in uranium, vanadium, and radium and is radioactive; colored bright lemon yellow; H, 2-3.

PHENAKITE: Beryllium silicate, $Be_2SiO_4$; hexagonal-rhombohedral; luster glassy; colorless, white; H, 7.5-8; S.G., 3; fracture conchoidal; cleavage poor prismatic; transparent to translucent. Prismatic crystals are main distinguishing characteristic; resembles *quartz*.

PHLOGOPITE: Hydrous potassium, magnesium, aluminum silicate, $KMg_3AlSi_3O_{10}(OH)_2$; monoclinic-prismatic; luster pearly to metallic; color brown; H, 2.5-3; S.G., 2.7; flexible elastic leaves; cleavage perfect basal; translucent.

PHOSPHURANYLITE: Hydrous calcium uranium phosphate of indeterminate composition, $Ca,(UO_2),(PO_4)\cdot xH_2O$; orthorhombic; luster glassy; color light yellow; H, soft; cleavage basal; brittle; transparent. Usually found as a crust, nonfluorescent.

PICROLITE: Columnar *serpentine, q.v.*

PIEDMONTITE: Calcium aluminum manganese silicate, $Ca_2(Al,Mn)_3(SiO_4)_3(OH)$; reddish variety of *epidote, q.v.* Luster glassy to greasy; H, 6-7; S.G., 3.2-3.5; fracture conchoidal; cleavage one perfect; translucent to transparent monoclinic crystals.

PINITE: Greenish mica pseudomorphs after *spodumene, q.v.*

PISOLITE: A limestone composed of rounded concretions about the size of a pea, giving rise to the adjective "pisolitic."

PISTACITE: Distinctively "pistachio green" *epidote, q.v.*

PITCHBLENDE: Impure *uraninite, q.v.,* in black pitchlike masses.

PITCHSTONE: Dull, partially altered *obsidian, q.v.*

PLAGIOCLASE: A continuous series of sodium calcium aluminum silicates from *albite* ($NaAlSi_3O_8$), through *oligoclase, andesine, labradorite, bytownite* to *anorthite* ($CaAl_2Si_2O_8$); triclinic-pinacoidal; luster glassy; color black, reddish-gray, yellow, white; H, 6; S.G., 2.6-2.8; fracture conchoidal; cleavage two good at 94°, two poor prismatic; translucent to transparent.

PLATINUM: Element, Pt; cubic-hexoctahedral; luster metallic; color grayish-white; H, 4-4.5; S.G., 14-19 (usually very impure); fracture hackly; no cleavage; malleable, ductile.

PLUMBAGO: Old name for *graphite, q.v.,* meaning "black lead."

PLUME AGATE: A moss *agate* in which the mossy dendritic growths form delicate lacy plumes in clear *chalcedony, q.v.*

POLKA-DOT AGATE: *Agate, q.v.,* characterized by spheroids of opaque *chalcedony* embedded in translucent *chalcedony*. The inclusions may be colored brown, red, reddish-brown, brownish-black, yellow.

POLYHALITE: Hydrous sulphate of potassium, calcium, and magnesium, $K_2Ca_2Mg(SO_4)_4 \cdot 2H_2O$; triclinic-pinacoidal; luster resinous; colorless to white; H, 3.5; S.G., 2.8; splintery; one good cleavage.

PRASE: *Quartz, q.v.,* containing millions of dark grayish-green *actinolite* inclusions.

PRECIOUS OPAL: Supreme form of *opal, q.v.,* reserved for specimens showing color play.

PREHNITE: Hydrous calcium aluminum silicate, $Ca_2Al_2Si_3$-

$O_{10}(OH)_2$; orthorhombic-rhombic pyramidal; luster glassy; color greens, white; H, 6-6.5; S.G., 2.8-2.9; fracture uneven; cleavage basal; translucent to nearly transparent.

PROUSTITE: Silver arsenic sulphide, $Ag_3AsS_3$; hexagonal-ditrigonal pyramidal; luster adamantine; color reds; H, 2-2.5; S.G., 5.6-5.7; fracture conchoidal; cleavage rhombohedral; brittle; translucent to transparent.

PSILOMELANE: Basic barium oxide plus manganese, $BaMn$-$Mn_8O_{16}(OH)_4$; orthorhombic; luster dull to submetallic; color black to steel gray; H, 5-6; S.G., 3.3-4.7; streak brownish-black to black; fracture conchoidal to smooth; no cleavage; brittle.

PYRITE: Iron sulphide, $FeS_2$; cubic-diploidal; luster metallic; color bright yellow; H, 6-6.5; S.G., 5; fracture conchoidal; no cleavage; brittle; also termed "fool's gold."

PYROLUSITE: Manganese dioxide, $MnO_2$; tetragonal-ditetragonal bipyramidal; luster metallic; color steel gray to black; streak black; H, 6-6.5; S.G., 4.4-5; fracture uneven; cleavage prismatic; brittle to soft.

PYROMORPHITE: Lead chlorophosphate, $Pb_5PO_4,AsO_4)_3Cl$; hexagonal-hexagonal bipyramidal; luster resinous; color greens, gray, brown; H, 3.5-4; S.G., 6.5-7.1; fracture subconchoidal to uneven; cleavage prismatic; brittle; translucent.

PYROPE GARNET: See *garnet*. Magnesium aluminum silicate, deep red color, $Mg_3Al_2Si_3O_{12}$; S.G., 3.5.

PYROPHYLLITE: Hydrous aluminum silicate, $Al_2Si_4O_{10}$-$(OH)_2$; monoclinic-prismatic; luster pearly to greasy; color greenish, silvery, white (often stained brown to black); H, 1-2; S.G., 2.8-2.9; flexible flakes; cleavage perfect micaceous; opaque to translucent.

PYROXENE: Group name for a series of magnesium and magnesium iron silicates: *enstatite-hypersthene, diopside-hedenbergite, augite, acmite-aegirite, jadeite, spodumene, rhodonite, q.v.*

QUARTZ: Silicon dioxide, $SiO_2$; hexagonal-trigonal trapezohedral; luster glassy; colorless, clear, amethyst, rose, brown, smoky, black, white, almost any tint due to impurities; H, 7; S.G., 2.6; fracture conchoidal; cleavage rhombohedral; transparency dependent on impurities and color. Four types of quartz include the following:

CRYSTALLINE: *amethyst, asteriated quartz, aventurine, citrine, cristobalite, ferruginous quartz, rock crystal; sagenite, smoky quartz, tridymite.*

CRYPTOCRYSTALLINE-AMORPHOUS: *agate, bloodstone (heliotrope), chalcedony, chrysoprase, gastroliths, jasper* and subvarieties, *plasma, prase.*

INTERMEDIATE FORMS: *chert, diatomite, flint, novaculite, siliceous sinter, tripolite.*

MASSIVE QUARTZ: *milky quartz, quartzite, rose quartz, sandstone.*

QUARTZ PORPHYRY: See *leopardite.*

QUARTZITE: Metamorphosed sandstone cemented by silica so that breakage is through, not around, the individual grains; often highly colored by impurities. For characteristics, see *quartz.*

RAINBOW OBSIDIAN: Iridescent *obsidian, q.v.*

REALGAR: Arsenic sulphide, AsS; monoclinic-prismatic; luster resinous; color orange-red; H, 1,5-2; S.G., 3.5; fracture subconchoidal; cleavage perfect side, fair basal; sectile; translucent to transparent.

RETINALITE: Waxy, translucent *serpentine, q.v.*, bright yellow to yellow-green.

RHODOCHROSITE: Manganese carbonate, $MnCO_3$; hexagonal-hexagonal scalenohedral; luster vitreous to pearly; color brown, gray, pinks; H, 3.5-4; S.G., 3.4-3.6; fracture conchoidal; cleavage perfect rhombohedral; brittle; translucent to transparent.

RHODOLITE: Pale red to rose *garnet, q.v.*

RHODONITE: Manganese silicate, $MnSiO_3$; triclinic-pinacoidal; luster glassy; color gray to pink; H, 5.5-6; S.G., 3.4-3.7; fracture splintery; cleavage prismatic; brittle; translucent to transparent.

RHYOLITE: Light-colored felsitic extrusive igneous rock, often characterized by flow lines.

RICOLITE: Fine-grained, curiously banded *serpentine, q.v.*, found near Rico, New Mexico.

ROCKBRIDGEITE: Variety of *dufrenite, q.v.*

ROCK CRYSTAL: Transparent colorless *quartz, q.v.*

ROSE QUARTZ: Massive rose pink, translucent to transparent *quartz, q.v.*

ROSOLITE: Rose pink *grossularite garnet, q.v.*

RUBELLITE: Red *tourmaline, q.v.*

RUBY: Red *corundum, q.v.*

RUBY-ZINC: Bright red *sphalerite, q.v.*

RUTILATED QUARTZ: *Rock crystal (quartz, q.v.)* containing needlelike inclusions of *rutile, q.v.*

RUTILE: Titanium oxide, $TiO_2$; tetragonal-ditetragonal bipyramidal; luster metallic-adamantine; color black, golden to brownish-red; H, 6-6.5; S.G., 4.2-4.3; streak brownish; fracture subconchoidal to uneven; cleavage basal and prismatic; brittle; thinly translucent to transparent.

SAGENITE: All *quartz* containing needlelike inclusions is collectively known by this term. Usually, however, it relates to *sagenitic agate,* or *chalcedony sagenite,* in which slender needles of foreign mineral materials penetrate and crisscross in translucent *chalcedony.*

SAGENITIC AGATE: See *sagenite.*

SANIDINE: Variety of *orthoclase, q.v.,* peculiar to volcanic rocks as flat tabular crystals, bluish. See *moonstone.*

SAPPHIRE: Blue *corundum, q.v.*

SARD: Pale brown *chalcedony, q.v.*

SARDONYX: *Sard* or *carnelian, q.v.,* showing alternating white bands.

SATELITE: Fibrous *serpentine, q.v.,* silky, grayish-green, opaque, chatoyant.

SATIN SPAR: Fibrous variety of *calcite, q.v.;* term also applied to a silky variety of gypsum.

SCAPOLITE: Group name for a series of aluminum silicates with sodium and calcium (*meionite, missonite, marialite,* and *wernerite*); tetragonal; luster dull to greasy; color gray, milky, blue, pink, violet, yellow, white; H, 5.5-6; S.G., 2.7; fracture subconchoidal; cleavage poor prismatic, translucent to transparent; may fluoresce orange to yellow, and red.

SCHEELITE: Calcium tungstate, $CaWO_4$; tetragonal-tetragonal bipyramidal; luster adamantine; color brownish, greenish, white; H, 4.5-5; S.G., 5.9-6.1; fracture uneven; cleavage three; translucent to transparent; fluorescent blue to yellow.

SCHORL: Black *tourmaline, q.v.*

SCORODITE: Hydrous ferric arsenate, $Fe(AsO_4)\cdot2H_2O$; orthorhombic-rhombic bipyramidal; luster glassy to subadamantine; color brownish-green to green; H, 3.5-4; S.G., 3.1-3.3; fracture uneven; cleavage poor; brittle; translucent to transparent.

SCORZALITE: High-iron magnesium aluminum phosphate, $(Fe,Mg)Al_2(PO_4)_2(OH)_2$; see *lazulite.*

SELENITE: Variety of *gypsum, q.v.,* occurring as transparent crystals, monoclinic; H, 2; glassy.

SERPENTINE: Hydrous magnesium silicate, $Mg_3Si_2O_5(OH)_4$; monoclinic-prismatic; luster greasy, silky, waxy; color brown, black, red, yellow, green, white; H, 2-5; S.G., 2.2-2.6; fibrous; cleavage none; opaque to translucent; sometimes fluorescent; greasy feel; includes *antigorite* (platy), *chrysotile (asbestos), marmolite* (micaceous), *ophiolite, picrolite, retinalite, williamsite.* The popular *verde antique* type is used in building decoration, meaning "ancient green."

SHALE: Solidified clay, always bedded sedimentary.

SIDERITE: Iron carbonate, $FeCO_3$; hexagonal-hexagonal scalenohedral; luster vitreous to pearly; color brown, gray, white; H, 3.5-4; S.G., 3.8-3.9; fracture conchoidal; cleavage rhombohedral; brittle; translucent to transparent.

SILICEOUS OÖLITE: Limestone in which many spherical concretions are replaced by silica; color black, red.

SILICEOUS SINTER: Variety of *geyserite, q.v.,* an *opal* that occurs on dry lake bed surfaces in the western states.

SILICIFIED CORAL: Fossil coral replaced by *chalcedony, q.v.*

SILLIMANITE: Aluminum silicate, $Al_2SiO_5$; orthorhombic-rhombic bipyramidal; luster satiny; color brownish, greenish, white; H, 6-7; S.G., 3.2-3.3; fracture splintery; cleavage perfect pinacoid; translucent to transparent.

SILVER: Element, Ag; cubic-hexoctahedral; luster metallic; color bright white, usually tarnished to black; H, 2.5-3; S.G., 10-11; malleable and ductile.

SLATE: Metamorphosed clay, resembling shale; characterized by small mica flakes.

SMITHSONITE: Zinc carbonate, $ZnCO_3$; hexagonal-hexagonal scalenohedral; luster subadamantine; color bluish, greenish, yellow, white; H, 5; S.G., 4.3-4.4; fracture conchoidal; cleavage rhombohedral; brittle; translucent.

SMOKY QUARTZ: *Rock crystal, q.v.,* colored blackish, or smoky.

SNOWFLAKE OBSIDIAN: A variety of *obsidian, q.v.,* in which light gray to bluish-gray spots occur, looking like snowflakes.

SODA-DRAVITE: Brown *tourmaline, q.v.,* $NaMg_3B_3Al_3(Al_3Si_6O_{27})(OH)_4$.

SODALITE: Sodium aluminum silicate with chlorine, $Na_4Al_3Si_3O_{12}Cl$; cubic-hexoctahedral; luster glassy; colorless, blue, pink, violet, white; H, 5.5-6; S.G., 2.2-2.3; fracture conchoidal to uneven; cleavage poor dodecahedral; translucent to transparent; often fluorescent yellow-orange.

SPECULARITE: Jaspery material laced with bands of dark steel-gray *hematite, q.v.*

SPESSARTITE GARNET: See *garnet;* Manganese aluminum silicate, $Mn_3Al_2Si_3O_{12}$; color dark brown to pinkish, reddish, black; S.G., 4.2.

SPHALERITE: Zinc sulphide, ZnS: cubic-hextetrahedral; luster adamantine; colorless through black, reddish-brown, yellow; H, 3.5-4; S.G., 3.9-4.1; fracture conchoidal; cleavage perfect dodecahedral; brittle; opaque to transparent.

SPHENE: Calcium titanium silicate, $CaTiSiO_5$; monoclinic-prismatic; luster adamantine; color gray, green, brown, yellow; H, 5-5.5; S.G., 3.4-3.5; fracture conchoidal; cleavage fair prismatic; translucent to transparent; see *titanite.*

SPINEL: Magnesium aluminum oxide, $MgAl_2O_4$; cubic-hexoctahedral; luster glassy; color blue, green, black, violet, orange-brown, white; H, 7.5-8; S.G., 3.5-4.1; fracture conchoidal; cleavage none; brittle; opaque to transparent.

SPODUMENE: Lithium aluminum silicate, $LiAlSi_2O_6$; monoclinic-prismatic; luster glassy; color buff, greenish, lavender, opaque, white; H, 6.5-7; S.G., 3.1-3.2; fracture uneven; cleavage perfect prismatic; translucent to transparent; thermoluminescent; often fluorescent and/or phosphorescent orange.

STAUROLITE: Iron aluminum silicate, $FeAl_4Si_2O_{10}(OH)_2$;

orthorhombic-rhombic bipyramidal; luster glassy; color brown; H, 7-7.5; S.G., 3.6-3.7; fracture subconchoidal; cleavage fair pinacoidal; translucent to transparent; also *fairy crosses.*

STEPHENITE: Silver antimony sulphide, $Ag_5SbS_3$; orthorhombic-pyramidal; luster metallic; color iron-black; H, 2-2.5; S.G., 6.2-6.3; fracture subconchoidal to uneven; cleavage two poor; brittle; darkens to black on standing.

STIBNITE: Antimony sulphide, $Sb_2S_3$; orthorhombic-bipyramidal; luster metallic; color steel gray; H, 2; S.G., 4.5-4.6; fracture subconchoidal; cleavage perfect side pinacoid; sectile.

STILBITE: Hydrous calcium, sodium, aluminum silicate, $(Ca,Na)_3Al_5(Al,Si)Si_{14}O_{40}.15H_2O$; monoclinic-prismatic; luster glassy; color brown, reddish, yellow, white; H, 3.5-4; S.G., 2.1-2.2; irregular fracture; cleavage one perfect; translucent to transparent.

STRONTIANITE: Strontium carbonate, $SrCo_3$; orthorhombic-rhombic bipyramidal; luster glassy; colorless, green, pink, yellow to brownish, white; H, 3.5-4; S.G., 3.7; fracture uneven; cleavage one good, one poor; brittle; translucent to transparent.

SUCCINITE: Mineralogic name for *amber, q.v.*

SULPHUR: Element, S; orthorhombic-bipyramidal; luster resinous; color yellow to amber; H, 2; S.G., 2-2.1; fracture conchoidal; cleavage basal; brittle.

SUNSTONE: A *feldsapar, q.v.,* which contains inclusions of *hematite* and *goethite;* a type of *aventurine, q.v.*

SWEETWATER AGATE: A name applied to small, dark-gray, translucent *chalcedony* nodules containing dendritic growths that form starlike patterns.

TALC: Hydrous magnesium silicate, $Mg_3Si_4O_{10}(OH)_2$; monoclinic-prismatic; luster greasy to pearly; color blackish, gray, greenish, white; H, 1; S.G., 2.7-2.8; cleavage micaceous; greasy feel; translucent to opaque.

TANTALITE: Trantalate of iron and manganese, $(Fe,Mn)(Ta,Cb)_2O_6$; orthorhombic-rhombic-bipyramidal; luster submetallic to resinous; colorless to black or reddish-brown; H, 6; S.G., 5.2-8; streak brown to black to white; fracture uneven; cleavage front and side pinacoid; brittle; opaque to transparent.

TEKTITES: Small, round, vitreous objects resembling glass with internal "swirl" marks, or grooved and channeled on the outside; Texas variety, known as *bediasites,* has H, 5-6; S.G., 2.3-2.4; color greenish to black and dark brown; fracture conchoidal, tough; variety of *meteorites, q.v.*

TELLURIUM: Element, Te; hexagonal-trigonal trapezohedral; luster metallic; color tin-white; H, 2-2.5; S.G., 6.1-6.3; fracture uneven; cleavage prismatic good; poor basal; brittle.

TETRAHEDRITE: Sulphide of copper, iron, and antimony, $(Cu,Fe)_{12}Sb_4S_{13}$; cubic hextetrahedral; luster metallic; color gray to black; H, 3-4.5; S.G., 4.6-5.1; fracture subconchoidal to uneven; cleavage none; brittle; associated with *tennantite,* $(Cu,Fe)_{12}As_4S_{13}$, rare.

TEXAS PLUME AGATE: Brewster Co. *agate, q.v.,* of particularly attractive plumes, black spreading through clear to milky *chalcedony,* found mostly as nodules with rough exteriors.

THAUMASITE: Variety of snow-white, chatoyant *prehnite, q.v.*

THENARDITE: Sodium sulphate, $Na_2SO_4$; orthorhombic-rhombic bipyramidal; luster glassy; colorless to brown or yellow; H, 2.5-3; S.G., 2.7; fracture uneven; cleavage good basal; translucent to transparent; fluorescent greenish-yellow.

THOMSONITE: A *zeolite* mineral, *q.v.;* complex hydrous calcium sodium aluminum silicate, $(Ca,Na_2)Al_2Si_2O_8$.-$2\frac{1}{2}H_2O$; orthorhombic; color white with concentric markings in cream, black, and green; H 5; S.G., 2.3-2.4; fibrous; extremely compact.

THULITE: Fluorescent pink *zoisite, q.v.*

THUNDEREGG: Special type of nodule, concretion or aggregation of chalcedony with external rind of silicified volcanic ash and star-shaped core of translucent, usually banded *chalcedony* (rarely deep-red *carnelian);* externally covered by "warty" protuberances, while interior *chalcedony* is often beautifully patterned with fine plume, sagenitic, or moss agate; occur sometimes as singles (usually), doubles, and/or triples.

TIGER'S EYE: See *hawk's eye.*

TITANITE: Alternate name for *sphene, q.v.*

TOPAZ: Aluminum fluosilicate, $Al_2SiO_4(F,OH)_2$; orthorhombic-rhombic bipyramidal; luster glassy; colorless, bluish, browns, yellow-brown, yellow; white; H, 8; S.G., 3.5-3.6; fracture conchoidal; cleavage perfect basal; translucent to transparent.

TOPAZOLITE: Variety of topaz-yellow *andradite garnet, q.v.*

TORBERNITE: Hydrous copper uranium phosphate, $Cu(UO_2)(PO_4)_2 \cdot 8\text{-}12(H_2O)$; luster vitreous to pearly; color green; H, 2-2.5; S.G., 3.2-3.6; no fracture; cleavage perfect basal; brittle; translucent to transparent.

TOURMALINE: A series name for aluminum silicates that include *schorl, soda-dravite, lime dravite,* and *lithia-tourmaline, q.v.,* found in pegmatites; luster glassy, color black, blue, brown, green, pink, red, white, and colorless; H, 7-7.5; S.G., 3-3.3; hexagonal-ditrigonal pyramidal; fracture conchoidal to uneven; cleavage poor prismatic and rhombohedral; transparent to opaque; often two or more colors per crystal; characteristic bulging triangular cross-section.

TRAVERTINE: A water-deposited *calcite, q.v.,* laid down by hot springs; soft, porous; variously colored by impurities.

TREMOLITE: Calcium magnesium silicate, $Ca_2Mg_5Si_8O_{22}(OH)_2$; monoclinic-prismatic; light-colored *actinolite, q.v.*

TRIDYMITE: Silicon dioxide, $SiO_2$; orthorhombic-rhombic bipyramidal; luster glassy; colorless to white; H, 7; S.G., 2.3; fracture conchoidal; cleavage prismatic; translucent to transparent; see *quartz,* but distinguishable by tabular crystallization; a high-temperature silicate.

TRIPHANE: Colorless to yellow *spodumene, q.v.*

TRIPHYLITE: Lithium iron phosphate, $LiFePO_4$; orthorhombic-rhombic bipyramidal; luster glassy; color blue-green-gray; H, 4.5-5; S.G., 3.4-3.6; fracture uneven; cleavage one fair, two imperfect; brittle; translucent to transparent; usually associated with *lithiophilite,* $LiMnPO_4$.

TROOSTITE: Brownish, opaque variety of *willemite, q.v.*

TUNGSTITE: Tungsten oxide plus water, $WO_3 \cdot xH_2O$; orthorhombic; color yellow; H, 2.5; S.G., 5.5; streak yellow; powdery; cleavage two; closely associated with *huebnerite* and *wolframite.*

TURQUOISE: Hydrous basic aluminum phosphate with copper, $CuAl_6(PO_4)_4(OH)_8 \cdot 4H_2O$; luster porcelaneous; color greenish blue to sky-blue; H, 5-6; S.G., 2.6-2.8; fracture smooth; brittle; thinly translucent.

TURRITELLA AGATE: Masses of small spiral snail shells, *turritellas,* reproduced in clear *chalcedony* as *petrifactions.*

ULEXITE: Hydrous sodium calcium borate, $NaCaB_5O_9 \cdot 8H_2O$; triclinic-pinacoidal; luster silky; color white; H, 1; S.G., 1.6; soft and cottony; translucent.

UNAKITE: A light green *epidote, q.v.,* in which is mixed an equal proportion of bright red to pink feldspar; named after Unaka Mountains between North Carolina and Tennessee.

URANINITE: Uranium dioxide, $UO_2$; cubic hexoctahedral; luster dull, submetallic; color steel gray to brownish-black; streak gray, brownish-black, olive-green; H, 5-6; S.G., 6.4-9.7; fracture conchoidal; cleavage none; brittle; opaque; radioactive; see *pitchblende.*

URANOPHANE: Hydrous calcium uranium silicate, $CaU_2Si_2O_{11} \cdot 7H_2O$; orthorhombic-rhombic bipyramidal; luster glassy to pearly; color orange-yellow to yellow; H, 2-3; S.G., 3.8-3.9; translucent; moderately fluorescent greenish-yellow.

UVAROVITE GARNET: See *garnet;* calcium chromium silicate, $Ca_3Cr_2Si_3O_{12}$; color emerald-green; S.G., 3.8.

VANADINITE: Lead chlorovanadate, $Pb_5(VO_4)_3Cl$; hexagonal-hexagonal bipyramidal; luster resinous; color brown, yellow-brown, red-orange-brown; H, 2.7-3; S.G., 6.7-7.1; fracture uneven; no cleavage; brittle; translucent to transparent.

VARISCITE: Hydrous aluminum phosphate, $Al(PO_4).2H_2O$; orthorhombic-rhombic bipyramidal; luster porcelaneous; color green; H, 3.5-4.5; S.G., 2.2-2.8; fracture conchoidal to smooth; no cleavage; brittle; thinly translucent.

VERDE ANTIQUE: Impure, translucent variety of *serpentine, q.v.,* used as a building decorative stone.

VIVIANITE: Hydrous iron phosphate, $Fe_3(PO_4)_2.8H_2O$; monoclinic-prismatic; luster glassy to pearly; colorless to greenish-blue, indigo, violet; H, 1.5-2; S.G., 2.6-2.7; streak white;

fracture subconchoidal (striated); cleavage micaceous; leaves flexible; translucent to transparent.

WARDITE: Hydrous sodium calcium aluminum phosphate, $Na_4CaAl_{12}(PO_4)_8(OH)_{18} \cdot 6H_2O$; tetragonal-tetragonal pyramidal; luster glassy; color bluish-green to white; H, 5; S.G., 2.8-2.9; fracture conchoidal; cleavage good basal; brittle; translucent to transparent.

WASCOITE: Silica-rich jaspery sediment from bottom of Lake Wasco, Wasco Co., Washington; color brown; variety of patterns resembling petrified wood.

WAVELLITE: Hydrous basic aluminum phosphate, $Al_3(OH)_3$-$(PO_4)_2 \cdot 5H_2O$; orthorhombic; luster glassy to silky; color black, brown, green, gray, yellow, white; H, 3.5-4; S.G., 2.4; fracture subconchoidal to uneven; splintery; cleavage domal and side pinacoid; brittle; translucent to transparent.

WHEELERITE: Fossil resin (amber, q.v.) found in Sandoval Co. New Mexico.

WILLEMITE: Zinc silicate, $Zn_2SiO_4$; hexagonal-rhombohedral; luster glassy to resinous; colorless to white or stained reddish-brown; H, 5.5; S.G., 3.9-4.2; fracture conchoidal to uneven; cleavage basal; translucent to transparent.

WILLIAMSITE: Variety of noble serpentine, q.v.

WITHERITE: Barium carbonate, $BaCO_3$; orthorhombic-rhombic bipyramidal; luster glassy; color gray, yellowish, white; H, 3-3.5; S.G., 4.3-4.7; fracture uneven; cleavage one good, two poor; brittle; translucent; fluorescent blue.

WOLFRAMITE: Iron and manganese tungstates, $(Fe,Mn)$-$WO_4$; includes ferberite ($FeWO_4$) and huebnerite ($MnWO_4$): monoclinic-prismatic; luster submetallic; color reddish-brown to black; H, 4-4.5; S.G., 7.1-7.5; fracture uneven; cleavage perfect side pinacoid; brittle; opaque.

WOLLASTONITE: Calcium silicate, $CaSiO_3$; triclinic-pedial; luster glassy to silky; colorless, gray, pink, white; H, 4.5-5; S.G., 2.8-2.9; fracture splintery; cleavage perfect pinacoidal; translucent; sometimes fluorescent orange or yellow.

WONDERSTONE: Variety of colorfully banded rhyolite, q.v.

WULFENITE: Lead molybdate, $PbMoO_4$; tetragonal-tetragonal pyramidal; luster adamantine; color brown, gray, orange, yellow, off-white; H, 2.7-3; S.G., 6.8; fracture sub-conchoidal; cleavage pyramidal good, two poor; translucent to transparent.

ZEOLITE: Family name for *analcite, chadazite, heulandite, natrolite,* and *stilbite, q.v.* The group totals some 30 members.

ZINCITE: Zinc oxide, ZnO; hexagonal-dihexagonal pyramidal; luster subadamantine; color orange-yellow to red; H, 4; S.G., 5.4-5.7; streak orange-yellow; fracture conchoidal; cleavage prismatic; brittle; translucent to transparent.

ZINC-BLENDE: *Sphalerite, q.v.*

ZIRCON: Zirconium silicate, $ZrSiO_4$; tetragonal-ditetragonal bipyramidal; luster adamantine; color bluish, brown, green, gray, reddish, violet, and colorless; H, 6.5-7.5; S.G., 4-4.7; fracture conchoidal; cleavage two poor; translucent to transparent; fluorescent yellow-orange.

ZOISITE: Hydrous calcium aluminum silicate, $Ca_2Al_3(SiO_4)_3$-(OH); orthorhombic-rhombic bipyramidal; luster glassy; color brown, gray, pink *(thulite, q.v.)*; H, 6; S.G., 3.3-3.4; fracture subconchoidal to uneven; cleavage perfect side pinacoid; translucent; sometimes fluorescent yellow-orange.

# Bibliography

/\.\/\.\/\.\/\.\/\.\/\.\/\.\/\.\/\.\

## GEMS AND MINERALS

Anderson, B. W., *Gem Testing*. Emerson, N.Y., 1948. The science of gemology, including easy, practical testing of gem stones.

Ball, S. H., "The Mining of Gems and Ornamental Stones by American Indians," *Bureau of American Ethnology, Anthropological Papers, No. 13, Bureau Ethnology Bulletin 128*, 1941, Smithsonian Institution, Washington, D.C.

Ballard, Thomas J., and Conklin, Quentin E., *The Uranium Prospector's Guide*. Harper & Brothers, N.Y., 1955. Detailed information on mineral maps, staking claims, uranium mineralogy.

Brown, R. W., "Plantlike Features in Thundereggs and Geodes," *Smithsonian Report for 1956*, pp. 329-39. Washington, D.C., 1957. Describes the formation of dendritic and mossy inclusions in chalcedony.

Brown, Vinson, and Allan, David, *Rocks and Minerals of California and Their Stories*. Naturegraph Company, San Martin, Calif., 1955.

Dake, H. C., Fleener, F. L., and Wilson, B. H., *Quartz Family Minerals*. Whittlesey House. McGraw-Hill Book Company, Inc., N.Y., 1938. This popular reference book describes the many varieties of silicon dioxide gem stones.

Dana, Edward S. and Ford, W. E., *Dana's Textbook of Mineralogy*, 4th ed. John Wiley and Sons, Inc., N.Y., 1932. A college textbook and authority.

Dana, James D. and Hurlbut, Cornelius S., Jr., *Dana's Manual of Mineralogy*, 16th ed. John Wiley and Sons, Inc., N.Y., 1952. An intermediate textbook dealing with crystals, properties of minerals and gem stones, descriptions, and identifications.

―――― *Minerals and How to Study Them*, 3rd ed. John Wiley and Sons, Inc.,

N.Y., 1949. An elementary textbook describing mineral properties, descriptions, and how to grow crystals.

English, George L., *Getting Acquainted with Minerals.* McGraw-Hill Book Company, Inc., N.Y., 1934. A well-illustrated introductory textbook of interest to rock collectors.

Fenton, Carroll L. and Fenton, Mildred A., *The Rock Book.* Appleton-Century-Crofts, Inc., N.Y., 1943. An excellent elementary discussion of rocks and minerals, well illustrated.

Feuchtwanger, L., *A Popular Treatise on Gems.* D. Appleton & Company, N.Y., 1859. Of historical interest mainly, but describes a number of localities in North America.

Ford, W. E., *A Textbook of Mineralogy.* John Wiley and Sons, Inc., N.Y., 1932. An advanced college textbook, not for amateurs.

Fritzen, D. K., *The Rock-Hunter's Field Manual.* Harper & Brothers, N.Y., 1959. Description and identification keys for rocks and minerals.

George, Russell D., *Minerals and Rocks.* Appleton-Century-Crofts, Inc., N.Y., 1943. A comprehensive compilation of mineral and gem-stone lore.

Graves, Howard B., Jr., *The Mineral Key.* McGraw-Hill Book Company, Inc., N.Y. Simple outline identification of minerals.

Grout, Frank F., *Kemp's Handbook of Rocks.* D. Van Nostrand Company, Inc., N.Y., 1940. An introductory textbook on rocks.

Hager, DeWitte, *Complete Guidebook to Rocks and Gems.* Trend Books, Inc., Los Angeles, Calif., 1960. Covers rock and mineral descriptions, localities, and jewelry-making with many illustrations.

Kraus, Edward H., Hunt, W. F., and Ramsdell, L. S., *Mineralogy.* McGraw-Hill Book Company, Inc., N.Y., 1951. A college text.

Kraus, E. H. and Slawson, C. B., *Gems and Gem Materials,* 5th ed. McGraw-Hill Book Company, Inc., N.Y., 1947. A popular book on gemology.

Liddicoat, R. T., Jr., *Handbook of Gem Identification.* Gemological Institute of America, Los Angeles, Calif., 1948.

Merrill, G. P., *Handbook and Descriptive Catalogue of the Collections of Gems and Precious Stones in the United States National Museum.* Smithsonian Institution, U.S. National Museum Bulletin 118, Washington, D.C., 1922.

Murdock, Joseph and Webb, R. W., *Minerals of California,* Bulletin 173, California State Division of Mines, San Francisco, California, 1956.

Nininger, Harvey H., *Out of the Sky: An Introduction to Meteoritics.* University of Denver Press, Denver, Colo., 1952. A survey of meteoritic minerals, structures, falls, and craters.

Palache, C., Berman, H., and Frondel, C., *Dana's System of Mineralogy.* John Wiley and Sons, Inc., N.Y.; Vol. I, 1944, Vol. II, 1951. Modern revision of Dana's original work.

Pearl, Richard M., *How to Know the Minerals and Rocks.* McGraw-Hill Book Company, Inc., N.Y., 1955. A Signet Key pocket book describing specific minerals and their localities.

——— *Mineral Collectors Handbook.* Mineral Book Company, Colorado Springs, Colo., 1949.

——— *Popular Gemology.* John Wiley and Sons, Inc., N.Y., 1948. A layman's book surveying gems and gem stones.

—— *Rocks and Minerals.* Barnes & Noble, Inc., N.Y., 1956. An everyday handbook of the mineral kingdom.

Pirsson, L. V., and Knopf, Adolph, *Rocks and Rock Minerals.* John Wiley and Sons, Inc., N.Y., 1947. A general textbook on igneous, sedimentary, and metamorphic rocks.

Pough, F. H., *A Field Guide to Rocks and Minerals.* Houghton Mifflin Company, Boston, 1953. A well-illustrated handbook.

Ransom, Jay E., "Arizona's Copper Minerals," "The Pegmatite Gems of California," *Lapidary Journal,* Vol. 8, No. 1, (April, 1954), Lapidary Journal, Inc., Palm Desert, Calif.

Rogers, Austin F., *Introduction to the Study of Minerals.* McGraw-Hill Book Company, Inc., N.Y., 1937. A college textbook.

Smith, G. F. H., *Gemstones,* 13th ed., revised by F. C. Phillips. Methuen & Co., Ltd., London, 1958. This is probably the most complete and thorough treatment of gemology in English.

Smith, Orsino C., *Identification and Qualitative Chemical Analysis of Minerals,* 2nd. ed. D. Van Nostrand Company, Inc., N.Y., 1953. A reference textbook with tables of properties of minerals and gem stones; many color plates.

Spencer, L. J., *A Key to Precious Stones,* 2nd ed. Emerson Books, Inc., N.Y., 1947. An introduction to the study of gems.

Spock, L. E., *A Guide to the Study of Rocks.* Harper & Brothers, N.Y., 1953.

Webster, R., *The Gemologist's Compendium.* N. A. G. Press, Ltd., London, A very complete reference book of minerals and gems.

Whitlock, Herbert P., *The Story of the Gems.* Emerson Books, Inc., N.Y., 1941. A well-illustrated introductory book on gem lore.

Winchell, Alexander N., *Elements of Mineralogy.* Prentice-Hall, Inc., N.Y., 1942. A college textbook.

Zinner, Paul, and the Staff of the Bureau of Mines, *Mineral Facts and Problems,* Bulletin 556, U.S. Bureau of Mines, U.S. Department of the Interior. Government Printing Office, Washington, D.C. 1956. Commercially slanted focus on minerals, metals, and fuels with historical data, uses, and mining localities; included various gem stones.

## MAGAZINES AND PERIODICALS

*American Mineralogist.* Journal of the Mineralogical Society of America, Department of Mineralogy, University of Michigan, Ann Arbor. A highly technical, professional journal.

*Desert Magazine.* Palm Desert, California. Excellent regional data.

*Earth Science.* Box 1357, Chicago 90, Ill. This magazine popularly describes all aspects of the earth sciences.

*Gems & Gemology.* Gemological Institute of America, 11940 San Vicente Blvd., Los Angeles 49, Calif. Carries occasional articles on popular gem stones.

*Gems & Minerals.* Box 687, Mentone, Calif. Has taken over the *Mineralogist* and covers all aspects of rock-collecting lore.

*Lapidary Journal.* Box 518, Del Mar, Calif. Although devoted primarily to the lapidary arts, the annual *Rockhound Buyers Guide Issue* describes collecting areas.

*Mineralogist.* Now important primarily for back issues, was absorbed by

*Gems & Minerals* in June, 1960. Put out by Mineralogist Book Publishing Co., 329 S.E. 32nd Ave., Portland, Oregon.

*Rocks & Minerals.* Box 29, Peekskill, N.Y. Popular magazine devoted to the earth sciences.

## GUIDEBOOKS

Bitner's *Arizona Rock Trails.* Bitner's, Scottsdale, Ariz., 1957. Contains a series of charts showing 60 Arizona gem-stone and specimen mineral localities.

Dake, H. C., *Northwest Gem Trails.* Mineralogist Publishing Company, 329 S.E. 32nd Ave., Portland, Oregon, 1950. Covers gem-stone localities in Oregon, Washington, Idaho, Montana, and Wyoming.

———— *The Agate Book.* Mineralogist Publishing Co., Portland, Oregon, 1951. A handbook for the agate collector and cutter.

———— *California Gem Trails.* Mineralogist, Publishing Company, Portland, Oregon, 1952. Covers California localities.

———— *Popular Prospecting.* Mineralogist Publishing Company, Portland, Oregon, 1955. Data and localities on gem stones, uranium, strategic metallic and nonmetallic minerals.

Henry, Darold J., *Gem Trail Journal.* Gordon's, Long Beach, Calif., 1952. Locality information in the western states.

———— *California Gem Trails,* 3rd ed., revised. Gordon's, Long Beach, Calif.. Mainly southern California gemstone localities.

———— *The Rock Collector's Nevada and Idaho.* Gordon's, Long Beach, Calif., 1953. Many gem-stone sites and what to find.

Johnson, H. Cyril, *Gem Hunters Atlas—Southwest,* 4th ed. Box 288, Susanville, Calif., 1960. Detailed maps of Arizona, Utah, New Mexico, Colorado, and West Texas showing gem-stone sites.

———— *Gem Hunters Atlas—Northwest.* Box 288, Susanville, Calif., 1960. Detailed maps of gem-stone localities in Oregon, Washington, Idaho, Montana, Wyoming, and parts of British Columbia and South Dakota.

———— *Gem Hunters Atlas—California-Nevada.* Box 288, Susanville, Calif., 1960. Detailed maps of the indicated states, showing gem-stone and mineral-collecting areas.

New Hampshire Planning & Development Commission, *The Geology of New Hampshire.* Gives fairly detailed list of localities.

Pearl, Richard M., *Colorado Gem Trails,* 2nd ed. Mineral Book Company, Colorado Springs, Colo., 1951. Description of gem-stones and their localities in Colorado.

Ransom, Jay Ellis, *Arizona Gem Trails and the Colorado Desert of California.* Mineralogist Publishing Company, Portland, Oregon, 1955. Gem-stone localities with detailed descriptions.

———— *Petrified Forest Trails.* Mineralogist Publishing Company, Portland, Oregon, 1955. Locality information on petrified forests of the United States with technical data on petrifactions.

Simpson, B. W., *Gem Trails of Texas.* Granbury, Texas, 1958.

Sinkankas, John, *Gemstones of North America.* D. Van Nostrand Company, Inc., N.Y., 1959. Probably the most comprehensive book on gem and gem-stone characteristics and localities in North America.

# Mineral Museums by States and Cities

/\\/\\/\\/\\/\\/\\/\\/\\/\\/\\/\\/\\/\\/\\/\\/\\/\\/\\

The following pages list alphabetically by states and cities the principal rock and mineral museums which are open to the public. These museums afford many opportunities for the casual rock collector to become acquainted with regional gem stones, minerals, geology, and locations where the best specimens may be found.

Often, too, the curators are most helpful in providing directions and gemological information regarding easily reached localities. Of course, most museums have on exhibit prize speciments from far distant regions, and these examples of the mineral kingdom are especially valuable as guides to understanding the techniques used for display as well as the chemical and mineral makeup of the individual specimens.

The starred items show where there is either a public or a college library available with unclassified geological and mineralogical reports. Such reports describe and locate various strategic or commercially valuable minerals, ores, and other natural resources. Oftentimes, detailed maps and diagrams are included to help the prospector and rock collector in his search for interesting specimens or gem stones.

ALABAMA
Auburn: *Alabama Polytechnic Institute*
Spring Hill: *Spring Hill College*

Talladega: *Talladega College*
*University: *Alabama Museum of Natural History*

199

**ALASKA**
College: *University of Alaska Museum*
**ARIZONA**
Holbrook: Petrified Forest National Monument Museum
*Phoenix: Arizona Museum
Tucson: *University of Arizona
**ARKANSAS**
Conway: Hendrix College
Fayetteville: *University of Arkansas Museum
**CALIFORNIA**
Berkeley: *University of California
Claremont: *Pomona College
*Los Angeles:
   California State Exposition Building
   Los Angeles County Museum of History, Science, and Art
   Occidental College
   University of California at Los Angeles
   * University of Southern California
Oakland: Oakland Public Museum
Pacific Grove: Pacific Grove Museum Association, Pacific Grove Museum
Palm Springs: Palm Springs Desert Museum
Palo Alto: * Stanford University Natural History Museum
Pasadena:
   * California Institute of Technology
   Pasadena Junior College
Riverside: Riverside Municipal Museum
* Sacramento: California Museum Association
San Diego: San Diego Society of Natural History, Natural History Museum
* San Francisco:
   California Academy of Sciences
   California State Division of Mines Museum
   Memorial Museum
Santa Barbara: Santa Barbara Museum of Natural History

Santa Clara: University of Santa Clara Museum
Stockton: College of the Pacific
Twenty-Nine Palms: Desert Branch, Southwest Museum
Yosemite: Yosemite National Park Museum
**COLORADO**
Boulder: *University of Colorado, University Museum
Colorado Springs:
   Colorado College Museum
   El Paso County Pioneer association, Pioneer Museum
Denver:
   Colorado Museum of Natural History
   *State Bureau of Mines Museum
   University of Denver Museum
Fort Collins: *Colorado State College of Agriculture and Mechanic Arts
Golden: *Colorado School of Mines Museum
Sterling: Logan County Historical and National History Society Museum
**CONNECTICUT**
Bridgeport: Bridgeport Scientific and Historical Society
Greenwich: Bruce Museum
*Hartford: *Trinity College Museum of Natural History Wadsworth Athenaeum
Middletown: *Wesleyan University
New Britain: New Britain Institute Museum
New Haven: *Yale University, Peabody Museum of Natural History
Stamford: Stamford Museum, Stamford Natural History Society
Storrs: *Connecticut Agricultural College
Wallingford: Choate School
**DELAWARE**
Newark: *University of Delaware
*Wilmington: Society of Natural History of Delaware

**DISTRICT OF COLUMBIA**
*Washington:
  *Catholic University of America*
  *Columbian College, George Washington University*
  *Georgetown University Museum*
  *Smithsonian Institution, United States National Museum*
  * *United States Bureau of Mines*
**FLORIDA**
De Land: *John B. Stetson University, Monroe Heath Museum of Natural History*
Gainsville: *University of Florida*
St. Augustine: *Crichlow Museum of Natural History*
Winter Park: *Rollins College Museum*
**GEORGIA**
Athens: *University of Georgia*
Atlanta:
  *Atlanta University*
  *Georgia State Museum*
Macon: *Mercer University*
Oxford: *Emory University Academy Museum*
**IDAHO**
Moscow: *University of Idaho*
**ILLINOIS**
Abington: *Hedding College*
Bloomington: *Illinois Wesleyan University Museum*
Carlinville: *Blackburn College*
Carthage: *Carthage College*
*Chicago:
  *Chicago Academy of Sciences*
  *Chicago Museum of Natural History*
  *University of Chicago Walker Museum*
Decatur: *Millikan University*
Elgin: *Elgin Scientific Society*
Evanston: *Northwestern University*
Galesburg: *Knox College*
Lake Forest: *Lake Forest College Museum*
Lincoln: *Lincoln College, Millikin University*
Naperville: *Northwestern College*

Rock Island: *Augustana College*
*Springfield: *Illinois State Museum*
Sterling: *Whiteside County Historical Society*
Urbana: *University of Illinois Museum of Natural History*
**INDIANA**
Bloomington: *Indiana University Museum*
Brookville: *Brookville Society of Natural History*
Crawfordsville: *Wabash College*
Franklin: *Franklin College of Indiana*
Hanover: *Hanover College*
Indianapolis:
  *Butler College*
  *Children's Museum*
  *Indiana State Museum*
Lafayette: *Purdue University*
Newcastle: *Henry County Historical Society Museum*
New Harmony: *Workingmen's Institute*
Notre Dame: *Notre Dame University*
Richmond: *Earlham College*
Terre Haute: *Rose Polytechnic Institute*
Upland: *Taylor University*
**IOWA**
Cedar Falls: *Iowa State Teachers College*
Cedar Rapids: *Coe College*
College Springs: *Amity College*
Dubuque: *Hermann Museum of Natural History*
Fayette: *Upper Iowa University*
Independence: *Independence Public Library*
Iowa City: *State University of Iowa*
Mount Vernon: *Cornell College*
Muscatine: *Muscatine Academy of Science*
Sioux City: *Sioux City Academy of Science and Letters*
Toledo: *Western College*

INDIANA *(Cont'd.)*
Waterloo: *Young Men's Christian Association*
Waverly: *Wartburg Normal College*
KANSAS
Baldwin City: *Baker University*
Emporia:
*College of Emporia*
*Kansas State Normal School*
Lawrence: *\*University of Kansas*
Lindsborg: *Bethany College*
Manhattan: *Kansas State Agricultural College*
McPherson: *McPherson College*
Salina: *Kansas Wesleyan University*
\*Topeka: *Washburn College Museum*
KENTUCKY
Bowling Green: *Ogden College*
Danville: *Centre College*
Frankfort: *Kentucky Geological Society*
Lexington:
*Transylvania University*
*\*University of Kentucky*
\*Louisville: *Louisville Public Library Museum*
LOUISIANA
Baton Rouge: *\*Louisiana State University*
\*New Orleans:
*Louisiana State Museum*
*\*Tulane University*
MAINE
Augusta:
*Augusta Public Library*
*Kennebec Historical Society*
*Maine State Museum*
Brunswick: *Bowdoin College*
Brinckley: *Bates Museum*
Lewiston: *Bates College Museum*
Orono: *\*University of Maine*
Paris: *Hamlin Memorial Hall*
Portland: *Portland Society of Natural History Museum*
Thomaston: *Knox Academy of Arts and Science Museum*
Waterville: *Colby College*

MARYLAND
Annapolis:
*State House*
*United States Naval Academy*
\*Baltimore:
*Goucher College Museum*
*\*Johns Hopkins University*
*Maryland Academy of Sciences*
Ellicot City: *Rock Hill College*
Westminister: *Western Maryland College*
MASSACHUSETTS
Amherst:
*\*Amherst College Museum*
*Massachusetts State College*
\*Boston
*Boston Society of Natural History, New England Museum of Natural History*
*Boston University Museum*
Cambridge:
*\*Harvard University, University Museum, Geological Museum*
*\* Massachusetts Institute of Technology*
Chestnut Hill: *Boston College Museum*
Dover: *Dover Historical and Natural History Society*
Fall River: *Fall River Public Library*
Fitchburg: *Wallace Public Library*
Framingham: *Framingham Historical and Natural History Society*
Gloucester: *Cape Ann Scientific Literary, and Historical Association*
Jamaica Plain: *Children's Museum*
Leominster: *Leominster Public Library Museum*
Marion: *Marion Natural History Society*
Marlborough: *Marlborough Society of Natural History*
Northampton: *Smith College Museum*
Pittsfield: *Museum of Natural History and Art*

**MASSACHUSETTS** (*Cont'd.*)

Salem: *Peabody Historical Society Museum*

Somerville: *Tufts College Museum*

South Hadley: *Mount Holyoke College*

Springfield: *Museum of Natural History*

Taunton: *Bristol County Academy of Sciences*

Wellesley: *\*Wellesley College*

Williamstown: *Williams College, Williams College Museum*

\*Worcester:
Clark University
Holy Cross College
Worcester Natural History Society, Worcester Museum of Natural History

**MICHIGAN**

Adrian: *Adrian College*

Alma: *Alma College Museum*

Ann Arbor: *\*University of Michigan, Natural Science Museum*

Battle Creek: *Public Schools Museum of Natural History*

Bloomfield Hills: *Cranbrook Foundation, Cranbrook Institute of Science*

\* Detroit: *Detroit Children's Museum*

East Lansing: * *Michigan State College of Agriculture and Applied Science*

Grand Rapids: *Kent Scientific Museum*

Houghton:
Hillsdale College
* Michigan College of Mining and Technology Museum

Kalamazoo: *Kalamazoo Museum and Art Institute*

Port Huron: *Port Huron Public Library Museum*

Three Oaks: *Edward K. Warren Foundation, Chamberlin Memorial Museum*

**MINNESOTA**

Collegeville: *St. John's University*

Minneapolis:
Minneapolis Museum Federation, Public Library Science Museum
\*University of Minnesota Museum of Natural History

Northfield:
Carlton College
St. Olaf College

\*St. Paul:
Hamline University Museum
St. Paul Institute of Arts and Science, Science Museum

St. Peter: *Gustavus Adolphus College*

Winona: *Winona State Teachers College*

**MISSISSIPPI**

Jackson: *Millsaps College*

State College: * *Mississippi State College*

University: *\*University of Mississippi*

**MISSOURI**

Canton: *Culver-Stockton College*

Columbia: *\*University of Missouri Museum*

Fayette: *Central College*

Fulton: *Westminster College*

Glasgow: *Pritchett College*

Jefferson City: *Missouri Resources Museum*

\*Kansas City:
Public Library Museum
Missouri Bureau of Geology and Mines

Rolla: *\*Missouri School of Mines and Metallurgy Museum*

St. Joseph: *St. Joseph's Museum*

\*St. Louis:
St. Louis Public Schools Educational Museum
\*Washington University

**MONTANA**

Agate: *Cook Museum of Natural History*

Bozeman: *Montana State College*

Butte: *\*Montana School of Mines*

MONTANA (Cont'd.)
Ekalaka: *Carter County Geological Society*
*Helena: *Montana State Library Museum*
Missoula: *University of Montana*
NEBRASKA
Hastings: *Hastings College*
Lincoln: *University of Nebraska Museum*
University Place: *Nebraska Wesleyan University*
NEVADA
Reno: *University of Nevada Mackay School of Mines Museum*
NEW HAMPSHIRE
Durham:
New Hampshire College of Agriculture and Mechanic Arts
*University of New Hampshire*
Hanover: *Dartmouth College Museum*
Keene:
Keene High School
Keene Natural History Society
Manchester: *Manchester Institute of Arts and Sciences*
Wolfeboro: *Libby Museum*
NEW JERSEY
Dover: *Dover High School*
Hoboken: *Stevens Institute of Technology Museum*
Jersey City: *New Jersey Public Library Museum*
Newark: *Newark Museum Association*
Paterson:
Paterson Museum
*Princeton University Museum*
*Trenton: *State Museum of New Jersey*
West Caldwell: *Potwin Memorial Library*
NEW MEXICO
Albuquerque: *University of New Mexico*
Mesilla Park: *New Mexico College of Agriculture and Mechanic Arts*

*Santa Fe: *New Mexico Historical Society*
Socorro: *New Mexico School of Mines*
NEW YORK
*Albany: *New York State Museum*
Aurora: *Wells College*
Binghamton: *Binghamton Academy of Science*
*Brooklyn:
Brooklyn Institute of Arts and Sciences, Brooklyn Museum
Brooklyn Institute Of Arts and Sciences, Brooklyn Children's Museum
Long Island Historical Society
Polytechnic Institute of Brooklyn
Bryn Mawr: *Bryn Mawr College*
*Buffalo:
Buffalo Museum of Science
Cassius College
State Normal School
Canton: *St. Lawrence University*
Clinton: *Hamilton College*
Cortland: *Public Library*
Genesee: *Genesee Valley Museum*
Geneva: *Hobart College*
Hamilton: *Colgate University, Museum of Natural History*
Ithaca: *Cornell University*
New Rochelle: *Glen Island Museum of Natural History*
*New York City:
Academy of Mount St. Vincent
*American Museum of Natural History*
*College of the City of New York*
Columbia University Geology and Mineralogy Museum
Cooper Union for the Advancement of Science and Art
Fordham University
Manhattan College
Metropolitan Museum of Art
New York University
Society of Ethical Culture
Staten Island Institute of Arts and Sciences

## NEW YORK (Cont'd.)

Niagara Falls: *Niagara University*
Poughkeepsie: *Vassar College*
Rochester: *Rochester Museum of Arts and Sciences*
Schenectady: *Union College
Schoharie: *Schoharie County Historical Society*
Seaford: *Fox Museum of Natural History*
Skaneateles: *Library Association*
Syracuse: *Syracuse University Natural History Museum*
Troy: *Rensselaer Polytechnic Institute*
West Point: *United States Military Academy*
Yonkers: *Yonkers Museum of Science and Arts*

## NORTH CAROLINA

Chapel Hill: *University of North Carolina*
Davidson: *Davidson College*
Durham: *Duke University Museum of Natural History*
Raleigh:
*North Carolina State College
North Carolina State Museum*
Tryon: *Polk County Museum*

## NORTH DAKOTA

Fargo: *North Dakota Agricultural College*
Grand Forks: *University of North Dakota*
Wahpeton: *North Dakota State School of Science*

## OHIO

Alliance: *Mount Union College*
Antioch: *Antioch College*
Athens:
*Ohio University
State Normal College*
Berea: *Baldwin-Wallace College Museum*
Bowling Green: *State College
*Cincinnati:
*Cincinnati Museum Association*

Cincinnati Society of Natural History
*University of Cincinnati
*Cleveland:
Albert College
Case School of Applied Science
Cleveland Museum of Natural History
Western Reserve University
*Columbus:
Ohio State Museum
*Ohio State University
*Dayton: Dayton Public Library Museum
Delaware: Ohio Wesleyan University
Fremont: Hayes Memorial Library Museum
Greenville: Carnegie Library Museum
Hiram: Hiram College
Marietta: Marietta College Museum
Oberlin: *Oberlin College
Sandusky: Sandusky High School
Tiffin: Heidelberg University
*Toledo: Toledo Institute of Natural Science
Urbana: Urbana University
Westerville: Otterbein University
Wooster: Wooster College

## OKLAHOMA

Bacone: *Bacone College*
Norman: *University of Oklahoma*

## OREGON

Corvallis: *Oregon Agricultural College*
Eugene: *University of Oregon Museum of Natural History*
*Portland: *City Free Museum*
Salem: *Willamette University*

## PENNSYLVANIA

Allentown: *Muhlenberg College
Annville: Lebanon Valley College
Beaver Falls: Geneva College
Bethlehem: *Lehigh University
Carlisle: Dickinson College
Chester: Pennsylvania Military College

PENNSYLVANIA (Cont'd.)
Easton:
*Lafayette College
Northampton County Historical
and Genealogical Society
Erie: Erie Public Museum
Gettysburg: Gettysburg College
Harrisburg: Pennsylvania State Library and Museum
Haverford: Haverford College
Lancaster: Franklin and Marshall College Museum
Lewisburg: Bucknell University
Meadville: Allegheny College Natural History Museum
Media: Delaware County Institute of Science
Myerstown: Albright College
New Brighton: Merrick Art Gallery
New Wilmington: Westminster College
*Philadelphia: Philadelphia Academy of Natural Sciences
Pittsburgh: *Carnegie Institute, Carnegie Museum
Scranton: Everhart Museum of Natural History, Science and Art
Warren: Warren Academy of Sciences
Washington: Washington and Jefferson College
West Chester: State Teachers College
Westtown: Westtown Friends School
Wilkes-Barre: Wyoming Historical and Geological Society
RHODE ISLAND
Kingston: Rhode Island State College
*Providence:
Brown University
Park Museum
Westerley: Public Library
SOUTH CAROLINA
Charleston:
Charleston Museum
College of Charleston
South Carolina Military Academy

Clemson: *Clemson College
Clinton: Thornwell Museum
Columbia: *University of South Carolina
Greenville: Furman College
Newberry: Newberry College
Orangeburg: Clafin University
Rock Hill: Winthrop College
Spartanburg: Wofford College
SOUTH DAKOTA
Rapid City: *South Dakota State School of Mines
Vermillion: *University of South Dakota
Yankton: Yankton College
TENNESSEE
Clarksville: Southwestern Presbyterian University
Harriman: Public Museum
Jackson: Union University
Jefferson City: Carson and Newman College
Knoxville: *University of Tennessee
Lebanon: Cumberland University
Maryville: Maryville College
Memphis:
Cossitt Library Museum Association
Southwestern College
Milligan: Milligan College
Nashville:
*Fisk University
*Tennessee Division of Geology
Vanderbilt University
Walden University
TEXAS
Alpine: West Texas Historical and Scientific Society, Big Bend Historical Memorial
*Austin: *University of Texas Geological Museum
Brownwood: Payne College
*Dallas:
Dallas Museum of Natural History
Texas Institute of Natural Resources and Industrial Development

TEXAS (Cont'd.)
El Paso:
El Paso Museum
University of Texas, College of
Mines Museum
*Houston: Houston Museum and
Scientific Society, Houston
Museum of Natural History
*San Antonio:
San Antonio Scientific Society
Witte Memorial Museum
Waco: Baylor University
UTAH
Bryce Canyon National Park:
Bryce National Park Museum
Provo: *Brigham Young University
Museum
*Salt Lake City:
*University of Utah
Westminster College
Zion National Park: Zion National
Park Museum
VERMONT
Burlington: *University of Vermont
Middlebury: *Middlebury College
Montpelier: *State Building
St. Johnsbury: Fairbanks Museum
of Natural Science
Westfield: Hitchcock Memorial Mu-
seum
VIRGINIA
Blackburg: *Virginia Polytechnic In-
stitute
Charlottesville: *University of Vir-
ginia
Emory: Emory and Henry College
Lexington:
Virginia Military Institute
Washington and Lee University

Roanoke: Virginia Museum of Nat-
ural History
Salem: Roanoke College
WASHINGTON
Burton: Vashon College
Port Angeles: Klahhane City Mu-
seum
Pullman: *State College of Wash-
ington
*Seattle:
State Museum
*University of Washington
*Spokane: Public Museum
Tacoma: Washington State His-
torical Society
Walla Walla: Whitman College
WEST VIRGINIA
Morgantown: *West Virginia Uni-
versity
WISCONSIN
Appleton: Lawrence College
Beloit: Beloit College
Green Bay: Neville Public Museum
Madison: *University of Wisconsin
Milton: Milton College
* Milwaukee: Milwaukee-Downer
College Museum
New London: New London Public
Museum
Oshkosh: Oshkosh Public Museum
Racine: Racine Memorial Museum
Ripon: Ripon College
Watertown: Northwestern College
WYOMING
*Cheyenne: Wyoming State Geo-
logical Department Museum
Laramie: *University of Wyoming
Yellowstone National Park: Yellow-
stone Museum

# Index

∧∨∧∨∧∨∧∨

209